ASPECTS OF THE
ORGANIC CHEMISTRY
OF SULPHUR

ORGANIC CHEMISTRY MONOGRAPHS

Consultant Editors

Dr J. W. COOK, F.R.S.
Vice-Chancellor, University of Exeter

and

PROFESSOR M. STACEY, F.R.S.
*Mason Professor and Head of Department of Chemistry
University of Birmingham*

Aspects of the Organic Chemistry of Sulphur

FREDERICK CHALLENGER

D.Sc. (Birmingham), Ph.D. (Göttingen), B.Sc. (London), F.R.I.C.

Emeritus Professor of Organic Chemistry
University of Leeds

LONDON
BUTTERWORTHS SCIENTIFIC PUBLICATIONS

1959

BUTTERWORTHS PUBLICATIONS LTD.
88 KINGSWAY, LONDON, W.C.2

AFRICA: BUTTERWORTH & CO. (AFRICA) LTD.
DURBAN: 33/35 Beach Grove

AUSTRALIA: BUTTERWORTH & CO. (AUSTRALIA) LTD
SYDNEY: 8 O'Connell Street
MELBOURNE: 430 Bourke Street
BRISBANE: 240 Queen Street

CANADA: BUTTERWORTH & CO. (CANADA) LTD.
TORONTO: 1367 Danforth Avenue

NEW ZEALAND: BUTTERWORTH & CO. (AUSTRALIA) LTD.
WELLINGTON: 49/51 Ballance Street
AUCKLAND: 35 High Street

U.S.A. Edition published by
ACADEMIC PRESS INC., PUBLISHERS
111 FIFTH AVENUE
NEW YORK 3, NEW YORK

Made and Printed in Great Britain by
The Garden City Press Limited
Letchworth, Hertfordshire

PREFACE

THE subjects discussed in four of these six essays are those of which I have had personal laboratory experience during twenty to thirty years. I value greatly my brief association with the late Professor John Cadman (afterwards Lord Cadman) in the Mining Department of the University of Birmingham, where many problems of petroleum technology were discussed, and my happy collaboration in the University of Manchester with Dr (now Professor) T. K. Walker on the chemistry of mould metabolism.

Dr Constance Higginbottom's identification of Gosio-gas as trimethylarsine in the University of Leeds demonstrated for the first time the phenomenon of mycological methylation, and opened a way to many further studies. The fundamental researches of Dr Paul Haas in seaweed chemistry, his scientific curiosity regarding the smell noticed at low-water mark, and the laboratory skill of Dr Margaret Simpson led to the isolation in Leeds of the first natural sulphonium salt, and to the widespread recognition of the importance of these compounds in plant and animal biochemistry. My association with all these colleagues and friends has been most warmly appreciated. The study of Co-enzyme A brings together much of interest in the chemistry of sulphur and of the natural nucleotides. Chapter 6 has been written mainly from the standpoint of the organic chemist and, with the exception of some account of the importance of Co-enzyme A in the metabolism of fatty acids, its wide biochemical significance is only touched upon.

It is a pleasure to acknowledge my great indebtedness to Dr Philip Taylor, for the care which he has devoted to the correction of the proofs. The editors of *Quarterly Reviews*, *Journal of the Chemical Society*, *Biochemical Journal*, *Endeavour* and *The Manufacturing Chemist* have kindly allowed me to incorporate, with or without modification, extracts from articles which I have contributed to these periodicals; the publishers of *Federation Proceedings* and Dr H. Mahler readily agreed to my making use of his article on Co-enzyme A in Volume 12. The permission of Verlag Chemie to include short verbatim extracts in German from early publications by Will and Körner and by Gerlich in *Liebig's Annalen der Chemie* and the *Berichte der deutschen chemischen Gesellschaft* enabled me to explain concisely the position which work on mustard oil had reached almost one hundred years ago. Here I must thank Dr A. Kjaer of Copenhagen for the many reprints which he has sent me in connection with his own rapidly extending work on the natural *iso*thiocyanates and their glucosides; they have been of great assistance.

I have had the privilege of discussing with Dr G. A. Snow his work on the effect of ethyl mercaptan and its derivatives in tubercular infections, and of having access to unpublished results. The publications of Professor J. Baddiley and his colleagues, of Dr R. L. M. Synge and Dr S. F. Birch have proved most valuable sources of information on the chemistry of Co-enzyme A and of the sulphur compounds present in vegetables and in petroleum respectively. The production of this book has been greatly furthered by the kindness of Professor W. Bradley who, for several years, has extended to me the generous hospitality of his department. Finally, it is a pleasure to thank the publishers for the consideration which they have shown to me throughout the preparation of the book.

Department of Colour Chemistry and Dyeing,　　　　　　F. C.
The University,
LEEDS
December, 1958

CONTENTS

vii

SIMPLE ORGANIC COMPOUNDS OF SULPHUR. PROPERTIES, PREPARATION AND BIOLOGICAL SIGNIFICANCE

In this chapter it will be convenient to include mercaptans (thiols), monosulphides, sulphido-acids, sulphoxides and disulphides. It is not proposed to summarize or discuss more than a few of their properties, reactions and methods of preparation but to emphasize those which are useful in their characterization, are less well known or have been used in the work discussed in the following chapters.

Acidity of mercaptans—As they are derivatives of hydrogen sulphide the mercaptans exhibit acidity, which however is weaker than that of the parent substance[1]. They dissolve in aqueous alkali hydroxides to form mercaptides, e.g. $C_2H_5 \cdot S \cdot K$ and form insoluble compounds with the salts of heavy metals such as mercury, lead, thallium, copper and silver. These, like metal sulphides, are sometimes coloured, usually yellow or orange. The name mercaptan is an indication of the ready reaction of these compounds with mercuric oxide or cyanide to give mercaptides.

$$2C_2H_5 \cdot S \cdot H + HgO = H_2O + Hg(S \cdot C_2H_5)_2$$

The phrase *Corpus mercurio aptum* (compounds combining readily with mercury) was abbreviated to mercaptan by Zeise[2,3]. The acidity of the mercaptans diminishes with increase in molecular weight and they are weaker acids than hydrogen sulphide, owing to the electron-donating effect of the alkyl group which causes the hydrogen atom to be more firmly fixed to the sulphur. Mercaptans containing four or more atoms of carbon are only partially removed from solution in light petroleum by shaking with aqueous sodium hydroxide, whereas hydrogen sulphide is completely extracted under such conditions. Again these higher mercaptans can be liberated by dilution of their alkaline solutions and partly extracted from solution in alkali by light petroleum. Finally, as was shown by Birch and Norris[1] they are progressively liberated from their alkaline solutions by boiling.

Oxidation of mercaptans—Mercaptans are readily oxidized to disulphides $R \cdot S \cdot S \cdot R$ by air, especially in alkaline or ammoniacal solution or by iodine or sulphuric acid. This property must always be taken into account when working with mercaptans. The disulphides have no acidic properties and their separation from mercaptans presents no serious difficulty. It is often desirable, however, to work in an atmosphere of nitrogen. Nitric acid oxidizes mercaptans to sulphonic acids, $R \cdot SO_2 \cdot OH$.

Metal derivatives of mercaptans[4]—The mercaptides of such metals as gold, platinum, iridium and palladium are unattacked by dilute acids and can be prepared from the chlorides of these metals. As auric chloride is an oxidizing agent the aurous mercaptide and a disulphide are formed when it reacts with a mercaptan.

$$AuCl_3 + 3R \cdot SH = R \cdot S \cdot Au + R \cdot S \cdot S \cdot R + 3HCl \ (R = C_n H_{2n+1}).$$

The lead and copper mercaptides are usually yellow in colour and these metallic derivatives have proved to be of great value in the identification of mercaptans by m.p. or by analytical determination of the metal.

Most mercaptides yield a metal sulphide and an organic sulphide on heating:

$$(CH_3 \cdot S \cdot)_2 Pb = CH_3 \cdot S \cdot CH_3 + PbS$$

Those of mercury behave in a similar manner, but a second reaction involving the formation of a disulphide also occurs

$$(RS)_2 Hg = Hg + R \cdot S \cdot S \cdot R$$

Which reaction predominates probably depends on the nature of the alkyl groups and possibly on the experimental conditions.

MERCAPTANS AND MERCURIC CYANIDE

Owing to the solubility of many mercaptides in dilute mineral acids they are best prepared from the salts of metals with weak acids such as lead acetate, mercuric acetate or mercuric cyanide:

$$Hg(CN)_2 + 2RSH = Hg(SR)_2 + 2HCN$$

There is an added advantage in this procedure, as alkyl sulphides do not form insoluble compounds with 4 per cent mercuric cyanide or acetate. The same is true of dialkyl disulphides $R \cdot S \cdot S \cdot R$. The reaction of these sulphur compounds with mercuric salts is discussed later. The controlled use of different salts of mercury for the separation of simple aliphatic or hydroaromatic compounds of sulphur has proved of great value both in university and industrial laboratories.

Most mercaptides crystallize well and have fairly sharp melting points. Occasionally the mercaptide $(RS)_2 Hg$ is contaminated with a compound containing co-ordinated mercuric cyanide and the melting point is depressed. This can be removed by boiling with water or by long shaking with cold water or on recrystallization, when the pure mercaptide is obtained. If this is not realized the incorrect impression may be gained that the mercaptan under examination is a mixture. This point is of importance when small quantities of mercaptans, such as are obtained in biochemical investigations, are in question; the matter has been studied in the case of methyl mercaptan by Dr P. A. Briscoe[5]. He found that the co-ordination of the mercuric cyanide occurs both when the mercaptan is added to excess of 4 per cent aqueous mercuric cyanide or when the pure mercaptide $(CH_3S)_2Hg$ is shaken with aqueous mercuric cyanide varying in strength from one to eight per cent.

Pure mercury dithiomethoxide $(CH_3S)_2Hg$ melts at 174°–175°C and decomposes at 177°C. Crude specimens prepared directly from the mercaptan and mercuric cyanide may sinter from as low as 121°C, melt from 130°–143°C and decompose at 177°C. Calculations based on the loss in weight of a crude sample of the mercaptide which had been shaken first with 4 per cent, then with 8 per cent mercuric cyanide and finally extracted with water, indicated the co-ordination of one molecule of cyanide by one of the mercaptide. The same conclusion was reached by noting the increase in weight on shaking the mercaptide with mercuric cyanide. Such crude addition compounds sintered at 132°–133°C and melted and decomposed at 141°–142°C. On shaking with water for 12 hours the m.p. rose to 175°C (decomp.) indicating regeneration of the pure mercaptide. The best solvents for mercury dithiomethoxide are ethyl acetate or pyridine.

MERCAPTANS AND MERCURIC CHLORIDE

The use of mercuric chloride for the preparation of mercaptides $(RS)_2Hg$ is usually undesirable because insoluble compounds of high melting point are often obtained. These have the structure $R \cdot S \cdot HgCl$ and may be accompanied by co-ordination compounds

of the type $R \cdot \overset{+}{S} \diagup^{\textstyle HgCl}_{\diagdown \overline{\overline{Hg}}Cl_2}$ and also by the mercaptides $(RS)_2Hg$. The

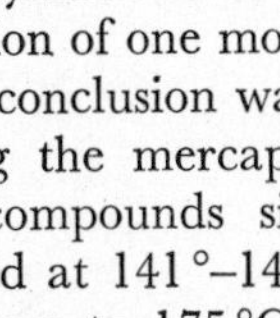

resulting mixture is often difficult to separate by simple crystallization. The author and Rawlings[6] found that when ethyl or n-propyl mercaptan reacts with suitable quantities of aqueous mercuric chloride any one of the three compounds may be obtained at will though not necessarily as the only product.

Influence of hydrogen sulphide on the course of the reaction between mercaptans and mercuric chloride—A further complication is found in the observation of the same authors that if ethyl mercaptan contains traces of hydrogen sulphide a red precipitate quickly becoming pink is produced when aqueous mercuric chloride is added. With more mercuric chloride the precipitate becomes white. This does not occur with the perfectly pure mercaptan; specimens which give a clean yellow precipitate with lead acetate (absence of lead sulphide) give only a white precipitate with mercuric chloride. On introduction of a few bubbles of hydrogen sulphide into the mercaptan the pink precipitate is readily obtained on addition of mercuric chloride.

This phenomenon is presumably due to the formation of the red compound $(C_2H_5S)_2Hg \cdot 2HgS$ probably $Hg(S \cdot Hg \cdot S \cdot C_2H_5)_2$ prepared by Sachs and Balassa[7] who also describe a yellow isomer. The disappearance of the red colour is probably due to removal of the mercuric sulphide as the double compound $HgCl_2 \cdot 2HgS$, probably $Hg(S \cdot HgCl)_2$, as described by Jolibois and Bouvois[8]. The yellow 'isomer' of $(C_2H_5S)_2Hg \cdot 2HgS$ mentioned by Sachs and Balassa is probably responsible for observations which have been made from time to time when ethyl or methyl mercaptans arising from biological processes, and therefore contaminated with hydrogen sulphide, are absorbed in mercuric cyanide. Thus, Rübner[9] obtained yellow precipitates when methyl mercaptan produced by boiling vegetables with water was passed through mercuric cyanide solution. Hydrogen sulphide would also be present under such conditions.

The methyl mercaptan evolved by the higher fungus *Schizophyllum commune* on a glucose-inorganic salts medium containing ammonium sulphate is contaminated with traces of hydrogen sulphide[10,11]. Consequently some of the deposits obtained when the evolved gases were passed through aqueous mercuric cyanide were yellowish in colour, but yielded the pure mercaptide $(CH_3S)_2Hg$ on recrystallization. An alkaline solution of a mercaptan can be converted to the insoluble mercury mercaptide $Hg(SR)_2$ by addition to aqueous mercuric cyanide[12]. The mercury salt is so poorly ionized that no mercuric oxide is precipitated. This device may often prove convenient in practice.

Preparation of Mercaptans (Alkane- and Arene-thiols)

Methods for the preparation of mercaptans have recently been summarized in Houben-Weyl's monumental work *Die Methoden der*

Organischen Chemie, Band IX, Schwefel, Selen, Tellur Verbindungen[13] where numerous references are collected. Only such reactions as have been simplified or improved by modern laboratory procedure or possess some special interest or are particularly simple or convenient will be discussed here. Similar considerations will determine the treatment of the alkyl sulphides and disulphides.

1. Where possible the use of alkyl halides in the preparation of mercaptans from an alkali-metal hydrosulphide, e.g. NaSH should be replaced by sodium alkyl sulphates which, in many cases, as Meyer and Jacobson point out, need not be isolated. Ingold *et al.*[14] have used both methods. Probably, as is certainly the case with the preparation of the alkyl sulphides from sodium sulphide, dimethyl and diethyl sulphates could be used and the previous preparation of the sodium alkyl sulphates avoided[15].

2. Many alkyl mercaptans are readily prepared by the alkylation of thiourea with alkyl halides or sulphates, followed by the decomposition of the resulting S-alkylthiouronium salt with sufficient alkali to liberate the free base, which then undergoes thermal decomposition

$$S:C(NH_2)_2 + R \cdot X = \left[R \cdot S \cdot C \overset{\overset{+}{N}H_2}{\underset{NH_2}{\diagdown}} \right] \bar{X} \xrightarrow{\text{NaOH}} R \cdot SH + C \overset{N}{\underset{NH_2}{\diagup}} + NaX + HOH$$

Full details for the preparation of several mercaptans by this method are given by Dijkstra[16]. S-methylthiouronium sulphate is obtained from thiourea and dimethyl sulphate, and on warming with two equivalents of sodium hydroxide evolves a steady stream of methyl mercaptan. This method is convenient for the evolution of known quantities of very volatile mercaptans which can be removed in a slow stream of nitrogen to the appropriate reagent.

3. Houben-Weyl[17] refers to the interaction of hydrogen sulphide and an alcohol in presence of thoria at 300°–350°C as a method for the preparation of mercaptans.

4. The formation of a mercaptan by the reduction of a sulphinic acid by sodium bisulphite or by zinc and hydrochloric acid, often at room temperature, is a delicate test for sulphinic acids.

Biological formation of mercaptans—Many instances of this will be considered in detail later and at present they may be summarized with little or no comment.

1. Methanethiol* is almost certainly present in intestinal gases[18]

---

* The terms mercaptan or thiol will be used throughout this book as is found more convenient.

and is evolved during the putrefaction of protein matter by bacteria[19] or along with hydrogen sulphide by heating keratin with water at 150°C[20]. It presumably arises from methionine $CH_3 \cdot S \cdot CH_2 \cdot CH_2 \cdot CH(NH_2) \cdot COOH$.

2. The wood-destroying fungus *Schizophyllum commune* evolves methanethiol when grown on a glucose-inorganic salts medium containing ammonium sulphate[21].

3. Methanethiol is present in the urine after ingestion of asparagus[22] and in cases of severe necrosis of the liver, when it appears also to be evolved in the breath, probably along with dimethyl disulphide and possibly dimethyl sulphide[23].

4. Mercaptans are formed by the biological fission of disulphides $R \cdot S \cdot S \cdot R$ e.g. by the mould *Scopulariopsis brevicaulis*[24,25], when the corresponding alkyl methyl sulphides $R \cdot S \cdot CH_3$ are also formed. The cystine–cysteine relation and the oxidation and reduction of glutathione furnish other examples of this reaction.

$$[COOH \cdot CH(NH_2) \cdot CH_2 \cdot S]_2 \underset{O}{\overset{2H}{\rightleftharpoons}} 2COOH \cdot CH(NH_2) \cdot CH_2 \cdot SH$$

Cystine   Cysteine

Thioctic acid[29-32] or lipoic acid (I) occurs in liver and in green plants and has been identified with a factor required by *Streptococcus faecalis* and is concerned with the oxidation of pyruvate. It may be involved in the processes occurring in photosynthesis and is a cyclic disulphide which readily undergoes reductive fission to a di-thiol acid.

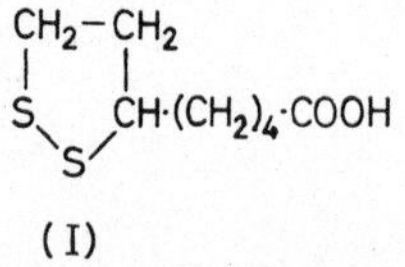

(I)

5. Methanethiol occurs in several plants, e.g. in the radish[26], 1-propanethiol in the onion[27] and 1-butanethiol in the anal secretion of the skunk[28].

6. Ergothioneine (II) is the betaine of thiolhistidine and occurs in ergot and in blood.

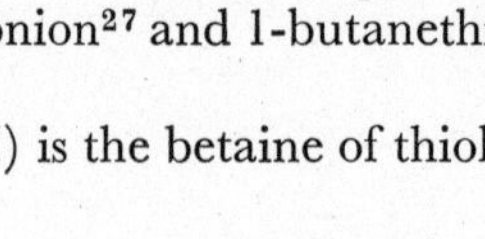

(II)

6

7. The remarkable biological catalyst Co-enzyme A (*see* Chapter 6) contains the terminal group —CO·NH·CH$_2$·CH$_2$·SH.

8. Mercaptans are frequently present in petroleum distillates and a large number have been identified, especially in fractions of boiling point below 180°C (*see* Chapter 3). On account of the biological origin of petroleum its content of mercaptans may conveniently be cited in this section.

Detection of thiol and disulphide groups in tissue slices—The well-known alkaline nitroprusside reaction for —SH groups and (after treatment of a disulphide with potassium cyanide) for —S—S— groups has been developed by a number of workers to permit of its use in chemical histology. (The potassium cyanide causes fission of the —S—S— group to give —SK and —SCN.) The procedure has been summarized in *Histochemische Methoden* by Lipp[33]. The same publication contains details for the detection of the thiol groups of proteins by a method which does not involve the use of sodium nitroprusside[34-36]. The reagent used is 2 : 2'-dihydroxy-6 : 6'-dinaphthyl disulphide (III) and when present in excess at pH 8·5

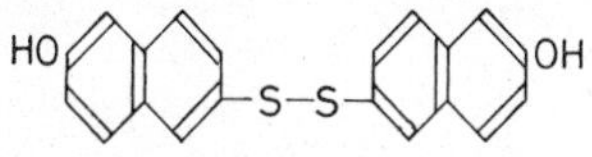

(III) 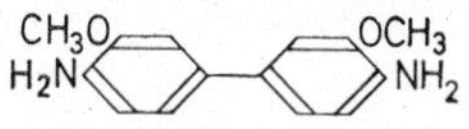   (IV)

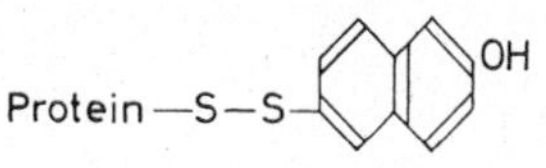

(V) 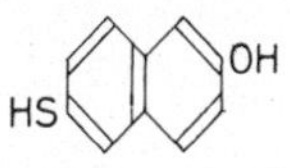   (VI)

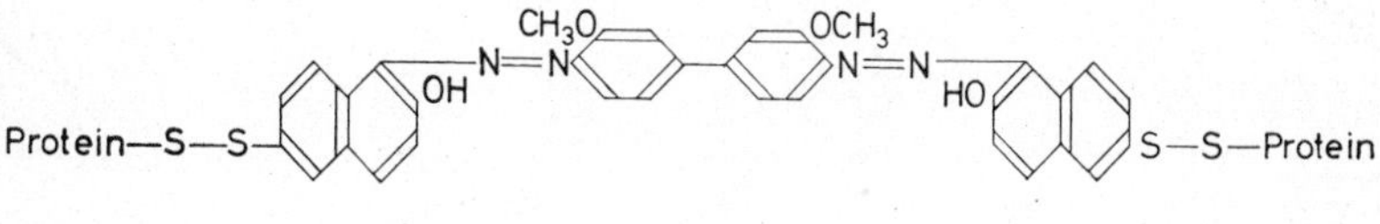

(VII)

it reacts with the —SH groups of tissue proteins to form a colourless compound (V) due to the preliminary fission of the —S—S— group of the reagent by the —SH of the protein. This product (V) is insoluble in water or in alcohol–ether, whereas the reagent and the second product of the fission—the thiol (VI)—can be removed by organic solvents. The tissue, now containing compound (V) is treated with the tetrazo-derivative of *o*-di-anisidine (IV) when a red or a blue dyestuff is produced according to whether coupling occurs once or twice. The scheme set out on p. 7 shows the formation of the blue dyestuff (VII). This appears in the tissue at the site of the original protein —SH linkage. The method can also be adapted as a test for the disulphide link, —S—S—, either alone or in presence of a thiol group.

DIALKYL SULPHIDES

The dialkyl sulphides $C_nH_{2n+1} \cdot S \cdot C_nH_{2n+1}$ are usually liquids. Dimethyl sulphide boils at 38 °C and diethyl sulphide at 92 °C. The odour of the lower members—methyl to *n*-propyl—is much less unpleasant than that of the corresponding mercaptans. If traces of mercaptans or disulphides be removed by heating with copper powder at about 260 °C or by washing with dilute alkali and repeated fractionation, the odour is not unpleasant. Dimethyl sulphide when largely diluted with air has an odour of seaweed and, as will be seen later, some marine algae evolve pure dimethyl sulphide on removal from the sea. The higher sulphides, e.g. *n*-butyl and *n*-amyl sulphides have an unpleasant smell, the rancid odour characteristic of many butyl and amyl compounds becoming apparent. The sulphides are all immiscible with water.

Reactions of the alkyl sulphides—1. Most of the reactions are due to the two pairs of unshared electrons on the sulphur atom. Crystalline addition products are sometimes formed with bromine or iodine. The dibromide of dimethyl sulphide $(CH_3)_2SBr_2$ was used by Haas[37] to characterize the dimethyl sulphide evolved by the marine alga *Polysiphonia fastigiata*. Chlorine gives substitution products with diethyl sulphide and in absence of a solvent causes the material to inflame.

2. A characteristic reaction of the alkyl sulphides is the formation of crystalline, often deliquescent, sulphonium salts $(R_1 \cdot R_2 \cdot R_3 \cdot \overset{+}{S}) \overline{X}$ with alkyl halides, particularly the iodides, halogenated fatty acids and their esters and halogenated ketones. Thus 2-bromopropionic acid and ω-bromoacetophenone give with dimethyl sulphide $(CH_3)_2 \cdot \overset{+}{S}(\overline{Br}) \cdot CH_2 \cdot CH_2 \cdot COOH$ and $(CH_3)_2 \overset{+}{S}(\overline{Br}) CH_2 \cdot CO \cdot C_6H_5$ respectively. Sulphuric acid dissolves alkyl sulphides giving odourless solutions in which the presence of a sulphonium sulphate e.g. $[(CH_3)_2\overset{+}{S}H] H\overline{S}O_4$ must be assumed. This is decomposed on dilution with water and the sulphide is regenerated. This recalls the similar behaviour of diethyl ether. Its odourless solution in sulphuric

8

acid presumably contains the analogous oxonium salt. Solution in sulphuric acid, followed by cautious dilution has been used to absorb and regenerate alkyl sulphides formed in very small quantities in some biochemical processes[38].

3. The halides of mercury, platinum and palladium (MX_2) form co-ordinated addition products with the dialkyl sulphides in which the sulphur acts as the donor atom. These have not always a simple structure. That from dimethyl sulphide and mercuric chloride[11,14,25] has the composition $2(CH_3)_2S \cdot 3HgCl_2$. The diethyl derivative $(C_2H_5)_2S \cdot 2HgCl_2$ and the methyl n-propyl compound[24] $2(CH_3 \cdot S \cdot C_3H_7) \cdot 5HgCl_2$ may be mentioned. Co-ordination compounds of this type have been carefully studied by Mann[39], Wardlaw and Cox[40,41] and others. It should be emphasized that they do not contain a C—Hg link, that is to say, they are co-ordination compounds and not mercuration products. Consequently they are readily decomposed by heat or hot water and to some extent by hot solvents and particularly by cold sodium hydroxide, when the characteristic odour of the sulphide is apparent. This test is carried out with minute quantities of material. The resulting alkaline mercuric oxide does not oxidize the dialkyl sulphides either in hot or cold suspension. The alkyl sulphides can therefore be purified through their mercurichlorides (which can be crystallized from hot alcohol, benzene or aqueous mercuric chloride) and regenerated with alkali[24,40]. The same is true of the dialkyl selenides $R \cdot Se \cdot R$[42,43]. The dialkyl tellurides, however, are oxidized to the telluroxides R_2TeO and mercury is deposited[44].

Very often a dialkyl sulphide or selenide forms two co-ordination compounds in which the ratio of sulphide or selenide to mercuric chloride is different. In such cases one of these, that with the higher proportion of organic component, loses some volatile sulphide or selenide on exposure to air and the melting point slowly changes to that of the other derivative. The same result can often be achieved by recrystallization of the 'lower' mercurichloride from hot aqueous 3 per cent mercuric chloride solution. Thus methyl ethyl selenide forms two mercurichlorides (A) $CH_3 \cdot Se \cdot C_2H_5 \cdot HgCl_2$, m.p. 98 °C and (B) $CH_3 \cdot Se \cdot C_2H_5 \cdot 2HgCl_2$, m.p. 141 °C[43]. The dimercurichloride is stable in air but the mono-derivative gradually loses methyl ethyl selenide and rises in m.p. on exposure to air. When recrystallized from aqueous mercuric chloride A gives rise to B. Aqueous mercuric chloride solution is an excellent reagent for removing and detecting small quantities of sulphides (also selenides, tellurides and arsines) evolved from plants or mould cultures, as the mercurichlorides are sparingly soluble in water. Some of them are

9

slowly dissociated in an air stream and consequently a sulphide mercurichloride suspended in water or dilute mercuric chloride will be gradually transferred to a second (clear) mercuric chloride solution under such conditions.

When mercuric chloride is used as an absorbent for an alkyl sulphide, selenide or arsine evolved from a culture the precipitate which forms in the 3–5 per cent aqueous solution should be removed occasionally and the mercuric chloride replaced by a fresh supply. This has two advantages. It affords an opportunity of checking (by determination of m.p.) the nature of the volatile compound emerging from the cultures and detecting any change in its composition. This procedure also prevents the gradual precipitation of a 'lower' mercurichloride through the slow fall in concentration of the absorbent due to separation of the insoluble mercurichloride.

4. With nitric acid dialkyl sulphides form sulphoxides R_2SO. As these are basic the product consists of the crystalline nitrate, e.g. dimethylhydroxysulphonium nitrate $(CH_3)_2\overset{+}{S}(OH)\overline{N}O_3$. Distillation with barium carbonate gives the sulphoxide.

5. Oxidation with potassium permanganate or with hydrogen peroxide in glacial acetic acid converts dialkyl sulphides to the sulphones, R_2SO_2. These are crystalline, non-basic, very stable, soluble in water and somewhat volatile with steam. They can be reduced to the corresponding sulphide with lithium aluminium hydride[45]. With Raney nickel they are converted with loss of oxygen and sulphur to hydrocarbons or their substitution products[46].

$$R \cdot SO_2 \cdot R' \xrightarrow[H]{Ni} RH + R'H + NiS + 2H_2O$$

When heated with sodium hydroxide sulphones form ethylenic hydrocarbons and the sodium salt of a sulphinic acid. This reaction was studied by Ingold and his collaborators during their early work on the mechanism of elimination reactions[47,48].

$$\overline{O}H + CH_3 \cdot CH_2 \cdot SO_2 \cdot CH_2 \cdot CH_3 \rightarrow$$
$$H_2O + CH_2 : CH_2 + CH_3 \cdot CH_2 \cdot S\overline{O}_2$$

6. With the sodium derivatives of N-chloroamines, $R' \cdot SO_2N(Cl)$ Na, sulphidimines $R_2\overset{+}{S}\text{-}\overline{N} \cdot SO_2 \cdot R'$ are produced from dialkyl sulphides, (see Chapter 2). Chloramine-T [N-chloro-N-sodiotoluene-p-sulphonamide, $CH_3 \cdot C_6H_4 \cdot SO_2N(Cl)Na$] is particularly convenient for this purpose. The sulphidimines crystallize well, have sharp melting points, can be separated by paper chromatography and

10

regenerate the dialkyl sulphide with tin and hydrochloric acid or with sodium bisulphite.

Preparation of Dialkyl Sulphides

1. A convenient process is the use of a salt of an alkylsulphuric acid or of dimethyl sulphate instead of an alkyl halide.

$$Na_2S + 2R \cdot O \cdot SO_2 \cdot ONa = R_2S + 2SO_2(ONa)_2$$
$$R \cdot S \cdot Na + R' \cdot O \cdot SO_2 \cdot ONa = R \cdot S \cdot R' + SO_2(ONa)_2$$

Modern work along these lines was carried out by Ingold and his colleagues[14].

2. Dialkyl sulphides may be obtained by passing a mercaptan over cadmium sulphide at 300°C[49].

3. By addition of a mercaptan to an olefine a sulphide is formed. The literature on this reaction is very considerable and, as is well known, its course is affected by the presence of light or of peroxides[50,51]. Ethanethiol, for example, combines with propylene to give $(CH_3)_2 \cdot CH \cdot S \cdot C_2H_5$ but in presence of peroxides ethyl n-propyl sulphide $CH_3 \cdot CH_2 \cdot CH_2 \cdot S \cdot CH_2 \cdot CH_3$ is formed[52]. The addition of hydrogen sulphide to olefines gives mercaptans which can then react with the original olefine to give sulphides. Here again peroxides and ultra-violet light affect the course of the reaction so that the Markownikoff rule[53] is not followed.

4. The addition of a mercaptan to an $\alpha\beta$-unsaturated acid gives a sulphido-acid. The reaction can occur in both neutral and acid solution[54] (see p. 19).

5. The decomposition of a sulphonium compound $(R_3 \overset{+}{S}) \overline{X}$ by nucleophilic reagents gives a sulphide which is accompanied by an alcohol and very frequently by both an alcohol and an olefine or two olefines. Considerable attention has been paid to the mechanism of these decompositions by Ingold and his co-workers[48] and to the effect on the proportions of alcohol and olefine produced by alterations in the groups attached to sulphur, and in the nature of the reagent. Frequently the method adopted was to study the thermal decomposition of the sulphonium hydroxide. Crane and Rydon[55] have described the alkaline fission of sulphonium iodides of the type

$[R \cdot CH_2 \cdot CH_2 \cdot \overset{+}{S}(CH_3)_2]\overline{I}$ and find that where $R = C_6H_5 \cdot CO \cdot O$— or $C_6H_5 \cdot O$—acetylene is eliminated according to the equation

$$[R \cdot CH_2 \cdot CH_2 \cdot \overset{+}{S}(CH_3)_2]\overline{I} = RH + CH \equiv CH + (CH_3)_2S + HI$$

An interesting example of olefinic decomposition of sulphonium salts is the action of alkali on the salt of a β-thetin, e.g. dimethyl–

β–propiothetin halide $(CH_3)_2\overset{+}{S}(\overline{X})\cdot CH_2\cdot CH_2\cdot COOH$ whereby dimethyl sulphide and acrylic acid are formed[49]:

$$(CH_3)_2\overset{+}{S}(\overline{X})\cdot CH_2\cdot CH_2\cdot COOH =$$
$$(CH_3)_2S + HX + CH_2 : CH\cdot COOH.$$

6. Hydrogen sulphide, in presence of ammonia or dilute alkali, to increase ionization, combines with $\alpha\beta$-unsaturated ketones such as benzalacetone $C_6H_5CH : CH\cdot CO\cdot CH_3$[56], benzalacetophenone[56] $C_6H_5CH : CH\cdot CO\cdot C_6H_5$ and carvone to form the so-called 'hydrosulphides' (VIII and IX).

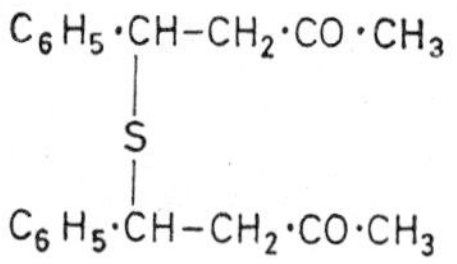

$C_6H_5\cdot CH-CH_2\cdot CO\cdot CH_3$

$C_6H_5\cdot CH-CH_2\cdot CO\cdot CH_3$

(VIII)

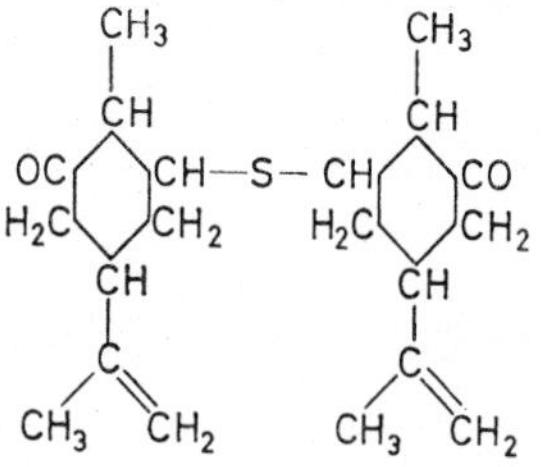

(IX)

That the addition of hydrogen sulphide takes place at the double bond adjacent to the carbonyl group and not at the carbonyl group itself is shown by the formation of a tetrabromide of carvone hydrosulphide. Carvotanacetone hydrosulphide in which the $CH_3\overset{|}{C}=CH_2$ groups are replaced by $CH_3\overset{|}{C}H\cdot CH_3$ does not combine with bromine[57]. On treatment with alkali these 'hydrosulphides' regenerate the original ketone; this reaction affords a method for the purification of carvone.

Biological Formation of Dialkyl Sulphides

1. Certain marine algae, e.g. *Polysiphonia fastigiata, Polysiphonia nigrescens*[58] and *Enteromorpha intestinalis*[59] evolve dimethyl sulphide when removed from the sea. The evolution is more rapid when the weed is treated with cold sodium hydroxide.

2. Various green plants, including bracken (*Pteridium aquilinum*) and several species of *Equisetum* (horse tails) e.g. *E. arvense* evolve dimethyl sulphide on boiling with sodium hydroxide[59].

3. Dimethyl sulphide is probably evolved in the breath of the dog[60] and of man[61] after administration of thiourea. In the case of dogs the odorous substance in the breath was not absorbed by 40 per

cent sodium hydroxide, by dilute solutions of the salts of heavy metals or by mercuric cyanide. This indicates the absence of a mercaptan. The breath when collected in a gasometer and passed through a hot tube into pure sodium hydroxide produced sodium sulphate. Concentrated sulphuric acid or saturated aqueous mercuric chloride absorbed it completely and liberated the odour again on dilution. This suggests that the substance is a sulphide (*see* p. 8). From our knowledge of the processes of biological methylation it is extremely probable that the breath of the dogs contained dimethyl sulphide. Moreover in experiments in which thiourea was given to patients suffering from hyperthyroidism[61] the sweetish odour exhaled in the breath was stated to resemble that of seaweed, [*see* (1) on p. 12]. The —SH group of the *iso*thiourea presumably undergoes biological methylation and finally appears as dimethyl sulphide.

4. The evolution of an unidentified organic sulphide from the sponge *Suberites domuncola* is described by Henze[62] but it was not investigated. Unpublished experiments by the author and Dr J. O. Smith suggested that an unsaturated sulphide was evolved.

5. A few essential oils are stated to contain small quantities of dimethyl sulphide, e.g. African and Réunion oil of geranium[63].

6. Numerous alkyl sulphides have been isolated from petroleum, often from the acid sludge obtained during the refining of the 'kerosene' fraction with sulphuric acid. The question is discussed in detail in Chapter 3.

7. When the urine of dogs is boiled with sodium hydroxide methyl-*n*-propyl sulphide and much smaller quantities of a second sulphide, which is most probably methyl-*n*-butyl sulphide, are evolved, (*see* Chapter 2). These are almost certainly produced by the decomposition of two sulphonium compounds $(CH_3 \cdot \overset{+}{S} \cdot C_3H_7 \cdot R)\overline{X}$ and $(CH_3 \cdot \overset{+}{S} \cdot C_4H_9 \cdot R')\overline{X}$ (*see* p. 11). The nature of the groups R and R' has not been determined.

DIALKYL DISULPHIDES

The dialkyl disulphides are colourless liquids of boiling points higher than those of the monosulphides. Dimethyl and diethyl disulphides boil at 112 °C and 153 °C, the corresponding mono-sulphides at 38 °C and 92 °C respectively. The disulphides have a more unpleasant odour than the monosulphides, but it is not so objectionable as that of the mercaptans. The structure is $C_nH_{2n+1} \cdot S \cdot S \cdot C_nH_{2n+1}$[64]. Most of the reactions of disulphides depend

13

upon the ready fission of the —S—S— link by chemical or biological reducing agents, by hydrolysis, by reaction with alkyl halides, with Grignard reagents or with mercuric chloride.

Properties of Dialkyl Disulphides

1. *Reductive fission*—Reductive fission to mercaptans can be effected by almost any of the common reducing agents, including 'sodium bisulphite'.

2. *Fission by halogens*—Bromine in an inert solvent gives the sulphenic bromides R·S·Br theoretically derived from the sulphenic acids, R·S·OH. In the aliphatic series these bromides are frequently unstable at room temperature but can be preserved for some time at −15 °C. The aromatic sulphenyl bromides are more stable, especially if the benzene nucleus is substituted. This is also true of the chlorides. The halogen atom is very reactive and can be replaced by —OH, —NH₂, —NH·Alkyl, —NH·Aryl or by —SCN or —CN. The last reaction affords a method for the preparation of substituted aryl thiocyanates from diaryl disulphides[65,66].

If chlorine be passed into dimethyl disulphide suspended in water at below 6 °C oxidative fission occurs and methanesulphonyl chloride $CH_3 \cdot SO_2Cl$ is formed[67]. This affords a good method for its preparation, although products of higher boiling point may also be produced. A similar fission occurs with aromatic disulphides in glacial acetic acid in presence of water, the reaction being carried further giving the corresponding sulphonic acid.

3. *Fission by water*—Hydrolytic fission by hot water under pressure has been observed with diethyl disulphide[68]. In a sealed tube at 170°C for five hours ethanethiol, hydrogen sulphide and metaldehyde were formed. In a copper autoclave with water at 200°–210 °C for four hours copper sulphide and copper dithioethoxide, copper ethyl mercaptide, $Cu (S \cdot C_2H_5)_2$, were formed and also acetaldehyde, characterized as the 2 : 4-dinitrophenylhydrazone. The ethanethiol was liberated by acid and characterized as mercury dithioethoxide $Hg(S \cdot C_2H_5)_2$.

The deposit in the autoclave on distillation in nitrogen gave diethyl sulphide, characterized as the mercurichloride, (*see* p. 9).

$$(CH_3 \cdot CH_2 \cdot S)_2Cu = CuS + CH_3 \cdot CH_2 \cdot S \cdot CH_2 \cdot CH_3$$

The reaction presumably first yields ethanethiol and ethanesulphenic acid $CH_3 \cdot CH_2 \cdot S \cdot OH$ and the sulphenic acid gives hydrogen sulphide and acetaldehyde according to a reaction which has been studied by Schöberl[69,70] and his co-workers with disulphidocarboxylic acids.

14

$$CH_3 \cdot CH_2 \cdot S \cdot S \cdot CH_2 \cdot CH_3 + H \cdot OH \ CH_3 \cdot CH_2 \cdot SH + HO \cdot S \cdot CH_2 \cdot CH_3$$
$$CH_3 \cdot CH_2 \cdot S \cdot OH = CH_3 \cdot CH : O + H_2S$$

The reaction has received much less attention in the case of simple disulphides.

4. *Fission by mercuric chloride*—The behaviour of aliphatic disulphides $R \cdot S \cdot S \cdot R$, where R = methyl to n-propyl, to aqueous mercuric chloride was studied by the author with Rawlings[6] and Blackburn[25]. The results proved of value in the separation of the mixtures of sulphide, disulphide and mercaptan liberated from mould cultures to which substrates containing sulphur had been added. They might be equally useful in the study of the sulphur compounds of petroleum fractions of low boiling point (*see* Chapter 3). The results will therefore be discussed in some detail.

When diethyl disulphide or di-n-propyl disulphide was added to excess of an aqueous 3 per cent solution of mercuric chloride a white insoluble solid formed during two or three days. The mixture was shaken from time to time, preferably continuously. When the disulphide had completely reacted the solids were separated and found to have the composition $CH_3 \cdot CH_2 \cdot S \cdot HgCl \cdot HgCl_2$ and $CH_3 \cdot CH_2 \cdot CH_2 \cdot S \cdot HgCl \cdot HgCl_2$. The —HgCl group is linked covalently to sulphur, the $HgCl_2$ forms a co-ordinate link. Analysis and determination of loss in weight on boiling with water, whereby the co-ordinated mercuric chloride is removed, completely established the composition. The chloromercuryethane and 1-propanethiols $CH_3 \cdot CH_2 \cdot S \cdot HgCl$ and $CH_3 \cdot CH_2 \cdot CH_2 \cdot S \cdot HgCl$ remaining were also analysed.

That the compounds $R \cdot S \cdot HgCl \cdot HgCl_2$ while readily evolving the thiol $R \cdot SH$ with acid gave no volatile sulphur compound with cold or hot sodium hydroxide, was indicated by aspiration into mercuric cyanide and mercuric chloride. With dimethyl disulphide exactly similar results were obtained but the exact composition of the original precipitate $CH_3 \cdot S \cdot HgCl$. x $HgCl_2$ was not determined. Di-n-butyl disulphide and di-n-amyl disulphide, though undergoing fission rather more slowly with aqueous mercuric chloride, form insoluble chloromercuryalkanethiols $R \cdot S \cdot HgCl$ and not the addition compound $R \cdot S \cdot HgCl \cdot HgCl_2$. These products were identical with those prepared from mercuric chloride and the thiol. Possibly the larger size of the n-butyl and n-amyl groups prevents co-ordination of mercuric chloride by the sulphur atom.

The reaction of the disulphides with mercuric chloride giving $R \cdot S \cdot HgCl$ might be expected to form $R \cdot S \cdot Cl$ as the other product. This would at once be decomposed by the water to give an alkane

15

sulphenic acid R·S·OH and it would be expected that in the acid solution disproportionation would occur[6,25], thus

$$2 \, R\cdot S\cdot OH = R\cdot SH + R\cdot SO_2H$$

The mercaptan would react further with the excess mercuric chloride and the sulphinic acid R·SO₂H would dissolve. This was shown to be the case with dimethyl and diethyl disulphides. The excess mercuric chloride was removed by use of sodium carbonate or hydrogen sulphide. In each case the neutralized filtrate was evaporated and the residue extracted with alcohol, yielding a sodium salt which, in the case of the ethyl compound, decolorized iodine in potassium iodide and acidified permanganate solution. With zinc and hydrochloric acid a strong odour of ethanethiol was produced. Treatment of the two sodium salts with *p*-nitrobenzyl halide in alcohol gave *p*-nitrobenzyl methyl sulphone and *p*-nitrobenzyl ethyl sulphone thus proving the presence of a sulphinic acid

$$NO_2\cdot C_6H_4\cdot CH_2\cdot Cl + Na\cdot SO_2\cdot R = NO_2\cdot C_6H_4\cdot CH_2\cdot SO_2\cdot R + NaCl$$

It might be suggested that the reaction of the disulphide is not with mercuric chloride in the first instance but with water to give an equilibrium which is very much to the left:

$$R\cdot S\cdot S\cdot R + HOH \rightleftharpoons R\cdot SH + R\cdot SOH$$

and that this is displaced to the right by removal of the mercaptan as its insoluble mercury derivative. If so, other salts of heavy metals which give insoluble mercaptides would be expected to react in a similar manner. Lead acetate solution, however, has no action on dialkyl disulphides. The first stage in the reaction may be the formation of an unstable co-ordination compound such as

$$
\begin{array}{c}
R - \overset{+}{S} - \overline{H}gCl_2 \\
| \\
R - S
\end{array}
$$

followed by fission.

THE SEPARATION OF ORGANIC COMPOUNDS OF SULPHUR BY MEANS OF MERCURY SALTS

The behaviour of organic sulphur compounds towards reagents, especially mercury salts, varies both with the sulphur compound and the mercury salt and it may be convenient to summarize our knowledge on the subject, some of which has resulted from work carried out in the author's laboratory[71]. Several of the reactions are also discussed by Birch and McAllan[72].

REACTIONS OF ORGANIC SULPHUR COMPOUNDS

1. *Mercaptans* R·SH
> Mercuric acetate: $(RS)_2Hg$ (sparingly soluble) and
> R·S·Hg-O-CO·CH$_3$ (soluble).
Mercuric cyanide: $(RS)_2Hg$ and some $(RS)_2Hg.Hg(CN)_2$.

Water removes the co-ordinated mercuric cyanide; acids regenerate the mercaptan.

> Mercuric chloride: R·S·HgCl, R·SHgCl·HgCl$_2$ and
> $(RS)_2Hg$. Acids regenerate the mercaptan.

2. *Dialkyl sulphides* R·S·R
> Mercuric acetate: Soluble co-ordination compounds,
decomposed by alkali or warm acid regenerating the sulphide.
Mercuric chloride: Sparingly soluble co-ordination compounds,
decomposed by alkali or warm acid, regenerating the sulphide.
Mercuric cyanide: Usually no precipitate, sulphide unchanged.

Methyl iodide: A sulphonium iodide, $[R_2\overset{+}{S}\cdot CH_3]\ \bar{I}$

3. *Polymethylene (cyclic) sulphides*—In general the behaviour of these sulphides to mercury salts is similar to that of the dialkyl sulphides. The cyclic sulphides, however, react rather more readily with aqueous mercuric acetate, leading to a separation of the two classes; moreover occasionally this reagent can be used to effect a partial separation of different cyclic sulphides (*see* Chapter 3).

4. *Thiophen and homologues*—The preparation, properties and occurrence of these compounds have been described at length in several recent authoritative monographs[73,74] and need not be considered here. Since, however, homologues of thiophen frequently accompany the other types of sulphur compound, especially in mineral oils[75], their behaviour with mercury salts is included for convenience.

> Mercuric acetate: Complex, insoluble mercurated compounds
> containing one or more C-Hg·O·CO·CH$_3$ linkages. The
> thiophen derivative is regenerated by warm acid but not by
> alkali.
> Mercuric chloride: R·C$_4$H$_2$S·HgCl is formed slowly by mercuration
> in presence of sodium acetate as a buffer (C—HgCl link). Can
> be crystallized. Sharp m.p. Stable to alkali; hot dilute acid
> regenerates the thiophen derivative.

17

Methyl iodide: No action.

Oxidation: Side chain → COOH or may be complete. Special conditions may yield sulphones or sesquioxides.

5. *Dialkyl disulphides* $R \cdot S \cdot S \cdot R$.

Mercuric cyanide: No action with a 4 per cent cyanide solution.

Mercuric chloride: Fission to $RS \cdot HgCl$ or $R \cdot SHgCl \cdot HgCl_2$ and to $R \cdot S \cdot OH$ which undergoes disproportionation to $R \cdot SH$ and $R \cdot SO_2H$.

Mercuric acetate: Fission occurs as with mercuric chloride but the resulting mercury derivatives $R \cdot S \cdot Hg \cdot O \cdot COCH_3$ are soluble.

Methyl iodide: Fission occurs giving two mols. of $[R \cdot \overset{+}{S} \cdot Me_2]\ \overset{-}{I}$.

Separation of Sulphur Compounds on the Small Scale

By suitable choice of mercuric salts in a certain order very small quantities of certain sulphur compounds can be separated and identified. If a mixture (M) of methyl mercaptan, dimethyl sulphide and dimethyl disulphide is passed successively in a stream of air or nitrogen through (1) aqueous 4 per cent mercuric cyanide and (2) aqueous 3 per cent mercuric chloride, the mercury dimethyl mercaptide $Hg(SCH_3)_2$ m.p. 174°–175 °C is precipitated in (1) usually accompanied by some of the compound $Hg(SCH_3)_2 \cdot Hg(CN)_2$ so that the m.p. of the deposit may be as low as 140 °C. Recrystallization or boiling with water removes the added cyanide and the pure mercaptide remains (*see* p. 3). In the mercuric chloride the dimethyl sulphide forms the insoluble co-ordinated compound $2(CH_3)_2S \cdot 3HgCl_2$, m.p. 157°–158 °C, but this is accompanied by the compound $CH_3 \cdot S \cdot HgCl$ or its addition compound with mercuric chloride, x $CH_3 \cdot S \cdot HgCl$. y $HgCl_2$, arising by fission of the disulphide. When this mixture is warmed with sodium hydroxide pure dimethyl sulphide is evolved and can be collected in mercuric chloride as the pure addition product m.p. 157°–158 °C. If the alkaline reaction mixture is then acidified and warmed pure methyl mercaptan is evolved and can again be collected in mercuric cyanide. If traces of hydrogen sulphide are present in the mixture (M) the original precipitate in the cyanide will be coloured yellow, yellowish-green or black according to the quantity present[76]. The yellow compound is of the type $(CH_3S)_2Hg \cdot HgS$. Warming with dilute acid will liberate CH_3SH and leave the HgS mainly unattacked. This method has been used for separations of this type where $R = CH_3$— to n-C_5H_{11}—. It has proved very useful for the analysis of the mixtures which are volatilized from cultures of the mould *Scopulariopsis brevicaulis* to which an alkyl disulphide has been added, which undergoes fission

18

and biological methylation giving $R \cdot SH$ and $R \cdot S \cdot CH_3$. Some disulphide volatilizes unchanged (*see* Chapter 5). The higher fungus *Schizophyllum commune* when grown on a medium containing glucose and inorganic salts including ammonium sulphate evolves the mixture (M) containing the three methylated sulphur compounds and slight traces of hydrogen sulphide. Mapstone[77] recommends the use of a 5 per cent solution of cadmium sulphate in N-sulphuric acid for the removal of hydrogen sulphide from its mixture with other sulphur compounds.

Alkylthioacids $R \cdot S \cdot (CH_2)_x COOH$—These acids or their simple derivatives or related compounds are frequently encountered in natural products[78,79]. A consideration of their structural relation to several compounds of biological importance shows that this is to be expected.

$$CH_3 \cdot S \cdot CH_2 \cdot CH(NH_2) \cdot COOH$$
Methylcysteine

$$(CH_3)_2 \overset{+}{S} (\overline{X}) \cdot CH_2 \cdot CH_2 \cdot COOH$$
Dimethyl-β-propiothetin salt

$$CH_3 \cdot S \cdot CH_2 \cdot CH_2 \cdot COOH$$
2-Methylthiopropionic acid

$$CH_3 \cdot S \cdot CH_2 \cdot CH_2 \cdot CH(NH_2) \cdot COOH$$
Methionine

$$CH_3 \cdot S \cdot CH_2 \cdot CH_2 \cdot CH_2 \cdot OH$$
Methionol

Preparation—1. If the sodium derivative of an alkanethiol reacts with the ester of a halogen fatty acid and the ester is hydrolysed with hot N-hydrochloric acid the alkylthioacid is obtained (*see* p. 20). The formation of the sodium mercaptide is conveniently carried out by reaction of the mercaptan with the sodium derivative of the alcohol containing the alkyl group in question, e.g.

$$CH_3 \cdot ONa + H \cdot SCH_3 = CH_3 \cdot S \cdot Na + CH_3OH$$
$$CH_3 \cdot SNa + Br \cdot CH_2 \cdot CH_2 \cdot COOC_2H_5 =$$
$$CH_3 \cdot S \cdot CH_2 \cdot CH_2 \cdot COOC_2H_5 + NaBr$$

2. An alkanethiol may react with an $\alpha\beta$-unsaturated acid or ester in either neutral[80,81] or acid solution[82,83] or in an anhydrous solvent in presence of sodium methoxide $CH_3 \cdot SH + CH_2 : CH \cdot COOCH_3 = CH_3 \cdot S \cdot CH_2 \cdot CH_2 \cdot COOCH_3$.

3. A mercaptide may react with a halogenated fatty acid in presence of sodium ethoxide in alcohol

$$COOH \cdot CH_2 \cdot Cl + NaS \cdot R = COOH \cdot CH_2 \cdot S \cdot R + NaCl$$

or a mercaptan in 30 per cent excess of aqueous sodium hydroxide may react with sodium chloroacetate, the mixture being strongly acidified on completion of the reaction.

4. The decomposition of the salt of an α-thetin by heating with water or dilute acid gives an S-alkylthioacid:

$$(CH_3)_2\overset{+}{S}\ (\overline{X})\cdot CH_2\cdot COOH + H_2O =$$
$$CH_3\cdot OH + HX + CH_3\cdot S\cdot CH_2\cdot COOH$$

Dimethyl sulphide and glycollic acid are also produced.

Natural occurrence of S-methylthioacids—The methyl ester of 2-methylthiopropionic acid, $CH_3\cdot S\cdot CH_2\cdot CH_2\cdot COOCH_3$, occurs in pineapple juice[78]. It is isomeric with dimethyl-β-propiothetin $(CH_3)_2\overset{+}{S}\cdot CH_2\cdot CH_2\cdot CO\overline{O}$ but interconversion by a reaction of the Willstätter type (*see* p. 21) has not yet been effected. The thetin has not been found in pineapple and the author has shown that it is absent from apples (Cox's orange pippins.) The ethyl ester of thioacetic acid, $HS\cdot CH_2\cdot COOC_2H_5$ has been found in beer[79].

THE ABNORMAL HYDROLYSIS OF METHYL 2-METHYLTHIOPROPIONATE AND OF METHYL 2-ETHYLTHIOPROPIONATE

This section describes some work arising from an unexpected observation made during the hydrolysis of the methyl ester of 2-methylthiopropionic acid $CH_3\cdot S\cdot CH_2\cdot CH_2\cdot COOCH_3$. Barger and Coyne[84] state that hydrolysis with boiling N-hydrochloric acid for four hours gives the corresponding acid as a liquid of b.p. 235°–240°C at 760 mm. Liu[85] confirmed this result.

Two other workers at Leeds employed 6N-hydrochloric acid for the same hydrolysis and both obtained entirely different results from those described above. During the heating, there was a marked odour of a volatile sulphur compound and also the acid obtained on extraction with ether was a solid and identified conclusively as bis-2-carboxyethyl sulphide $COOH\cdot CH_2\cdot CH_2\cdot S\cdot CH_2\cdot CH_2\cdot COOH$. Oxidation to the sulphone confirmed this conclusion. The volatile sulphur compound was shown to be dimethyl sulphide by conversion to the mercurichloride $2(CH_3)_2S\cdot 3HgCl_2$ and to the sulphidimine $(CH_3)_2\overset{+}{S} - \overline{N}\cdot SO_2\cdot C_6H_4\cdot CH_3$. It was entirely free from methanethiol as shown by its inertness to mercuric cyanide.

Origin of the Dimethyl Sulphide

It seemed possible that the dimethyl sulphide might arise from the intermediate formation and subsequent decomposition of dimethyl

β-propiothetin chloride $(CH_3)_2\overset{+}{S}(\overline{C}l)\cdot CH_2\cdot CH_2\cdot COOH$, possibly formed from the ester by isomeric change thus

(1.) $CH_3\cdot S\cdot CH_2\cdot CH_2\cdot COOCH_3 \rightarrow (CH_3)_2\overset{+}{S}\cdot CH_2\cdot CH_2\cdot CO\overset{-}{O}\xrightarrow{\text{_ HCl}}$

$(CH_3)_2\overset{+}{S}(\overline{C}l)\cdot CH_2\cdot CH_2\cdot COOH \rightarrow CH_2:CH\cdot COOH +$
$(CH_3)_2S + HCl$

Acrylic acid

Such a reaction would be analogous to the interconversion of trimethylacetobetaine ('betaine') and methyl dimethylaminoacetate demonstrated by Willstätter[86,87].

(2.) $(CH_3)_3\overset{+}{N}\cdot CH_2\cdot CO\cdot\overset{-}{O}\rightleftharpoons (CH_3)_2N\cdot CH_2\cdot COOCH_3$. Betaine, however, is an α-derivative and although it seems possible from Willstätter's publications that a similar relation might hold between trimethyl-β-propiobetaine and methyl-β-dimethylaminopropionate

(3.) $(CH_3)_3\overset{+}{N}\cdot CH_2\cdot CH_2\cdot CO\overset{-}{O} \rightarrow (CH_3)_2N\cdot CH_2\cdot CH_2\cdot COOCH_3$, his evidence for this is not so clear. The β-betaine on heating gives mainly trimethylamine and acrylic acid $CH_2:CH\cdot COOH$.

An interconversion of this type is however not involved in the formation of dimethyl sulphide during the abnormal hydrolysis. Under similar conditions the corresponding ethyl ester also gives dimethyl sulphide whereas methyl 2-ethylthiopropionate $CH_3\cdot CH_2\cdot S\cdot CH_2\cdot CH_2\cdot COOCH_3$ gives diethyl sulphide. Bis-2-carboxyethyl sulphide is formed in each case. Methyl ethyl sulphide is not produced in either case, and the reactions:

$$CH_3\cdot CH_2\cdot S\cdot CH_2\cdot CH_2\cdot COOCH_3 \rightarrow$$

$$\begin{array}{cc} CH_3\cdot CH_2 & CH_3\cdot CH_2 \\ \diagdown & \diagdown \\ \overset{+}{S}\cdot CH_2\cdot CH_2\cdot CO\overset{-}{O} \rightarrow & S + CH_2:CH\cdot COOH \\ \diagup & \diagup \\ CH_3 & CH_3 \end{array}$$

do not occur.

Probable Mechanism of the 'Abnormal Hydrolysis'

It seems fairly certain that the 'abnormal' reaction is brought about by the low pH (6N-acid) although traces of dimethyl sulphide and bis-2-carboxyethyl sulphide $S(CH_2\cdot CH_2\cdot COOH)_2$ are formed even under Barger and Coyne's conditions as shown by Hollingworth. Presumably a proton is co-ordinated by the unshared electrons of the sulphur atom of the methylthiopropionic acid to

21

form the complex ion $CH_3 \cdot \overset{+}{\underset{\cdot\cdot}{S}} \cdot CH_2 \cdot CH_2 \cdot COOH$. This might then be converted to the corresponding thetin by a process in which the positive charge on the sulphur might so attract the electrons of the CH_3—group as to allow bimolecular nucleophilic attack by the sulphur atom of a second molecule of 2-methylthiopropionic acid giving a transition state (X) leading to the formation of the thetin and 2-thiopropionic acid:

$$H \cdot \overset{+}{\underset{\cdot}{S}} \cdot CH_2 \cdot CH_2 \cdot COOH \qquad HS \cdot CH_2 \cdot CH_2 \cdot COOH$$

$$CH_3 \qquad\qquad \longrightarrow \qquad +$$

$$CH_3 \cdot S \cdot CH_2 \cdot CH_2 \cdot COOH \qquad (CH_3)_2 \overset{+}{S} \cdot CH_2 \cdot CH_2 \cdot COOH$$
$$(X)$$

Elimination of dimethyl sulphide from the thetin would leave the cation $\overset{+}{C}H_2CH_2 \cdot COOH$ which by union with 2-thiopropionic acid, followed by deprotonation, could give bis-2-carboxyethyl sulphide:

$$\overset{+}{C}H_2 \cdot CH_2 \cdot COOH + HS \cdot CH_2 \cdot CH_2 \cdot COOH =$$
$$\overset{+}{H} + S(CH_2 \cdot CH_2 \cdot COOH)_2$$

An alternative and somewhat less concise representation of the last stage in the process involves the decomposition of the thetin to dimethyl sulphide and acrylic acid as shown in (1) on p. 21

$$(CH_3)_2 \overset{+}{S} \cdot CH_2 \cdot CH_2 \cdot COOH = (CH_3)_2 S + CH_2 : CH \cdot COOH + H^+$$

By addition of the 2-thiopropionic acid, produced by breakdown of the transition complex shown above, to the acrylic acid, bis-2-carboxyethyl sulphide would be formed and its production during the abnormal hydrolysis explained

$$CH_2 : CH \cdot COOH + H \cdot S \cdot CH_2 \cdot CH_2 \cdot COOH =$$
$$S(CH_2 \cdot CH_2 \cdot COOH)_2$$

It was found that in hot 6N-hydrochloric acid 2-thiopropionic acid reacts with methyl acrylate to form bis-2-carboxyethyl sulphide in good yield. A similar reaction with thioacetic acid $H \cdot S \cdot CH_2 \cdot COOH$ gives the unsymmetrical sulphido-acid $COOH \cdot CH_2 \cdot S \cdot CH_2 \cdot CH_2 \cdot COOH$. These reactions are therefore possible under the conditions of the abnormal hydrolysis. Moreover, by heating a mixture of dimethyl-β-propiothetin chloride and 6N-hydrochloric acid with (a) 2-thiopropionic acid and (b) thioacetic acid the two sulphido-acids were readily obtained:

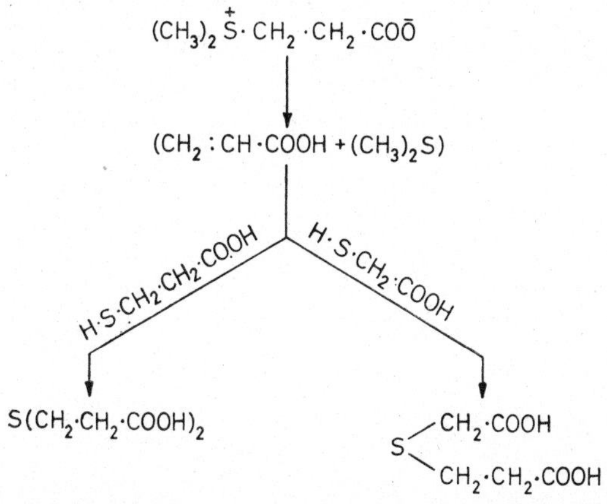

$$(CH_3)_2 \overset{+}{S} \cdot CH_2 \cdot CH_2 \cdot CO\bar{O}$$

$$\downarrow$$

$$(CH_2 : CH \cdot COOH + (CH_3)_2 S)$$

$$H \cdot S \cdot CH_2 \cdot CH_2 \cdot COOH \qquad\qquad H \cdot S \cdot CH_2 \cdot COOH$$

$$\downarrow \qquad\qquad\qquad\qquad\qquad \downarrow$$

$$S(CH_2 \cdot CH_2 \cdot COOH)_2 \qquad\qquad S \underset{CH_2 \cdot CH_2 \cdot COOH}{\overset{CH_2 \cdot COOH}{<}}$$

When 2-methylthiopropionic acid, thioacetic acid and 6N-hydrochloric acid were heated as before both the symmetrical and the unsymmetrical acids were obtained. None of these experiments, however, enables a final decision to be reached as to whether acrylic acid is an intermediate in the original abnormal hydrolysis.

Stability of S-Alkylthioacetic Acids to 6N-Hydrochloric Acid

These acids were recovered unchanged after boiling with the 6N acid. This is probably due to the proximity of the electrophilic carboxyl group to the sulphur atom, whereby the unshared electrons of the sulphur atom are rendered unavailable and co-ordination of a proton hindered. In the corresponding S-alkylthiopropionic acid derivatives this effect is damped by the second intervening —CH_2— group and protonization of the sulphur atom can occur. Since this co-ordination is the first step in the 'abnormal hydrolysis' the absence of such a phenomenon in the S-alkylthioacetic acids is explained.

Decomposition of S-Methylthio-α-amino Acids with Hot Mineral Acid

Methionine $CH_3 \cdot S \cdot CH_2 \cdot CH_2 \cdot CH(NH_2) \cdot COOH$—Butz and du Vigneaud[88] showed that methionine with boiling 18N-sulphuric acid gave homocysteine $HS \cdot CH_2 \cdot CH_2 \cdot CH(NH_2)COOH$ and an odour resembling that of dimethyl disulphide. Repetition of the experiment and aspiration of volatile products through mercuric

23

cyanide and chloride showed the presence of methanethiol, dimethyl sulphide and dimethyl disulphide (*see* p. 18). The monosulphide probably arose by decomposition of the thetin $\overline{\overline{SO}}_4[(CH_3)_2\overset{+}{S}\cdot CH_2\cdot CH_2\cdot CH(NH_2)\cdot COOH]_2$ produced by a reaction analogous to that observed in the 'abnormal hydrolyses' discussed in this section.

In a study of the formation of sulphonium salts derived from the S-alkyl derivatives of amino acids Lavine and Floyd[89-91] have shown that this thetin sulphate is actually formed during the action of sulphuric acid on methionine.

S-methylcysteine—With boiling 18N-sulphuric acid, the volatile products were the same as with methionine, but the yield of dimethyl sulphide was much greater, suggesting the greater instability of the thetin salt of S-methylcysteine as compared with that of methionine.

THE WORK OF LAVINE AND HIS COLLEAGUES ON ALKYLMETHIONINE SULPHONIUM SALTS

These authors have also studied the formation of homocystine by the action of sulphuric acid on methionine[89] by Butz and du Vigneaud's method. Their procedure could probably be used in many of the numerous cases where phosphotungstic acid needs to be removed from combination with a base. The methionine methylsulphonium phosphotungstate obtained by precipitation of the reaction mixture was dissolved in 90 per cent acetone and treated with tetraethylammonium bromide[90]. The sparingly soluble tetraethylammonium phosphotungstate was separated and the filtrate concentrated *in vacuo*. Neutralization with ammonia, concentration, solution in methanol and precipitation with ethanol yielded pure methionine methylsulphonium bromide. It was also shown that dimethyl sulphate in excess of 18N-sulphuric acid readily converts methionine to its methylsulphonium salt.

SCHÖBERL'S SYNTHESIS OF CARBOXYLIC DERIVATIVES OF ALIPHATIC SULPHONIUM COMPOUNDS

Preliminary synthetic work—In 1947 Schöberl and Wagner[92] found that thioacetic acid, $HS\cdot CH_2\cdot COOH$, 2-thiopropionic acid and 1-cysteine combine additively with acrylic acid in neutral or weakly acid solution giving, in the last named reaction, $COOH\cdot CH_2\cdot CH_2\cdot S\cdot CH_2\cdot CH(NH_2)COOH$. Schöberl[93-95] also carried out similar experiments in strongly acid aqueous solutions. In 2-N sulphuric acid containing a trace of hydroquinone, thioacetic acid and acrylic acid gave 87 and 75 per cent yields of the sulphido-acid, $COOH \cdot CH_2 \cdot S \cdot CH_2 \cdot CH_2 \cdot COOH$ in agreement with Hollingworth's results. The residues from the reaction, however, gave fractions in which the presence of C-methyl groups was indicated by the Kuhn–Roth analytical procedure. Consequently the formation of 1–5 per cent of the isomeric disulphido-acid $COOH \cdot CH_2 \cdot S \cdot CH(CH_3) \cdot$ COOH containing a branched chain appeared to have occurred. With 2-thiopropionic and acrylic acids the branched isomer $COOH \cdot CH_2 \cdot CH_2 \cdot S \cdot CH(CH_3) \cdot COOH$ was only produced in presence of alkaline catalysts (sodium hydroxide, trimethylamine or piperidine), to the extent of 0·5–1·5 per cent, as indicated by Kuhn–Roth analysis.

The addition of thioacetic acid to methacrylic acid in neutral solution proceeded normally:

$$HS \cdot CH_2 \cdot COOH + CH_2 : C(CH_3) \cdot COOH =$$
$$COOH \cdot CH_2 \cdot S \cdot CH_2 \cdot CH(CH_3) \cdot COOH$$

The same was true for 1-thiopropionic acid $CH_3 \cdot CH(SH) \cdot COOH$ and acrylic acid. None of the product which should be formed by

$$\begin{array}{c} CH_3 \\ \diagdown \\ \text{addition of} \qquad CH \cdot S\text{— to the } \alpha\text{-position in the double bond} \\ \diagup \\ COOH \end{array}$$

was detected.

The main reaction follows the course of the well-known addition of a polar molecule HM to $\alpha\beta$-unsaturated carbonyl compounds. A proton is added to the α-carbon atom of the unsaturated acid so producing a positive carbonium ion which is then attacked by the anion M^- of HM giving, in the case of acrylic acid, $M \cdot CH_2 \cdot CH_2 \cdot$ COOH.

Schöberl's new synthesis of sulphonium compounds—During these investigations, Schöberl found that when sulphido-acids of the type $COOH \cdot CH_2 \cdot CHR \cdot S \cdot (CH_2)_n \cdot COOH$ (where $n = 1, 2$) react with the unsaturated acid in presence of very concentrated halogen acid (HX) sulphonium compounds of the type $(COOH \cdot CH_2 \cdot CHR)_2 \cdot \overset{+}{S} \cdot (CH_2)_n COOH \Big] \overline{X}$ were obtained[96].

Tri-2-carboxyethylsulphonium chloride, $\overline{Cl}[\overset{+}{S} \cdot (CH_2 \cdot CH_2 \cdot COOH)_3]$, was prepared from 2-thiopropionic acid (4 g.) and acrylic acid (8 g.) in a mixture of hydrochloric acid (5·6 c.c.) and 2N-acetic acid (5·6 c.c.). On cooling in ice the sulphido-acid, bis-2-carboxyethyl

25

sulphide $S(CH_2 \cdot CH_2 \cdot COOH)_2$ was quickly deposited m.p. 128 °C (*see* p. 22). It was not separated. If the mixture was left for 24 hours the m.p. of the deposit rose to 155 °C. The solid was separated and on treatment with cold alcohol some sulphido-acid m.p. 128 °C was removed. The residue melted at 162 °–163 °C and was shown to be the tricarboxyethylsulphonium chloride. This was also obtained directly from bis-2-carboxyethyl sulphide and acrylic acid suspended in a small quantity of water by saturation with gaseous hydrogen chloride. The corresponding bromide was obtained by similar procedure. These salts are stable at room temperature but on thermal decomposition or on heating in aqueous solution one carboxyethyl group —$CH_2 \cdot CH_2 \cdot COOH$ is eliminated, presumably as 2-halogenopropionic acid:

$$S(CH_2 \cdot CH_2 \cdot COOH)_2 + CH_2 : CH \cdot COOH + HX \rightarrow \overline{X} \Big\{ \overset{+}{S}(CH_2 \cdot$$
$$CH_2 \cdot COOH)_3 \rightarrow S(CH_2 \cdot CH_2 \cdot COOH)_2 + X \cdot CH_2 \cdot CH_2 \cdot \overset{\cdot}{C}OOH$$

Carboxymethyl-di-2-*carboxyethyl sulphonium halide*—$COOH \cdot CH_2 \cdot \overset{+}{S}$ $(CH_2 \cdot CH_2 \cdot COOH)_2 \Big\} \overline{X}$ *and the corresponding Thetin,* (presumably) $(COOH \cdot CH_2 \cdot CH_2)_2 \overset{+}{S} \cdot CH_2 \cdot CO\overline{O}$. The sulphonium chloride was prepared from acrylic acid and thioacetic acid $HS \cdot CH_2 \cdot COOH$ by a similar process. When it was dissolved in hot water the thetin crystallized. The sulphonium salt was obtained on concentration of the mother liquors *in vacuo*. It undergoes considerable dissociation in water and the corresponding base is weaker than the tri-2-carboxy-ethylsulphonium base $H\overline{O} \Big\{ \overset{+}{S}(CH_2 \cdot CH_2 \cdot COOH)_3$ which yields no anhydride (thetin) under similar conditions. Since thetin formation depends on the replacement of a —$CH_2 \cdot CH_2 \cdot COOH$ residue by —$CH_2 \cdot COOH$, the latter group is presumably the one involved in thetin formation. The closer proximity to the sulphur atom of one of the three carboxyl groups presumably lowers the basic properties of the sulphonium ion.

Further instances of thetin formation in Schöberl's experiments—The thetin

$$\begin{array}{c} COOH \cdot CH_2 \cdot CH_2 \cdot \overset{+}{S} \cdot CH_2 \cdot COOH \\ | \\ CH_2 \cdot CO\overline{O} \end{array}$$

containing two —$CH_2 \cdot COO$ groups linked to sulphur is obtained at once when acrylic acid, hydrogen chloride and 1 : 1′-dicarboxy-dimethyl sulphide interact. Formation in acid solution of a thetin rather than its salt appears to be a new observation.

Neither sulphonium salt $\overline{X}\{\overset{+}{S}(CH_2 \cdot COOH)_3$ nor thetin $(COOH \cdot CH_2)_2 \overset{+}{S} \cdot CH_2 \cdot CO\overline{O}$ is obtained from the 1 : 1'-dicarboxy-dimethyl sulphide and bromoacetic acid. This thetin can however be prepared from the salts of the two acids in neutral solution

$$(COONa \cdot CH_2)_2 S + BrCH_2 \cdot COONa =$$
$$(COONa \cdot CH_2)_2 \overset{+}{S} \cdot CH_2 \cdot CO\overline{O} + NaBr$$

and, in agreement with the considerations already discussed, does not form a sulphonium salt with acids.

Sulphonium salts (XI) to (XIII) are also formed from S-ethylthio-acetic acid $CH_3 \cdot CH_2 \cdot S \cdot CH_2 \cdot COOH$, hydrogen halide and acrylic, crotonic $CH_3 \cdot CH : CH \cdot COOH$ and methacrylic $CH_2 : C(CH_3) \cdot COOH$ acids and others from S-*iso*propylthioacetic acid and acrylic and crotonic acids. Diethyl and di-*iso*propyl sulphides behave in a similar manner giving e.g. (XIV). The di-*iso*propylsulphonium salt was characterized as the picrate. The di- and tricarboxy-sulphonium compounds are not precipitated by picric acid. Many of them, however, form insoluble reineckates (XV).

$$R_2 \overset{R_1}{\underset{R_3}{\diagdown \underset{\diagup}{\overset{+}{S}}}} \left[\overline{Cr} \begin{array}{c} (SCN)_4 \\ (NH_3)_2 \end{array} \right] \text{(XV)}$$

$$\begin{array}{c} CH_3 \cdot CH_2 \cdot \overset{+}{S} \cdot CH_2 \cdot COOH \\ | \\ CH_2 \cdot CH_2 \cdot COOH \\ \text{(XI)} \end{array} \qquad \begin{array}{c} CH_3 \cdot CH_2 \cdot \overset{+}{S} \cdot CH_2 \cdot COOH \\ | \\ CH_3 \cdot CH \cdot CH_2 \cdot COOH \\ \text{(XII)} \end{array}$$

$$\begin{array}{c} CH_3 \cdot CH_2 \cdot \overset{+}{S} \cdot CH_2 \cdot COOH \\ | \\ CH_2 \cdot CH(CH_3) \cdot COOH \\ \text{(XIII)} \end{array} \qquad \begin{array}{c} CH_3 \cdot CH_2 \cdot \overset{+}{S} \cdot CH_2 \cdot CH_3 \\ | \\ CH_2 \cdot CH_2 \cdot COOH \\ \text{(XIV)} \end{array}$$

Schöberl's views on the mechanism of his sulphonium synthesis—Schöberl considers it improbable that the reaction proceeds by simple addition to the sulphide or sulphido-acid R_2S of a halogeno-fatty acid resulting from the action of HX on the unsaturated acid—acrylic, crotonic or methacrylic. The conditions were often such as to make addition of halogen acid to the double bond most improbable. The yield of sulphonium salt obtained when 2-bromopropionic acid and bis-2-carboxyethyl sulphide $S(CH_2 \cdot CH_2 \cdot COOH)_2$ were warmed in aqueous solution at 55 °C for 22 hours was very small. Nevertheless, Schöberl does not describe the behaviour of the sulphido-acid or sulphide with the halogeno-fatty acid under the strongly acid conditions which he employed. He suggests that the mechanism of the reaction is similar to that accepted for addition of a thiol to an unsaturated acid. A proton from the halogen acid is co-ordinated by the α-carbon atom of the unsaturated acid. The resulting positive ion is co-ordinated by the unshared electrons of the sulphur atom of the sulphide or sulphido-acid, thus producing a sulphonium ion:

$$CH_2 : CH \cdot COOH + H^+ = -\overset{+}{C}H_2 \cdot CH_2 \cdot COOH$$

$$R \cdot S \cdot CH_2 \cdot CH_2 \cdot COOH + -\overset{+}{C}H_2 \cdot CH_2 \cdot COOH$$

$$= R \cdot \overset{+}{S}(CH_2 \cdot CH_2 \cdot COOH)_2$$

Schöberl cites the analogous work of Barnett, Cook and Peck[97] who found that with styrene, pyridine and bromine, styrene dibromide $C_6H_5 \cdot CHBr \cdot CH_2Br$ was formed as well as a quaternary pyridinium salt, but that styrene dibromide and pyridine did not react during 24 hours, in agreement with the modern ionic mechanism involving formation of the ion $C_6H_5 \cdot \overset{+}{C}H \cdot CH_2Br$.

Schöberl's work clearly bears much similarity to that of the author and Hollingworth. Their experiments at Leeds whether (a) abnormal hydrolysis of S-alkyl-2-thiopropionic esters or (b) addition of a thio-acid to an unsaturated acid or (c) reaction of dimethyl-β-propiothetin chloride with a thio-aliphatic acid (see pp. 20–23) were carried out in boiling 6N-hydrochloric acid. Schöberl synthesized his carboxysulphonium compounds by two methods:

(1) interaction of hydrogen halide, an unsaturated acid and the sulphide or sulphido-acid in 2N-acid, with or without an organic solvent or (2) saturation of an aqueous mixture of the sulphide or sulphido-acid and the olefinic acid with gaseous hydrogen halide. Formation of one or more carboxysulphonium compounds of the type described by Schöberl might therefore be expected in Hollingworth's experiments (a), (b) and (c).

Trimethylsulphonium chloride, dimethyl sulphide and S-methylthioacetic acid were detected by Hollingworth when dimethylacetothetin chloride was boiled with 6N-hydrochloric acid. The more soluble reaction products of his other experiments should therefore be investigated.

28

REFERENCES

[1] Birch, S. F. and Norris, W. S. G. P., *J. chem. Soc.* **127** (1925) 899

[2] Zeise, W. C., *Liebig's Ann.* **11** (1834) 1

[3] See also Liebig, J., *ibid.*, **11** (1834) 14

[4] Meyer-Jacobson, *Lehrbuch der Organischen Chemie, Zweite Auflage, Erster Band, Erster Teil* (1907) 319

[5] Briscoe, P. A., *Thesis*, Univ. of Leeds, (1953) 66

[6] Challenger, F. and Rawlings, A. A., *J. chem. Soc.* (1937) 868

[7] Sachs, G. and Balassa, L., *Z. anorg. Chem.* **145** (1925) 194

[8] Jolibois, P. and Bouvois, P., *Compt. rend.* **170** (1920) 1497

[9] Rübner, M., *Arch. Hyg.* **19** (1893) 136

[10] Birkinshaw, J. H., Findlay, W. K. P. and Webb, R. A., *Biochem. J.* **36** (1942) 526

[11] Challenger, F. and Charlton, P. T., *J. chem. Soc.* (1947) 424

[12] Briscoe, P. A., Personal communication

[13] Houben-Weyl, *Die Methoden der Organischen Chemie*, Thieme. Stuttgart, **9** (1955) 7

[14] Ingold, C. K., Jessop, J. A., Kuriyan, K. I. and Mandour, A.M.M. *J. chem. Soc.* (1933) 533

[15] Meyer-Jacobson, *Lehrbuch der Organischen Chemie, Zweiter Auflage, Erster Band, Erster Teil* (1907) 318

[16] Dijkstra, N. D., *Thesis*, Univ. of Groningen, (1933) 12

[17] Houben-Weyl, *Die Methoden der Organischen Chemie*, Thieme, Stuttgart, **9** (1955) 33

[18] Nencki, L., *Monatsh.* **10** (1889) 862

[19] Nencki, L., *Ber. dtsch. chem. Ges.* **34** (1901) 201

[20] Bauer, R., *Z. physiol. Chem.* **35** (1902) 348

[21] Birkinshaw, J. H., Findlay, W. P. K. and Webb, R. A., *Biochem. J.* **36** (1942) 526

[22] Nencki, L., *Arch. exp. Path. Pharmak.* **28** (1891) 206

[23] Challenger, F. and Walshe, J. M., *Biochem. J.* **59** (1955) 372

[24] Challenger, F. and Rawlings, A. A., *J. chem. Soc.* (1937) 868

[25] Blackburn, S. and Challenger, F., *ibid.*, (1938) 1872

[26] Nakamura, N., *Biochem. Z.* **164** (1925) 31

[27] Challenger, F. and Greenwood, D., *Biochem. J.* **44** (1949) 87

[28] See Blackburn, S. and Challenger, F., *J. chem. Soc.*, (1938) 1872 for references.

[29] Kidder, G. W., *Federation Proc.* **13** (1954) 695

[30] O'Kane, D. J. and Gunsalus, K., *J. Bact.* **56** (1948) 499

[31] *Ann. Reports Chem. Soc.* **51** (1954) 244; **52** (1955) 231

[32] Calvin, M., *Conferences et Rapports*, 3ème Cong. Intern. de Biochimie, Brussels (1955) 222

[33] *Histochemische Methoden*, Sammlung herausgegeben von W. Lipp, Lieferung III 1954, 15, 21, 9, R. Oldenbourg, München

[34] Barrnett, R. J. and Seligman, A. M., *Science* **116** (1952) 323

[35] Barrnett, R. J. and Seligman, A. M., *J. Histochem. Cytochem.* **1** (1953) 392

[36] Barrnett, R. J. and Seligman, A. M., *J. nat. Cancer Inst.* **14** (1954) 769
[37] Haas, P., *Biochem. J.* **29** (1935) 1298
[38] See References 60 and 62
[39] Evans, R. C., Mann, F. G., Peiser, H. S. and Purdie, D., *J. chem. Soc.* (1940) 1215; Mann, F. G. and Purdie, D., *ibid.*, (1936) 130
[40] Cox, E. G., Saenger, H. and Wardlaw, W., *ibid.*, (1934) 182
[41] Angell, F. G., Drew, H. D. K. and Wardlaw, W., *ibid.*, (1930) 349; Drew, H. D. K., Preston, G. H., Wardlaw, W. and Wyatt, G. H., *ibid.*, (1933) 1294
[42] Dransfield, P. B. and Challenger, F., *ibid.*, (1955) 1153
[43] Bird, Miss M. L. and Challenger, F., *ibid.*, (1942) 573
[44] Bird, Miss M. L. and Challenger, F., *ibid.*, (1939) 163
[45] Bordwell, F. G. and McKellin, W. H., *J. Amer. chem. Soc.* **73** (1951) 2251
[46] Bonner, W. A., *ibid.*, **74** (1952) 1033, 1034, 5089
[47] Fenton, G. W. and Ingold, C. K., *J. chem. Soc.* (1928) 3127; (1929) 2338; (1930) 705
[48] Ingold, C. K., *Structure and Mechanism in Organic Chemistry*, G. Bell & Sons, Ltd., London, (1953) 420
[49] Houben-Weyl, *Die Methoden der Organischen Chemie.* Thieme, Stuttgart, **9** (1955) 141
[50] Smith, J. C., *Ann. Reports Chem. Soc.* **36** (1939) 219
[51] Mayo, F. R. and Walling, C., *Chem. Rev.* **27** (1940) 351
[52] Kharasch, M. S., Mansfield, J. Y. and Mayo, F. R., *J. Amer. chem. Soc.* **59** (1937) 1155
[53] Markownikoff, W. B., *Liebig's Ann.* **153** (1870) 228, 256
[54] Challenger, F. and Hollingworth, H. D., *Chem. & Ind.* (1954) 463
[55] Crane, C. W. and Rydon, H. N., *J. chem. Soc.* (1947) 766
[56] Fromm, E., *Liebig's Ann.* **394** (1912) 290
[57] Challenger, F., Smith, A. L. and Paton, F. G., *J. chem. Soc.* (1923) 1046
[58] Challenger, F. and Simpson, Miss M. I., *ibid.*, (1948) 1591
[59] Challenger, F., Bywood, R., Thomas, Mrs. P. and Hayward, Miss B. J., *Arch. Biochem. Biophys.* **69** (1957) 514
[60] Pohl, F., *Arch. exp. Path. Pharmak.* **51** (1904) 341
[61] For references see Challenger, F., *Chem. Rev.* **36** (1945) 335
[62] Henze, M., *Z. physiol. Chem.* **41** (1904) 122
[63] Schimmel and Co., Annual Reports; *Cent. Blatt.* (1909) I 1564
[64] Challenger, F. and Greenwood, D., *J. chem. Soc.* (1950) 26
[65] Zincke, T. and Farr, F., *Liebig's Ann.* **391** (1912) 57
[66] Zincke, T. and Baeumer, J., *ibid.* **416** (1918) 86
[67] Backer, H. J., *Rec. Trav. chim. Pays-Bas* **67** (1948) 902
[68] Taylor, B., cited by Challenger, F. and Rawlings, A. A., *J. chem. Soc.* (1937) 871
[69] Schöberl, A., *Liebig's Ann.* **507** (1933) 111
[70] Schöberl, A., *ibid.*, **522** (1936) 97
[71] Challenger, F., *Mfg. Chem.* **25** (1954) 151
[72] Birch, S. F. and McAllan, D. T., *J. Inst. Petrol.* **37** (1951) 443
[73] Steinkopf, W., *Die Chemie des Thiophens*, Steinkopf, Leipzig, (1941)

REFERENCES

[74] Hartough, H. D., *Thiophene and its Derivatives*, Interscience, New York, (1952) pp. 444–53

[75] Challenger, F., Haslam, J., Bramhall, R. J. and Walkden, J., *J. Inst. Petrol.* **12** (1926) 10

[76] Rübner, M., *Arch. Hyg.* **19** (1893) 156

[77] Mapstone, G. E., *J. Proc. Aust. chem. Inst.* **13** (1946) 373

[78] Haagen-Smith, A. J., Kirchner, J. G., Deasy, C. L. and Prater, A. N., *J. Amer. chem. Soc.* **67** (1945) 1651

[79] Obata, Y. and Yamanishi, T., *Bull. chem. Soc. Japan* **22** (1949) 247

[80] Ramberg, L., *Ber. dtsch. chem. Ges.* **40** (1907) 2588

[81] Hurd, C. D. and Gershbein, L. L., *J. Amer. chem. Soc.* **69** (1947) 2328, 2333

[82] Hollingworth, H. D., *Thesis*, Univ. of Leeds, (1952)

[83] Challenger, F. and Hollingworth, H. D., *Chem. & Ind.*, (1954) 463

[84] Barger, G. and Coyne, F. P., *Biochem. J.* **22** (1928) 1417

[85] Liu, Y. C., Personal communication

[86] Willstätter, R., *Ber. dtsch. chem. Ges.* **35** (1902) 584

[87] Willstätter, R. and Kahn, W., *ibid.*, **37** (1904) 401, 1853

[88] Butz, L. W. and du Vigneaud, V., *J. biol. Chem.* **99** (1932–1933) 135

[89] Lavine, T. F. and Floyd, N. F., *ibid.*, **207** (1954) 97

[90] Floyd, N. F. and Lavine, T. F., *ibid.*, **207** (1954) 119

[91] Lavine, T. F., Floyd, N. F. and Cammaroti, M. S., *ibid.*, **207** (1954) 107

[92] Schöberl, A. and Wagner, A., *Ber. dtsch. chem. Ges.* **80** (1947) 379

[93] Schöberl, A., *Angew. Chem.* **64** (1952) 224

[94] Schöberl, A., *ibid.*, **65** (1953) 321

[95] Schöberl, A., and Lange, G., *Liebig's Ann.* **599** (1956) 140

[96] De Lisle, A., *Ber. dtsch. chem. Ges.* **25** (1892) 2450

[97] Barnett, E. de B., Cook, J. W. and Peck, W. C., *J. chem. Soc.* **125** (1924) 1035

31

2

NATURAL SULPHONIUM COMPOUNDS, SULPHIDES, SULPHOXIDES, MERCAPTANS AND SULPHIDO-AMINO ACIDS

THE DIMETHYL SULPHIDE EVOLVED FROM THE MARINE ALGA *POLYSIPHONIA FASTIGIATA*

Historical introduction

THE work now to be discussed owes much to the fundamental and long-continued researches of Haas on the ingredients of certain marine algae. In 1921 he established the occurrence of 'ethereal sulphates' in carrageen (*Chondrus crispus*)[1,2]. He showed that these consisted of potassium and calcium salts of the acid sulphuric esters of polysaccharides. Compounds of this type were already known to occur in animals, e.g. in cartilage, but had not previously been detected in plants. In 1931 Haas isolated an octapeptide of glutamic acid[3] from the red alga *Polysiphonia fastigiata* and studied with Bird[4] the constituents of the cell-wall of *Laminaria*. He had always been particularly interested in the red algae and in 1923 with Miss Russell-Wells[5] had shown that *Polysiphonia fastigiata* also contains a polysaccharide sulphate.

Identification of Dimethyl Sulphide

In 1935 Haas investigated the nature of the odorous product which is evolved by this seaweed when exposed to air. He found that on aspirating air over the weed through (*a*) bromine in carbon tetrachloride, (*b*) mercuric chloride and (*c*) potassium chloroplatinite K_2PtCl_4, the dibromide $(CH_3)_2SBr_2$, the mercurichloride $2(CH_3)_2S \cdot 3HgCl_2$ and the platinochloride $2(CH_3)_2S \cdot PtCl_2$ which resulted, were identical with those of dimethyl sulphide[6]. *Polysiphonia nigrescens* also evolved this sulphide.

The author and Blackburn found[7] that in cultures of the mould *S. brevicaulis* carefully purified dimethyl disulphide gave rise to methanethiol, CH_3SH and dimethyl sulphide, in agreement with the reducing and methylating action exerted by this organism on other dialkyl disulphides (*see* Chapter 5).

In 1942 Birkinshaw, Findlay and Webb[8] reported that the wood-destroying fungus *Schizophyllum commune* when grown on a glucose medium containing inorganic salts and a trace of 'Marmite' converts ammonium sulphate to methanethiol. The author and Charlton[9] then showed that dimethyl sulphide and traces of dimethyl disulphide were also present.

On account of the frequency with which biological methylation is encountered, it seemed possible that the dimethyl sulphide evolved by the alga in Haas' experiments might arise by methylation of the polysaccharide sulphates of the weed. This would involve hydrolysis, reduction and further methylation. Such a process would resemble the metabolism of *S. commune*.

It appeared unlikely that the dimethyl sulphide was stored as such in the alga, and the possibility of its occurrence as a sulphonium compound suggested itself. It was therefore decided to attempt the identification of the precursor from which it appeared probable (*see* below) that the sulphide was eliminated by enzyme action.

Conditions under which Dimethyl Sulphide is formed

In some preliminary experiments in which the alga was placed in artificial sea-water containing sodium ethyl sulphate $C_2H_5 \cdot O \cdot SO_2 \cdot ONa$, no methyl ethyl sulphide but only dimethyl sulphide was evolved. This provided no support for the suggestion outlined above.

When the volatile products from the alga, removed from its host *Ascophyllum nodosum* and placed in tap or distilled water, were aspirated through (*a*) mercuric cyanide and (*b*) mercuric chloride, no precipitate was formed in (*a*), indicating the absence of methanethiol. The deposit in (*b*) consisted solely of the mercurichloride of dimethyl sulphide; mercurated fission products of dimethyl disulphide were absent. The sulphur compound was, therefore, homogeneous. Addition of cold sodium hydroxide to the alga accelerated the elimination of dimethyl sulphide.

The question arises whether the sulphide evolution is an essential life-process of the alga or whether it is a sign of death or damage. The well-known occurrence of trimethylamine, in the living flowers of many trees and plants may be cited. Cromwell[10] showed that in the case of *Chenopodium vulvaria* the amine arises by enzyme action from choline and not from betaine.

An enzyme is clearly concerned with the algal process also. Grinding the weed with sand or immersing it in distilled water facilitated the evolution[11]. Weed immersed in boiling water and allowed to cool evolved no dimethyl sulphide in an air stream, but long boiling with water or addition of sodium hydroxide (purely chemical hydrolysis) caused a fresh evolution. When the alga was left in alcohol for a few hours, and then suspended in water, air removed no dimethyl sulphide, but addition of alkali caused a ready evolution. Dimethyl sulphide formation still occurred when the weed was placed in water containing toluene and well shaken, so that it is unlikely that bacterial action was involved. The enzymic nature of the process has now been confirmed by Cantoni[12,13] (*see below*).

IDENTIFICATION OF THE PRECURSOR OF THE DIMETHYL SULPHIDE, AS DIMETHYL-β-PROPIOTHETIN

A concentrated alcoholic extract of the alga gave a precipitate with ammonium reineckate $NH_4[Cr(NH_3)_2(SCN)_4]$. After successive conversion to the sulphate, chloride, platinichloride and chloride, a picrate was obtained. Decomposition with hydrochloric acid gave a pure chloride $C_5H_{11}O_2ClS$. This was optically inactive and evolved dimethyl sulphide with cold sodium hydroxide. Its acidity and non-reactivity with 2 : 4-dinitrophenylhydrazine excluded such constitutions as $Cl^-\{^+S(CH_3)_2 \cdot CH_2 \cdot CO \cdot CH_2OH$ or $Cl^-\{^+S(CH_3)_2 \cdot CH(OH) \cdot CH_2 \cdot CHO$. It appeared probable that the chloride was either an α- or a β-thetin derivative (I) or (II).

$$Cl^-\{^+S(CH_3)_2 \cdot CH(CH_3)CO_2H \qquad Cl^-\{^+S(CH_3)_2 \cdot CH_2 \cdot CH_2 \cdot CO_2H$$
$$\text{(I)} \qquad\qquad\qquad \text{(II)}$$

The authentic bromides were converted to the chlorides, picrates, styphnates, and platinichlorides. Mixed m.p. determinations carried out with these compounds and with corresponding derivatives from *P. fastigiata* showed that the algal product is the chloride of the β–propiothetin derivative, dimethyl-2-carboxyethylsulphonium chloride[11] (II).

POSSIBLE BIOCHEMICAL SIGNIFICANCE OF THE THETIN

Cantoni and Anderson[12] have recently confirmed the conclusions of Challenger and Simpson[11] and have shown that *P. fastigiata* contains an enzyme which, although so far only obtained in a crude condition, is extremely active in effecting the decomposition of dimethyl-β-propiothetin to dimethyl sulphide, acrylic acid and H^+ (*see* p. 21),

$$(CH_3)_2\overset{+}{S} \cdot CH_2 \cdot CH_2 \cdot CO \cdot OH = (CH_3)_2S + CH_2 : CH \cdot COOH + H^+$$

Cantoni[13] remarks that this suggests that some important biological function may be performed by the thetin and the enzyme but he does not discuss the problem further. Challenger[14] has suggested that the fission might bear some analogy with the thiaminase reaction which has been studied by Woolley[15]. In that case the fission would liberate the cation $\overset{+}{C}H_2 \cdot CH_2 \cdot COOH$ which with ammonia or trimethylamine (both presumably available in the alga) could give β-alanine $NH_2 \cdot CH_2 \cdot CH_2 \cdot COOH$ or its betaine $(CH_3)_3 \overset{+}{N} \cdot CH_2 \cdot CH_2 \cdot COOH$ and in the first case, H^+.

$$(CH_3)_2 \overset{+}{S} \cdot CH_2 \cdot CH_2 \cdot COOH + NH_3 \rightarrow$$
$$(CH_3)_2 S + H_2 N \cdot CH_2 \cdot CH_2 \cdot COOH + H^+$$
$$(CH_3)_2 \overset{+}{S} \cdot CH_2 \cdot CH_2 \cdot COOH + (CH_3)_3 N \rightarrow$$
$$(CH_3)_2 S + (CH_3)_3 \overset{+}{N} \cdot CH_2 \cdot CH_2 \cdot COOH$$

The betaine might also arise by methylation of β-alanine by an algal transmethylase. The presence of small quantities of β-alanine, both free and combined probably as Co-enzyme A (*see* Chapter 6), has recently been demonstrated by paper chromatography in each of a larger number of marine algae which were examined by Ericson and Carlson[16]. It is noteworthy that the highest amount of β-alanine, 68 μg. per gram was found in *Polysiphonia fastigiata* and 30 μg. per gram in *Ulva lactuca*. In eleven other varieties the figures ranged from 12 to 54. It will be recalled that it was from *P. fastigiata* that dimethyl-β-propiothetin was isolated[11] (*see* p. 34). Cantoni[17] gives its concentration in the alga as 0·3 to 0·4 molar. *Ulva lactuca* almost certainly contains a dimethylsulphonium compound (probably the same thetin) as it evolves much dimethyl sulphide with cold alkali[18] (*see* p. 33).

These results need further amplification before the author's suggestion of a biological relation between the thetin, β-alanine or its betaine and ammonia or trimethylamine can be regarded as significant. β-alanine betaine has not yet been detected in marine algae. It should also be emphasized that the amount of thetin in *P. fastigiata* and probably in *Ulva lactuca* is much greater than that of β-alanine, free or combined. Ericson and Carlson[16] state—'the β-alanine occurring in bound form is, however, so high that it is improbable that all of it should exist in the form of pantothenic acid. β-alanine must therefore play some other role in the metabolism of marine algae . . . the concentration . . . is so high that it could well constitute part of a protein molecule. Further studies are required.'

THETIN SALTS AND MOULD CULTURES

As early as 1946 it was almost certain that the breakdown of the dimethyl-β-propiothetin salt in *Polysiphonia fastigiata* is due to enzyme action. It therefore became of interest to study the behaviour of thetin salts with different organisms[19] and *S. brevicaulis* and *Penicillium notatum* were chosen. The seaweed thetin chloride and bromide were almost unchanged in bread cultures of the first mould, only a 1–2 per cent yield of dimethyl sulphide being obtained. With *P. notatum* and the bromide, however, the yield was 36 per cent. The isomeric dimethyl-α-propiothetin bromide and chloride $(CH_3)_2\overset{+}{S}(\overline{X})CH(CH_3)\cdot COOH$ gave no dimethyl sulphide in cultures of *S. brevicaulis* and *P. notatum* respectively. Dimethyl-acetothetin bromide was also inert to both moulds. The sulphides were characterized and weighed as the mercurichloride. It was conclusively shown that, where a sulphide was evolved, this was not due to the culture becoming alkaline by formation of ammonia, with consequent liberation of the sulphide.

DIMETHYL-β-PROPIOTHETIN IN OTHER MARINE ALGAE

When Challenger and Simpson's work was published, no other instance of the occurrence of a sulphonium compound in plants had been recorded apart from that of sulphoxides (*see* p. 39). On account of their basic properties they may be regarded as 'potential' sulphonium compounds e.g., $(CH_3)_2SO + HX \longrightarrow X\text{-}\Big\{ {}^+S(OH)\cdot(CH_3)_2.$ In recent years the biological importance of sulphonium compounds has received much attention and their occurrence established both in plants (*see* below) and in animals[20,21] (*see* p. 43).

In 1953 Bywood[22], working in the author's laboratory isolated derivatives of dimethyl-β-propiothetin from alcoholic extracts of two green marine algae, *Enteromorpha intestinalis* and *Spongomorpha arcta*. In the first case the method of isolation was very similar to that employed for *P. fastigiata*, the reineckate being first obtained and then converted successively to the platinichloride, $R_2Pt\ Cl_6$, the picrate and the styphnate. From *Sp. arcta* a platinichloride was isolated which evolved dimethyl sulphide with cold alkali and had the m.p. of the platinichloride of dimethyl-β-propiothetin. Nicolai and Preston[23] carried out an X-ray examination of *Sp. arcta* and *Sp. lanosa* and of evaporated aqueous extracts; the diagrams obtained were similar to that of dimethyl-β-propiothetin bromide.

UNIDENTIFIED DIMETHYLSULPHONIUM COMPOUNDS IN OTHER PLANTS

Bywood[24] also examined a number of other marine algae, of which *Ulva lactuca* and *Enteromorpha compressa* readily evolved dimethyl sulphide with cold sodium hydroxide as did also two freshwater algae *Oedogorium sp.* and *Ulothrix sp.* Other marine algae, such as *Pelvetia caniculata, Halidrys siliquosa, Cladophora rupestris* and *Ceramium rubrum* only evolved the sulphide with boiling alkali. This was also the case with the freshwater alga *Microspora amoena.* The dimethyl sulphide was collected as the mercurichloride. *Spongomorpha arcta* evolved more dimethyl sulphide with hot alkali, after evolution with the cold reagent had ceased. This may possibly indicate that a portion of the sulphonium compound is more firmly linked than the rest, a suggestion which receives some support from the work of Nicolai and Preston[23]. No dimethyl sulphide was evolved when the dried mycelium of *S. brevicaulis,* grown on a glucose–inorganic salts medium, or *P. notatum* obtained from a penicillin factory were boiled with alkali.

In 1949 Karrer and his colleagues[25] detected dimethyl sulphone in various species of *Equisetum* (horse tails) e.g. in *E. palustre, E. arvense, E. hiemale* and probably *E. telmateia.* This observation suggested to the author the possible presence of a sulphonium compound in the *Equisetae* and on boiling some species with alkali, dimethyl sulphide was evolved and characterized as the mercurichloride[26]. It was shown to be extremely unlikely that the sulphide could have been formed by reduction of dimethyl sulphone by the alkali and organic matter of the plant.

The fresh green fronds and leaves of the common bracken (*Pteridium aquilinum*) evolved dimethyl sulphide with alkali[26], which was characterized as the sulphidimine (*see* p. 44) and as two other derivatives. It is probable that the precursor of the dimethyl sulphide in these cryptogams is a sulphonium compound but it has not yet been identified in either case.

Smythe suggested that, in animals, the sulphone may be formed by methylation and oxidation of hydrogen sulphide which is produced from cystine in presence of liver slices[27]. Oxidation of methionine to methylsulphonoacetic acid, followed by decarboxylation: $CH_3 \cdot SO_2 \cdot CH_2 \cdot COOH = CH_3 \cdot SO_2 \cdot CH_3 + CO_2$ is also a possibility. This decomposition readily occurs in presence of hot alkali. It would seem, however, that the most probable explanation is the fission of a dimethylsulphonium compound giving dimethyl sulphide followed by oxidation.

OCCURRENCE OF S-METHYL-L-CYSTEINE SULPHOXIDE IN CABBAGE

An interesting corollary to the work just described is the isolation by Synge and Wood[28] of the sulphoxide of (+)-S-methyl-L-cysteine $CH_3 \cdot \overset{+}{\underset{\underset{O-}{|}}{S}} \cdot CH_2 \cdot CH \cdot NH_2 \cdot COOH$ from a diffusate[29] from

cabbage. It was obtained by adsorption on a column of the ion-exchange resin Zeo-Karb 215 (H$^+$ form) and later displaced, along with aspartic and glutamic acids and some other amino acids by ammonia. It was separated from these by partition chromatography on kieselguhr. Crystallization from ethanol gave a product of m.p. 167°–168°C (decomp.) and $\left[\alpha\right]_D^{24} = + 118°$ in water. Its behaviour on paper chromatography was identical with that of a synthetic mixture of the diastereoisomers of S-methyl-L-cysteine sulphoxide obtained by oxidation of the amino acid with aqueous hydrogen peroxide. Such mixtures have been prepared from S-methylcysteine by two groups of workers, but no attempt was made to separate the diastereoisomers arising from the production of a new asymmetric centre, the sulphoxide group. Separation of such optical isomers does not need the use of a third optically active centre (*see* p. 41 and Chapter 3) and Lavine[30] separated the isomeric sulphoxides of L-methionine by crystallization of their picrates. Stoll and Seebeck[31] separated the diastereoisomers of S-allylcysteine- and S-propylcysteine sulphoxides by direct crystallization.

Separation of the synthetic diastereoisomers of S-methyl-L-cysteine sulphoxide—In order to complete the identification of the sulphoxide from cabbage, Synge and Wood attempted the separation of the synthetic diastereoisomers of S-methyl-L-cysteine sulphoxide by fractional crystallization of their picrates but though fractions of different optical rotations were obtained the method was unpromising as also was paper chromatography using collidine-water. Synge and Wood then tried to resolve the mixture by chromatography on a cation-exchange resin in view of the successful separation of the sulphoxides of methionine by this method reported by Moore and Stein[32]. Three zones were obtained on the column of which the first two were imperfectly resolved, but a third yielded after elution and purification on a column of Zeo-Karb 215 and elution with ammonia, a solid. This was identical in m.p. and mixed m.p. and in specific rotation with the natural dextrorotatory sulphoxide obtained by Synge and Wood from cabbage, which is therefore (+)-S-methyl-L-cysteine sulphoxide. The synthetic and natural products were also shown to be crystallographically identical. Moreover, the natural strongly dextrorotatory sulphoxide on reduction with aqueous sodium metabisulphite in a polarimeter tube at room temperature acquired during 3 weeks a slight laevo rotation. S-methyl-cysteine was obtained from the solution and identified by paper chromatography, analysis and specific rotation.

Hydrochloric acid decomposed both the natural and the synthetic sulphoxides giving S-methylcysteine. Oxidation of the new compound and of S-methylcysteine with hydrogen peroxide and molybdate gave solutions which behaved similarly on paper chromatography, presumably due to formation of the sulphone.

S-methyl-L-cysteine sulphoxide from the turnip—Morris and Thompson[33],[34] obtained, by the use of ion-exchange resins, a compound $C_4H_9O_3NS$ from the leaves and roots of turnips. It gave a brownish-blue ninhydrin reaction and was adsorbed on a mixture of copper carbonate and alumina. It behaved as a neutral compound on ion-exchange resins and appeared to be an amino acid. Hydrochloric acid eliminated ammonia but no amide group was present, as amides do not give the ninhydrin reaction. No hydrogen was taken up in presence of palladium, but potassium permanganate was reduced. No aldehyde, disulphide or sulphydryl groups were present. Treatment with hydriodic acid suggested that it was a sulphoxide and on paper chromatography it was found to be indistinguishable from S-methyl-L-cysteine sulphoxide in 3 different solvents. The product obtained with hydriodic acid was identical with S-methyl-L-cysteine in specific rotation and infra-red spectrum. The new compound was clearly the S-methyl-L-cysteine sulphoxide of Synge and Wood and had m.p. 169°–170°C and $\left[\alpha\right]_D^{25} = +125°$.

Natural occurrence of compounds related to S-methyl-L-cysteine sulphoxide—Synge and Wood consider that the new sulphoxide accounts for a considerable proportion of the organic sulphur of cabbage. When the results were announced they afforded the first instance of the occurrence of a derivative of S-methylcysteine in nature, nor had the amino acid itself then been recognized as a natural product. This had always seemed rather surprising in view of the wide occurrence of cysteine and cystine and of the closely related homologue methionine. S-methylcysteine has now been isolated from the common bean, *Phaseolus vulgare*.

A closely related compound, alliin[31] which is S-allylcysteine sulphoxide $\overset{+}{CH_2} : CH \cdot CH_2 \cdot \overset{+}{S} \cdot CH_2 \cdot CH(NH_2)COOH$ occurs in

garlic (*see* p. 54) and the isomeric (+) and (−) sulphoxides of biotin have been identified in milk[35],[36] and in the culture media of *Aspergillus niger* respectively[37-39]. Both isomers are formed by oxidation of biotin with hydrogen peroxide. Westall[40] (*see* p. 62) has isolated a new amino acid, felinine, from cats' urine. This is S-3-hydroxy*iso*amyl-L-cysteine HO·CH$_2$·CH$_2$·C(CH$_3$)$_2$·S·CH$_2$·CH· (NH$_2$)·COOH and it has been synthesized by Trippett[41]. It will be interesting to see whether the corresponding sulphoxide or sulphone will be recognized later as natural products.

Synge and Wood refer to the frequent occurrence of methyl mercaptan in plants or to its evolution during cooking processes, and suggest that it may sometimes arise by decomposition of S-methylcysteine sulphoxide. The breakdown of sulphoxides

$$R·CH_2·\overset{+}{\underset{|}{S}}·CH_2·R' \text{ to give } R·CHO \text{ and } R'·CH_2·SH \text{ has been studied}$$
$$\overset{|}{\underset{-}{O}}$$

by several workers cited by Challenger and Rawlings[63], but the reaction merits further examination by the use of simple symmetrical and unsymmetrical sulphoxides. The natural sulphoxides and sulphones which are related to the *iso*thiocyanates (mustard oils) are considered in Chapter 4.

THE OPTICAL ISOMERS OF METHIONINE SULPHOXIDE

Reference may here be made to some work on the optical isomers of methionine sulphoxide (γ-methylsulphinyl-α-aminobutyric acid). Toennies and Kolb[42] prepared the inactive sulphoxide by the oxidation of DL-methionine with hydrogen peroxide and showed that fractional crystallization of the picrate gave two picrates both of which were optically inactive and were converted to the sulphoxides. One fraction was an equimolecular mixture of L-methionine -(−)-sulphoxide and D-methionine-(+)-sulphoxide and the other a similar mixture of L-methionine-+-sulphoxide and D-methionine-(−)-sulphoxide.

Lavine[30] then oxidized L-methionine with iodine, iodine and mercuric chloride, to date (which is equivalent to hypoiodous acid) and also with hydrogen peroxide. Reduction values and oxygen absorption and finally isolation of the products and their analysis showed that the sulphoxide was formed in each case. It was found that varying amounts of the two diastereoisomeric sulphoxides were formed according to the method employed. Lavine considers that the different methods of oxidation which produced the second centre of asymmetry, the sulphoxide group, effected asymmetric synthesis (under the influence of the optically active carbon atom) in varying degree, presumably as a result of varying rates of reaction. With hydrogen peroxide the two diastereoisomers were produced in almost equal amount. These isomers, L-methionine-(+)-sulphoxide and L-methionine-(−)-sulphoxide were separated by means of the picrates. Picric acid was removed with amylamine. As before, the presence of the asymmetric carbon atom obviates the necessity of using an optically active acid for the separation. Lavine studied the factors influencing the rotatory power of the two asymmetric centres and the contribution of each to the observed rotations. Elimination of the asymmetry of the carbon atom by oxidation with chloramine-T (*see* Chapter 1) was complete in a few minutes and gave products that possessed, when freshly prepared, the rotation expected for the sulphoxide group. An aldehyde-sulphoxide was probably produced in this reaction, as indicated by the formation of a 2 : 4-dinitrophenylhydrazone. The sulphoxide group was not oxidized by the chloramine except after several days.

THE TOXIC SUBSTANCE IN AGENIZED FLOUR : METHIONINE SULPHOXIMINE

About 1950 much attention was devoted to the toxic action (resulting in hysteria and convulsions) which is exerted upon dogs and certain other animals by flour which has been treated with traces of nitrogen trichloride vapour in order to improve its baking properties. The original observation was made by Sir Edward Mellanby[43] and further work was carried out by him, by Moran[44] and by Reiner and their colleagues[45,46] who all arrived at similar results. The toxic factor arises from the action of the nitrogen trichloride ('agene') on the protein gluten contained in the wheaten flour. Other proteins, e.g. zein, 'casein', egg albumen, haemoglobin and rice protein also become toxic under this treatment, but keratin and arachin do not. The conclusion was finally reached that the proteins which become toxic have a relatively high methionine content while the others contain little or none of this amino acid. Moreover, when casein and zein are partially oxidized by hydrogen peroxide, whereby the methionine residues are affected, the resulting product does not become toxic on treatment with nitrogen trichloride. On the other hand free methionine or the products of hydrolysis of zein and casein yield no toxic product with 'agene', the products in the case of methionine being the sulphoxide or the sulphone.

It appeared, therefore, that isolation of the toxic substance would be achieved by the use of unhydrolysed protein rather than individual amino acids. Zein, gluten and egg albumen were therefore treated with nitrogen trichloride vapour ('agenized') and the resulting product hydrolysed either by the enzyme pancreatin or by

41

chemical means. A long series of operations, including dialysis, extraction with phenol, hydrolysis, extraction of by-products with butanol, precipitation with acetone, electro-dialysis, ion-exchange fractionation, partition chromatography and crystallization from alcohol finally yielded a crystalline product $C_5H_{12}O_3N_2S$. With Raney nickel α-amino-n-butyric acid and nickel sulphide were formed. Determination of —NH_2 nitrogen by the van Slyke method showed the presence of only one amino-group. The formula

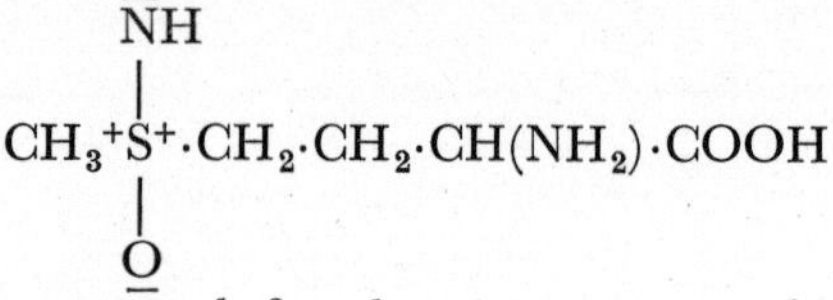

$$CH_3 \cdot \overset{+}{S}{}^+ \cdot \overset{\overset{\displaystyle \overline{N}H}{|}}{\underset{\underset{\displaystyle \overline{O}}{|}}{}} \cdot CH_2 \cdot CH_2 \cdot CH(NH_2) \cdot COOH$$

was therefore suggested for the new compound. This type of structure which resembles those of the sulphoxides $\overset{R}{\underset{R}{>}}\overset{+}{S}—\overline{O}$ and

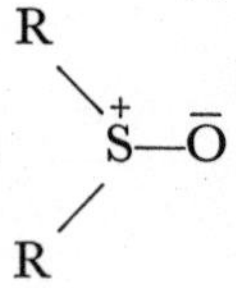

the sulphones $\overset{R}{\underset{R}{>}}\overset{\overset{\displaystyle \overline{O}}{}}{\underset{\overset{+}{S}}{\underset{\displaystyle O}{}}}$ was not previously known. The compound was named methionine sulphoximine and was synthesized from methionine sulphoxide and sodium azide in sulphuric acid–chloroform solution: $CH_3 \cdot \overset{+}{S}(\overline{O}) \cdot CH_2 \cdot CH_2 \cdot CH(NH_2) \cdot COOH + HN_3$

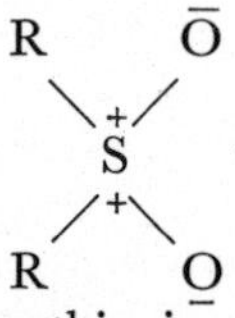

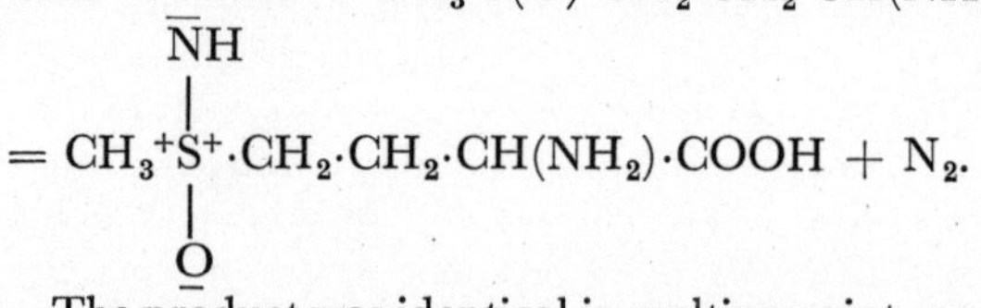

$$= CH_3 \cdot \overset{+}{S}{}^+ \cdot \overset{\overset{\displaystyle \overline{N}H}{|}}{\underset{\underset{\displaystyle \overline{O}}{|}}{}} \cdot CH_2 \cdot CH_2 \cdot CH(NH_2) \cdot COOH + N_2.$$

The product was identical in melting point, crystal form, chemical reactions, behaviour on a paper chromatogram and physiological action with the compound from 'agenized' protein. The simplest sulphoximine $(CH_3)_2\overset{+}{S}\overset{\overline{O}}{\underset{NH}{}}$ has been prepared in a similar manner from dimethyl sulphoxide. Several homologues have been synthesized, e.g. the di-n-amyl, diphenyl and p-tolyl methyl compounds,

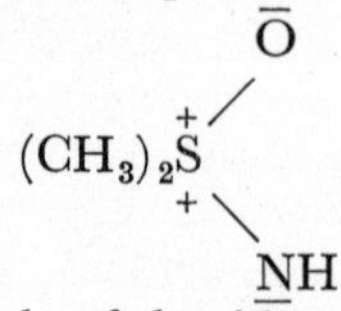

and also the sulphoximine of S-methylcysteine, $\mathrm{CH_3 \cdot \overset{O}{\underset{NH}{\overset{+}{\underset{+}{S}}} \cdot CH_2 \cdot}}$
$\mathrm{CH(NH_2) \cdot COOH.}$

THE SULPHONIUM COMPOUNDS OF DOGS' URINE AND THEIR DECOMPOSITION PRODUCTS

Abel[47] stated that on warming the urine of dogs with caustic soda diethyl sulphide was evolved, but no proof of identity was given. In particular the m.p. of the mercurichloride of the sulphide was 145°C and in a second experiment 150°C. Diethyl sulphide mercurichloride has m.p. 119°C. Nevertheless, later workers accepted Abel's statement and Neuberg and Grosser[48] claimed to have isolated the precursor of the diethyl sulphide as the phosphotungstate and iodobismuthate and to have identified it as diethylmethylsulphonium hydroxide. They stated that formation of this base is increased on administration of diethyl sulphide to dogs; the sulphide being methylated by the organism. No experimental details whatever were supplied by these authors and no further communication has appeared.

It has been shown, however, that the alkaline decomposition of diethylmethylsulphonium iodide gives mainly methyl ethyl sulphide which was characterized as the mercurichloride. The work of Ingold and Kuriyan[49] also suggests that ethyl methyl sulphide is the main product of this decomposition.

As these observations on dogs' urine had a bearing on other work in progress at Leeds a further study of the subject was begun by Dr Margaret Whitaker (Simpson) and continued by Dr D. Leaver[21] and several litres of dogs' urine were decomposed with alkali and the volatile sulphur compounds absorbed in (a) mercuric cyanide and (b) mercuric chloride. Very little mercaptan was detected in (a) but the sulphide mercurichloride in (b) was converted to the mercuribromide and to the benzylsulphonium picrate and styphnate $\mathrm{X^- \{ R \cdot \overset{+}{S} \cdot R'(CH_2C_6H_5). \}}$ Their m.p.s differed from those of the corresponding diethyl sulphide derivatives, approximating to those of the analogous derivatives of methyl-n-propyl sulphide, but were unsharp.

The sulphidimine $\mathrm{R \cdot R' \cdot \overset{+}{S} - \overset{-}{N} \cdot SO_2 \cdot C_6H_4 \cdot CH_3}$, however, was finally purified and its m.p. and mixed m.p. showed it to be identical with methyl-n-propyl sulphidimine. The presence of a small quantity of another sulphide in the natural sulphide was confirmed by two separate methods.

1. The crude sulphide from dogs' urine was converted to the methylsulphonium base. Paper chromatography of this presumed mixture of bases and comparison of the pattern with those given by known mixtures suggested the presence of dimethyl-*n*-propyl-sulphonium hydroxide and a much smaller quantity of dimethyl-*n*-butylsulphonium hydroxide.

2. The crude sulphidimine was chromatographed on paper and sprayed with a mixture of aqueous potassium iodide and hydrochloric acid which hydrolyses the sulphidimine to sulphoxide, RR'SO. This then liberates iodine. Undeveloped bands corresponding to the spots were separately boiled with sodium hydrogen sulphite, and the sulphides thus liberated by reduction of the sulphidimines were converted to mercurichlorides. That from the main band was shown by m.p. and mixed m.p. to be methyl-*n*-propyl sulphide mercurichloride. That from the smaller band was indistinguishable in m.p. from the mercurichloride of methyl-*n*-butyl sulphide.

The sulphide of dogs' urine is therefore mainly methyl-*n*-propyl sulphide with most probably some methyl-*n*-butyl sulphide. In spite of a prolonged investigation involving the use of ion-exchange resins, the sulphonium compounds in the urine which are the precursors of these two sulphides were not identified.

THE SULPHUR COMPOUNDS OF ASPARAGUS

The researches on the occurrence of sulphonium compounds in plants afford a link with an old, and still unsolved problem in bio-chemistry. Nencki[50] stated in 1891 that the strong odour which is readily detectable in the urine after ingestion of asparagus is due to methanethiol, of which he analysed the lead salt. Many years later Allison confirmed this by isolation of the silver salt[51]. The next serious investigation of the sulphur compounds of asparagus was made by Jansen[52] who, in 1948, isolated 2 : 2'-dithio*iso*butyric acid $HS \cdot CH_2 \cdot CH(CO_2H) \cdot CH_2 \cdot SH$ as the corresponding disulphide. He found, however, that this acid on ingestion by two individuals did not cause excretion of methanethiol, but the scale of the experiment was too small (*see* p. 47).

Two possible modes of formation of the methanethiol need to be envisaged. It is possible that the asparagus contains a methylated compound of sulphur from which the —SCH_3 group is eliminated as methanethiol, possibly enzymically, during passage through the body. This compound could hardly be methionine as other foodstuffs rich in this amino acid do not yield methanethiol in the urine. On the other hand the methyl group might be supplied by the human body and attached to the sulphur of a thiol or disulphide group to give an —SCH₃ derivative which might then undergo fission to yield methanethiol.

JANSEN'S IDENTIFICATION OF 2 : 2′-DITHIOISOBUTYRIC ACID IN THE FORM OF ITS DISULPHIDE IN ASPARAGUS

Isolation of the disulphide—Preliminary experiments showed that a press-juice obtained from asparagus contained both a thiol and a disulphide. On exposure to air only a disulphide was recognizable. Extraction with *n*-butanol removed a sulphur compound which was acidic and could be extracted from the butanol with sodium bicarbonate. Nine gallons (40 kilograms) of a commercial 'extract' of asparagus containing 62·5 per cent of solids were diluted with an equal volume of water and shaken (pH 4·5) with seven gallons of butanol for 20 minutes. After centrifugation the disulphide was extracted from the butanol with three gallons of dilute sodium bicarbonate from which, after acidification, the disulphide was again removed by butanol (4 gallons). Concentration *in vacuo* at 35°C to 270 c.c. followed by extraction with 1,300 c.c. of benzene, removal of insoluble matter, and extraction of the benzene three times with 330 c.c. of 5 per cent sodium bicarbonate gave a solution which was acidified to pH 2 with 10 per cent sulphuric acid and some black resin removed. The disulphide was then extracted three times with a total of two litres of ether, the extract dried and concentrated yielding 31·7 grams of a disulphide. This could not be recrystallized as it became viscous, and conversion to the thiol and re-formation of the disulphide caused much polymerization. The identification was effected by reduction to the thiol and formation of crystalline derivatives.

Reduction and identification of the disulphide from asparagus and formation of derivatives—The disulphide was reduced with sodium in liquid ammonia. Evaporation and acidification of the residue gave an acid m.p. 61°–62°C which had the empirical formula $C_4H_8O_2S_2$ and was shown to contain two SH groups by titration with *p*-chlorophenylmercuribenzoate $Cl \cdot C_6H_4 \cdot Hg \cdot O \cdot CO \cdot C_6H_5$, using sodium nitroprusside as an external indicator. The mercury reagent was standardized with specially purified cysteine hydrochloride. The determination depends on the reaction: $Cl \cdot C_6H_4 \cdot Hg \cdot O \cdot CO \cdot C_6H_5 +$

$HS \cdot R = Cl \cdot C_6H_4 \cdot Hg \cdot SR + C_6H_5COOH$. The acid was therefore 2 : 2'-dithio*iso*butyric acid, $HS \cdot CH_2 \cdot CH(COOH) \cdot CH_2 \cdot SH$. It was characterized as the S-dimethyl derivative $CH_3 \cdot S \cdot CH_2 \cdot CH(COOH) \cdot CH_2 \cdot S \cdot CH_3$. This acid was synthesized from *s*-dichlorohydrin which was converted first to dichloroacetone and thence through the bisulphite compound to the corresponding cyanohydrin and so to

the hydroxy-acid $Cl \cdot CH_2 \cdot C \overset{\displaystyle OH}{\underset{\displaystyle COOH}{\Big\langle}} CH_2 \cdot Cl$. On reduction with

hydriodic acid at 100° this gave 2 : 2'-di-iodo*iso*butyric acid

$I \cdot CH_2 \cdot C \overset{\displaystyle H}{\underset{\displaystyle COOH}{\Big\langle}} CH_2 \cdot I$. With ethanolic sodium methyl mercaptide the

corresponding S-dimethyldithio-acid $CH_3S \cdot CH_2 \cdot CH(COOH) \cdot CH_2 \cdot S \cdot CH_3$ was obtained. It was identical with that isolated on reduction of the disulphido-acid from asparagus followed by methylation.

*Desulphurization of the 2 : 2'-dithio*isobutyric acid from asparagus with *Raney nickel*—This was carried out in alcoholic solution and the *iso*butyric acid converted to its *p*-phenylphenacyl ester which was identical with an authentic sample. $(HS \cdot CH_2)_2 \cdot CH \cdot COOH \longrightarrow (CH_3)_2 \cdot CH \cdot COOH \longrightarrow (CH_3)_2 \cdot CH \cdot CO \cdot O \cdot CH_2 \cdot CO \cdot C_6H_4 \cdot C_6H_5$.

Further evidence of the presence of two thiol groups in the acid from Asparagus—The disulphido-acid was reduced as before and the product condensed with formaldehyde in 0·1 N hydrochloric acid, yielding an acid $C_5H_8O_2S_2$ which gave analytical figures corresponding to 1 : 3-dithiane-5-carboxylic acid.

$$CH_2O + \quad \overset{\displaystyle H \cdot S \cdot CH_2}{\underset{\displaystyle H \cdot S \cdot CH_2}{\Big\rangle}} CH \cdot COOH \longrightarrow CH_2 \overset{\displaystyle S \cdot CH_2}{\underset{\displaystyle S \cdot CH_2}{\Big\langle\Big\rangle}} CH \cdot COOH + H_2O$$

Possible biological behaviour of the dithio-acid from asparagus—Jansen points out that 2 : 2'-dithio*iso*butyric acid is closely related in structure to 'British Anti-Lewisite', 2 : 3-dimercaptopropanol $HO \cdot CH_2 \cdot CH(SH) \cdot CH_2 \cdot SH$ and suggests that it may protect the thiol enzymes of asparagus by removing heavy metals, or that like glutathione it may be an oxidation-reduction agent, concerned with hydrogen transfer. The question arises whether this compound is responsible for the elimination of methanethiol in the urine after

46

ingestion of asparagus. Allison has found that a large number of persons (69 out of 116 examined), do not, in fact, exhibit the methanethiol formation after consuming asparagus. Jansen's experiments with two individuals are inconclusive.

Allison and McWhirter[53] found that whereas some subjects excrete detectable amounts of methanethiol after ingesting only three or four sticks of asparagus, no significant amount of the compound occurs in the urine of others after ingestion of as much as a pound of asparagus. This metabolic difference and the genetic factors which control it are both under further investigation. The authors are chiefly concerned with the second aspect of the problem.

IDENTIFICATION OF THE METHYLMETHIONINESULPHONIUM ION IN ASPARAGUS

Dr Margaret Whitaker (Simpson[26]) found that a concentrated acetone extract of asparagus evolved dimethyl sulphide on boiling with alkali. (The seaweed thetin, *see* p. 34, evolves the sulphide in the cold.) By using two ion-exchange resins which retained (*a*) the basic amino acids and a sulphonium compound and (*b*) the amino acids, an eluate was obtained which gave a platinichloride and thence a picrate. Challenger and Miss Hayward[54] identified the source of the dimethyl sulphide as a methylmethioninesulphonium salt $\overline{X}\left\{\overset{+}{S}Me_2 \cdot CH_2 \cdot CH_2 \cdot CH(NH_2) \cdot CO_2H\right.$. Paper chromatography of (*c*) the chloride obtained from the picrate and (*d*) the methionine and homoserine from the alkaline decomposition of (*c*) confirmed the identity.

About six months previously this sulphonium compound had been isolated as a bromide from cabbage and detected in parsley, lettuce and turnip greens and other vegetables by Shive and his co-workers[55]. The dimethylsulphonium compound of horse-tails and of bracken may possibly be a methylmethioninesulphonium salt since these plants, as well as asparagus extracts, require fairly strong heating with alkali before the dimethyl sulphide is evolved.

Speculations on the origin of the methanethiol excreted after ingestion of asparagus—The simplest explanation would be that the methanethiol arises from methionine which has been shown to yield this mercaptan in cultures of *Scopulariopsis brevicaulis* on bread[56] and in cultures of *Aspergillus niger* and *Microsporum gypseum*[57]. There is also some evidence (*see* p. 51) that a similar fission may occur in man under pathological conditions[58,59]. Nevertheless, methionine is widespread in foodstuffs and yet considerable methanethiol excretion has only been recognized—in healthy persons—after consumption of asparagus. The same objection probably applies to the suggestion that the source of the methanethiol is a methylmethionine sulphonium salt. This occurs in asparagus, but also in many other vegetables. It yields some methanethiol in cultures of *A. niger* on bread[60], but this is probably due to a preliminary formation of methionine.

The isolation of S-methylcysteine sulphoxide from cabbage by Synge and Wood[28] and its detection in a large number of *Cruciferae*, but not yet in asparagus, may here be recalled. Sulphoxides yield mercaptans and aldehydes on fission by acids $R \cdot CH_2 \cdot SO \cdot CH_2 R \rightarrow R \cdot CHO + R \cdot CH_2 SH$. Synge and Wood consider that the evolution of traces of mercaptans and hydrogen sulphide during the cooking of cruciferous vegetables, reported by Niemann[61] and discussed by Rubner[62], may be due to decomposition of S-methylcysteine sulphoxide. Their evidence for the formation of methanethiol was the production of a greenish-yellow precipitate on aeration into mercuric cyanide (*see* p. 18) and a yellow precipitate when this was acidified with 3 per cent hydrochloric acid and volatile matter aspirated into 3 per cent lead acetate. In spite of the absence of analyses and formation of a derivative having a melting point, the conclusions of these earlier workers were probably correct. The simultaneous evolution of hydrogen sulphide is presumably due to the decomposition of sulphenic acids[63] $R \cdot CH_2 \cdot S \cdot OH$ arising by the hydrolytic fission of disulphides: $R \cdot CH_2 \cdot S \cdot OH = R \cdot CHO + H_2S$. For example, Synge and Wood cite the statement of Zwergal[64] that hydrogen sulphide and 'mercaptan' are produced on steam distillation of kohl-rabi with dilute acid. The methyl mercaptan was detected as 'mercury mercaptide'. Since a methylsulphinyl cyanide

$$CH_3 \cdot \overset{+}{\underset{\underset{O^-}{|}}{S}} \cdot CH : CH \cdot CH_2 \cdot CH_2 \cdot CH_2 \cdot CN$$ was also isolated from the

same plant by Zwergal (*see* Chapter 4, p. 120), the methyl mercaptan may arise by fission of this nitrile. Blackburn and Challenger[65] cite the work of Nakamura[66] who in 1925 isolated methyl mercaptan from the radish (*Raphanus sativus L.*), thus affording the first instance of its occurrence in fresh plant tissue. Air was slowly passed over the freshly crushed roots (acidified with oxalic acid) into aqueous mercuric cyanide. Traces of hydrogen sulphide caused the mercaptide to be yellow (*see* Chapter 1, p. 18) but on extraction with boiling acetone the solution deposited pure mercury dithiomethoxide $(CH_3S)_2Hg$. It will be recalled that Schmid and Karrer[67] isolated sulphoraphene $CH_3 \cdot \overset{+}{S} \cdot CH : CH \cdot CH_2 \cdot CH_2 \cdot N : C : S$ from radish

seeds. $\underset{O^-}{|}$

Koolhaas[68] in 1931 detected methanethiol in five species of *Lasianthus*. The mercaptan was isolated as the (analysed) mercury derivative by steam distillation of the leaves of *Lasianthus purpureus* and collection in potassium hydroxide followed by acidification and absorption in mercuric cyanide. Synge and Wood remark that 'methylcysteine sulphoxide may . . . give rise to methanethiol and related volatile compounds'. They do not appear, however, to have studied the volatile products of the decomposition of S-methyl-cysteine sulphoxide very fully as yet, since they remark that hot hydrochloric acid gives S-methylcysteine, ammonia, some carbon dioxide and an unpleasant cabbage-like odour. It seems very probable that methanethiol was present.

Comments on the preceding speculations—We are not yet in a position to hear the conclusion of the whole matter. The occurrence of α-amino-γ-dimethylbutyrothetin [the methylmethionine sulphonium ion $(CH_3)_2 \overset{+}{S} \cdot CH_2 \cdot CH_2 \cdot CH(NH_2) CO\overline{O}]$ and S-methylcysteine sulphoxide in both cabbage and turnip[56] and many other vegetables and the presence of the first compound in asparagus[55] renders desirable a search for the sulphoxide in asparagus. Should this be found, a study of its behaviour on administration to human subjects should be made. Should the sulphoxide be established as the precursor of the urinary methanethiol it will still be necessary to determine why the phenomenon is exhibited by asparagus so much more intensely than by other vegetables, e.g. cabbage.

So far as the author is aware no enzyme preparation has yet been obtained which produces a mercaptan from a sulphoxide. The only biological decompositions of sulphoxides so far reported are those of dimethyl and diethyl sulphoxides which, in bread cultures of *Scopulariopsis brevicaulis*, are reduced to the corresponding sulphides, the yield of mercurichloride in the first case being 60 per cent[69,70]. The author agrees with Synge and Wood that 'much further work is required to throw light on the reactivity of sulphoxide groups'.

Rubner states that methanethiol was detected in the vapours from the acidified urine of persons consuming cabbage, cauliflower and Teltower–Rübchen, by formation of a green colour with isatin in sulphuric acid. This evidence is hardly comparable with that furnished by the experiments with asparagus, where the odour in the urine was intense and metal derivatives of methanethiol were prepared.

Salkowski's experiments on rabbits fed exclusively on cabbage—Salkowski[71]

49

noticed an abnormal excretion of thiosulphate by rabbits fed only on cabbage; the evidence for its presence seems convincing. The urine on acidification with acetic acid evolved no mercaptan on boiling, but on heating with hydrochloric acid a mercaptan which gave a precipitate in mercuric cyanide was evolved. This was assumed to be methanethiol, because with isatin in sulphuric acid the usual green colour was produced. Sulphur arising from the decomposition of thiosulphate, and hydrogen sulphide were also produced.

An aqueous extract of cabbage produced the same results on administration to rabbits[72] and was decomposed by hot hydrochloric acid, but no details are given. Synge and Wood suggest that the aqueous extract of cabbage and the urine both contained S-methylcysteine sulphoxide and that the methanethiol is only evolved from the urine when it is boiled with acid and the sulphoxide decomposed.

THE EXCRETION AND PROBABLE EXHALATION OF METHANETHIOL (METHYL MERCAPTAN) IN MAN

Methyl mercaptan formation in necrosis of the liver—The presence of a characteristic odour (*foetor hepaticus*) in the breath of patients with severe liver disease has been known for many years and has been discussed by Schiff[73], Himsworth[74], Davidson[75] and Lichtman[76]. Davidson suggested that it was due to a mercaptan derived from cystine or methionine, but showed that its presence was not dependent upon methionine therapy. The same or a very similar odour[76] is sometimes present in the urine of patients manifesting *foetor hepaticus*. Recently a case of massive hepatic necrosis was studied in University College Hospital, London, in which the smell was very marked in the urine when passed and opportunity was taken to isolate and identify the compound responsible.

The urine was collected over thymol and stored at 4 °C. It seemed probable that the odorous substance in the urine was either an alkyl mercaptan, a dialkyl sulphide or a dialkyl disulphide or a mixture of all three. It was decided to employ the method developed by Challenger and Rawlings[63] and Blackburn and Challenger[77] for identification.

Paper-chromatographic examination of the plasma repeatedly showed a moderate increase in the concentration of the amino acids commonly found, but a very marked increase in methionine, as has been observed previously in cases of severe hepatitis. Death occurred after the patient had been in coma for 10 days. Post-mortem examination showed that the liver weighed only 840 g., due to almost complete destruction of the parenchymal cells.

Examination of the urine—A slow stream of nitrogen was passed through approximately 5–6 l. of the urine and then successively through tubes containing dilute sulphuric acid (to remove ammonia) and through (*a*) aqueous mercuric cyanide and (*b*) aqueous mercuric chloride. The volume of liquid in the tubes was about 5 ml. in each. A deposit formed in (*a*) which had a very faint yellow tint, gave an odour of methanethiol on acidification and melted unsharply and decomposed from 150° to 180°C. It was boiled with water, to remove mercuric cyanide from small quantities of the double compound $(CH_3S)_2Hg \cdot Hg(CN)_2$, (*see* Chapter 1, p. 3), filtered and recrystallized from much hot ethanol, when it separated in shining leaflets closely resembling in appearance mercury dimethyl mercaptide, $Hg(SCH_3)_2$. These melted and decomposed at 170°–174°C and at 168°C in admixture with an authentic sample of m.p. 167°–168°C (decomp.). $Hg(SCH_3)_2$ melts and decomposes at 174°–175°C. The authentic sample contained traces of mercuric cyanide, hence the lower m.p. Similar m.p's and mixed m.p's were obtained with the mercuric cyanide precipitate which had been heated with water, but not recrystallized.

The deposit in tube (*b*) in the original experiment was much smaller in amount than that in (*a*). It gave a scarcely perceptible odour with sodium hydroxide, indicating the absence of the double compound $2(CH_3)_2S, 3HgCl_2$ and hence of dimethyl sulphide from the urine (*see* p. 52, and Challenger and Rawlings[63]). With dilute acid the odour of methanethiol was readily detected. The solid sintered from 150°C and decomposed at 180°C without completely melting, a behaviour consistent with that of a mixture of $CH_3 \cdot S \cdot HgCl \cdot HgCl_2$ and $CH_3 \cdot S \cdot HgCl$. The deposit in the mercuric chloride arose either from traces of methanethiol which escaped precipitation in the cyanide, or more likely, by fission of dimethyl disulphide $CH_3 \cdot S \cdot S \cdot CH_3$ produced by atmospheric oxidation of the methanethiol in the urine. Disulphides pass unchanged through mercuric cyanide.

Possible origin of the methanethiol

The high concentration of methionine in the blood of the patient suggests that the methanethiol may have arisen from this amino acid by hydrolytic or reductive fission of the bond between the CH_3S-group and the adjoining carbon atom, giving homoserine, $HO \cdot CH_2 \cdot CH_2 \cdot CH(NH_2) \cdot COOH$ or α-aminobutyric acid, $CH_3 \cdot CH_2 \cdot CH(NH_2) \cdot COOH$ respectively as the second product. Such a fission has been observed with methionine and S-methylcysteine giving methyl mercaptan, in cultures of the mould

Scopulariopsis brevicaulis[78] and with the enzyme thionase occurring in liver tissue respectively[79].

It is well known that methionine can supply a methyl group for the biological synthesis of choline, creatine, anserine, adrenaline and N-methylnicotinamide (*see* Chapter 5, p. 174). The methionine is then re-formed and is maintained at a fairly constant level. Many of these transmethylations presumably take place in the liver and in cases of damage to that organ, methyl transfer is possibly inhibited and methionine may accumulate; such an accumulation has actually been observed in the case of this and other patients with severe parenchymal liver disease[80]. The organism may then employ fission of the other carbon–sulphur link with elimination of methanethiol, in order to deal with the excess of methionine. Dent[81] found in 1947 that, in normal subjects and especially in a case of the Fanconi syndrome, increased excretion of α-aminobutyric acid followed the administration of methionine, 'as if some direct desulphurization had taken place'. The fate of the CH_3S-group of the methionine was not investigated. Mercaptan production may, of course, be preceded by oxidative deamination of methionine and formation of the corresponding α-keto acid, $CH_3 \cdot S \cdot CH_2 \cdot CH_2 \cdot CO \cdot COOH$, which was shown by Challenger and Liu[82] to yield methanethiol and, by methylation, dimethyl sulphide in cultures of *S. brevicaulis*. Amination of the keto-acid to methionine followed by fission, was, however, not excluded.

The absence of dimethyl sulphide in the urine is noteworthy and may be due to impairment of the methylation processes of the liver. In man, methanethiol may be expected to be methylated, to some extent at least, to dimethyl sulphide. This sulphide is almost certainly exhaled by man on administration of thiourea, a type of mercaptan. The metabolism of thiourea in man and dogs has been discussed by Challenger and Liu, Astwood[83,84] and Himsworth[85], and by Pohl[86]. The odour of the breath of the patient was less unpleasant than that of the urine. This may have been due to the oxidation of the methanethiol to dimethyl disulphide, $CH_3 \cdot S \cdot S \cdot CH_3$, which has a less obnoxious odour. The breath was not examined chemically, so the presence of some dimethyl sulphide, $CH_3 \cdot S \cdot CH_3$, is not excluded.

1-PROPANETHIOL (*n*-PROPYL MERCAPTAN) IN ONIONS

Small quantities of 1-propanethiol $CH_3 \cdot CH_2 \cdot CH_2 \cdot SH$ are present in onions[87]. Sterile air was passed in three separate experiments through the onions (5–6 kg. in all), then through aniline to remove any allyl *iso*thiocyanate $CH_2 : CH \cdot CH_2 \cdot N : C : S$, then through dilute hydrochloric acid into mercuric cyanide and finally into mercuric chloride, both in aqueous solution. A precipitate slowly formed in the cyanide and after crystallization from ethanol was found to be pure mercury di-thio-*n*-propoxide $Hg(S \cdot CH_2 \cdot CH_2 \cdot CH_3)_2$ by analysis and by m.p. and mixed m.p. determinations. It depressed the m.p. of the corresponding allyl compound $Hg(S \cdot CH_2 \cdot CH : CH_2)_2$ the presence of which might have been expected.

The identity of the 1-propanethiol was further confirmed by decomposition of the mercury derivative with acid and aspiration through water into lead acetate. The precipitated lead di-thio-*n*-propoxide $Pb(S \cdot C_3H_7)_2$ was identified by comparison with an authentic specimen. In a similar manner the lead mercaptide was converted to the silver derivative. The corresponding allyl derivatives differ widely in m.p. from the lead and silver compounds obtained from the onion. The content of 1-propanethiol in the onion was estimated as being about 10 mg./kg.

n-Propanethiol had not previously been detected in nature, although Challenger and Rawlings[63] observed its formation from di-*n*-propyl disulphide in cultures of *S. brevicaulis*. It may be identical with a very volatile compound from onions mentioned by Walker, Lindegren and Bachmann[88]. Kohmann[89] reports the presence of propionaldehyde in onions from evidence based on the melting points and analyses of the 4-nitro- and 2 : 4-dinitrophenylhydrazones. It seems possible that, during the distillation of the onions under reduced pressure in presence of water at 50 °C, propionaldehyde might have arisen from propanethiol thus:

$$CH_3 \cdot CH_2 \cdot CH_2 \cdot SH \xrightarrow{O_2} (CH_3 \cdot CH_2 \cdot CH_2 S-)_2 \xrightarrow{H_2O}$$

$$CH_3 \cdot CH_2 \cdot CH_2 \cdot SH + CH_3 \cdot CH_2 \cdot CH_2 \cdot SOH \xrightarrow{-H_2S} CH_3 \cdot CH_2 \cdot CHO$$
$$\text{Propanesulphenic acid.}$$

This type of reaction was studied by Schöberl[90].

In 1924 Meirion Thomas[91] distilled onions in steam and treated the distillate with 'dimedone' (3 : 3-dimethyl*cyclo*-hexane-1 : 5-dione) obtaining crystalline derivatives which were identical with the 'dimedone' derivative of propionaldehyde, in confirmation of the work of Kohmann[89].

THE PRECURSORS OF DIALLYL DISULPHIDE IN GARLIC

In 1944 Cavallito[92-94] and his colleagues isolated an antibacterial oily substance from garlic cloves by steam distillation of an alcoholic extract. This had only a slight garlic odour, was soluble in water, had the composition $C_6H_{10}OS_2$ and was named allicin. The authors could not decide between the formulae

$$CH_2 : CH \cdot CH_2 \cdot \overset{+}{S}(\overline{O}) \cdot S \cdot CH_2 \cdot CH : CH_2$$
$$\text{and } CH_2 : CH \cdot CH_2 \cdot S \cdot O \cdot S \cdot CH_2 \cdot CH : CH_2$$

but preferred the first. No other compound of this type had hitherto been isolated from a natural product with the possible exception of $\beta\beta'$-dihydroxydiethyl sulphoxide. Stoll and Seebeck[95] found that oxidation of diallyl disulphide with hydrogen peroxide in glacial acetic acid gave an oil having the chemical and antibacterial properties of allicin, which should therefore be assigned the sulphoxide structure and may also be regarded as the allyl ester of allylthiosulphinic acid. Cavallito *et al.* also oxidized a number of dialkyl disulphides to analogues of allicin and studied their bactericidal properties.

Alliin—The Swiss authors[96] then isolated an amino acid from garlic which they named alliin and showed to be a precursor of allicin. Garlic cloves were mixed with solid carbon dioxide, thoroughly ground and extracted with methyl or ethyl alcohol containing about 10–15 per cent of water. The alcohol was removed *in vacuo* and the aqueous residue freed from fat by ether. Carbohydrate was removed by fractional precipitation with methyl alcohol, when the alliin was obtained as almost odourless, optically active crystals, $\left[\alpha\right]_D^{21} = + 62 \cdot 8°$, having the composition $2C_6H_{11}O_3NS \cdot H_2O$. The water can only be removed at a temperature at which decomposition occurs. Nevertheless the analysis of various derivatives of alliin which are anhydrous always indicates the formula $C_6H_{11}O_3NS$ for alliin. This is true, for dihydroalliin, desoxoalliin and the N-benzoyl and N-*p*-nitrobenzoyl derivatives. The molecular weight of alliin determined cryoscopically in water agrees with the formula $C_6H_{11}O_3NS$.

Potentiometric titration, the ninhydrin reaction and a van Slyke determination of the nitrogen content showed alliin to be an amino acid. Reduction with hydrogen and Raney nickel as catalyst established the presence of one double bond and gave dihydroalliin. Neither the oxygen nor the sulphur were removed. Cysteine was oxidized to cystine and hydrogen sulphide to sulphur. The last reaction explains the behaviour of alliin with thioacetic acid, $CH_3 \cdot COSH$ in glacial acetic acid solution. Sulphur slowly separates at room temperature. The other product of the reaction is an acid $C_8H_{13}O_3NS$ which with hydrogen and Raney nickel takes up one mol. of hydrogen. On warming the acid with sodium hydroxide it gives acetic acid, ammonia, pyruvic acid and a strong odour of allyl mercaptan. This was not characterized, but on carrying out a similar alkaline decomposition with the reduced acid, 1-propanethiol was obtained and characterized as its derivative with mercuric chloride, either $C_3H_7 \cdot S \cdot HgCl$ or its double compound with mercuric chloride.

The course of the alkaline hydrolysis would be explained if the acid $C_8H_{13}O_3NS$ were an allylmercapturic acid $CH_2 : CH \cdot CH_2 \cdot S \cdot CH_2 \cdot CH(NH \cdot CO \cdot CH_3) \cdot COOH$ produced from the corresponding sulphoxide, alliin, by acetylation of the amino group with thioacetic acid (*see* Chapter 6, p. 231). The hydrogen sulphide produced is then oxidized to sulphur (*see* p. 54) probably by an $-\overset{+}{S}-\overset{-}{O}$ group, which is reduced to $-S-$.

$$CH_2 : CH \cdot CH_2 \cdot \overset{+}{S}(\overset{-}{O}) \cdot CH_2 \cdot CH(NH_2) \cdot COOH \xrightarrow{\quad CH_3 \cdot CO \cdot SH \quad}$$

$$CH_2 : CH \cdot CH_2 \cdot S \cdot \overset{H \, | \, OH}{|} CH_2 \cdot CH(NH \overset{H \, | \, OH}{|} \cdot CO \cdot CH_3) \cdot COOH \xrightarrow{\quad 2H_2O \quad}$$

$$CH_2 : CH \cdot CH_2 \cdot SH + CH_2 : \underset{|}{C} \cdot COOH + CH_3COOH + H_2O$$
$$NH_2$$

The α-aminoacrylic acid gives ammonia and pyruvic acid on hydrolysis. The S-alkylcysteines readily yield mercaptans with alkali.

Further evidence confirmed the structure

$$CH_2 : CH \cdot CH_2 \cdot \overset{+}{S} \cdot CH_2 \cdot CH(NH_2) \cdot COOH$$
$$\underset{\underline{O}}{|}$$

for alliin. Sodium metabisulphite $Na_2S_2O_5$ removed an atom of oxygen forming desoxoalliin, which was synthesized from allyl bromide and the mercuric chloride double compound of cysteine and shown to have the structure $CH_2 : CH \cdot CH_2 \cdot S \cdot CH_2 \cdot CH(NH_2) \cdot COOH$. On acetylation with either acetic anhydride or thioacetic acid the acid $C_8H_{13}O_3NS$ was obtained, identical with that prepared from alliin and thioacetic acid.

Enzymic fission of alliin—Alliin has no antibacterial properties but on addition of an enzyme preparation obtained from garlic the solution acquires antibacterial properties[95], and contains allicin, pyruvic acid and ammonia:

$$2CH_2 : CH \cdot CH_2 \cdot \overset{+}{S} \cdot CH_2CH(NH_2) \cdot COOH + H_2O =$$
$$\mid$$
$$\overset{-}{O}$$

$$CH_2 : CH \cdot CH_2 \cdot \overset{+}{S} \cdot S \cdot CH_2CH : CH_2 + 2CH_3 \cdot CO \cdot COOH + 2NH_3$$
$$\mid$$
$$\overset{-}{O}$$

Stoll and Seebeck[97] suggested that alliin first breaks down to give (a) allylsulphenic acid $CH_2 : CH \cdot CH_2 \cdot S \cdot OH$, which they write as the corresponding tautomeric form, the sulphoxide $CH_2 : CH \cdot CH_2 \overset{+}{S} \cdot H$,

$$\mid$$
$$\overset{-}{O}$$

and (b) one molecule of α-amino-acrylic acid $CH_2 : C(NH_2)COOH$. Two molecules of the sulphenic acid are believed to give allicin and water while (b) with water gives pyruvic acid and ammonia. Finally allicin was shown on distillation with steam to yield diallyl disulphide. The oxygen acceptor in this reaction has not yet been identified.

A simpler explanation of the formation of allicin from alliin may be suggested, according to which the allylsulphenic acid undergoes disproportionation to allylsulphinic acid and allyl mercaptan (prop-2-ene-1-thiol). These two then interact to form allicin and water

$$2CH_2:CH \cdot CH_2 \cdot S \cdot OH \rightarrow CH_2:CH \cdot CH_2 \cdot \overset{+}{S} \cdot OH + HS \cdot CH_2 \cdot CH:CH_2$$
$$\mid$$
$$\overset{-}{O}$$

$$\rightarrow CH_2 : CH \cdot CH_2 \cdot \overset{+}{S} \cdot S \cdot CH_2 \cdot \overset{-}{C}H : CH_2 + H_2O$$
$$\mid$$
$$\overset{-}{O}$$

SYNTHESIS OF NATURAL ALLIIN [(+)-ALLYL-L-CYSTEINE SULPHOXIDE]
AND ITS THREE OPTICALLY ACTIVE ISOMERS

As the molecule of alliin $CH_2 : CH \cdot CH_2 \cdot \overset{+}{S} \cdot CH_2 \cdot CH(NH_2) \cdot COOH$
$$\mid$$
$$\overset{-}{O}$$

contains two asymmetric centres, the α-carbon of the amino acid residue and the sulphur of the sulphoxide group, the following isomers can exist

$$\begin{pmatrix} C- \\ S+ \end{pmatrix} \quad \begin{pmatrix} C- \\ S- \end{pmatrix} \quad \begin{pmatrix} C+ \\ S+ \end{pmatrix} \quad \begin{pmatrix} C+ \\ S- \end{pmatrix}$$

I   II   III   IV

Of these I and IV are optical antipodes (enantiomorphs) and so are II and III. On the other hand I and III and II and IV are diastereoisomers. Before commencing a study of the optically active alliins Stoll and Seebeck[98] decided to obtain preliminary experience with the corresponding n-propyl derivative $CH_3 \cdot CH_2 \cdot CH_2 \cdot \overset{+}{\underset{\underset{O}{|}}{S}} \cdot CH_2 \cdot$

$CH(NH_2) \cdot COOH$. This was obtained by oxidation of S-n-propyl-L-cysteine with hydrogen peroxide. The product was obviously racemic with respect to the sulphur atom but possessed laevorotation due to the C-atom of the L-cysteine residue. Consequently it should theoretically be possible to resolve it into $(-)$-S-n-propyl-L-cysteine sulphoxide and $(+)$-S-n-propyl-L-cysteine sulphoxide and this was done by fractional crystallization from aqueous acetone.

The second isomer $\begin{pmatrix} +S \\ -C \end{pmatrix}$ was found to be identical with the product of the catalytic reduction of natural alliin. This enables the structure $(+)$-S-allyl-L-cysteine sulphoxide to be assigned to natural alliin unless configurational change had occurred during hydrogenation. The above configuration was confirmed by a direct synthesis. Desoxoalliin $CH_2 : CH \cdot CH_2 \cdot S \cdot CH_2 \cdot CH(NH_2) \cdot COOH$ was synthesized by an improved method from allyl bromide and L-cysteine in sodium hydroxide. The product was oxidized with hydrogen peroxide. On fractional crystallization of the resulting sulphoxide from aqueous acetone $(+)$–S-allyl-L-cysteine sulphoxide was obtained identical with natural alliin in specific rotation and m.p. The mother liquors yielded the $(-)$-S-allyl-L-cysteine sulphoxide.

This synthesis of natural alliin confirms the constitution and configuration already assigned to it. Stoll and Seebeck decided to prepare the corresponding derivative of D-cysteine, but as this amino-acid is not readily available, S-allyl-DL-cysteine was prepared and converted to its N-formyl derivative by warming with formic acid in acetic anhydride. This was then resolved by fractional crystallization of its brucine salt from butanol when the salt of S-allyl-D-N-formylcysteine separated, $CH_2 : CH \cdot CH_2 \cdot S \cdot CH_2 \cdot CH \cdot (NH \cdot CHO) \cdot COOH$. The brucine was then removed by ammonia, the filtrate concentrated and the formyl group hydrolysed with hydrochloric acid. The resulting hydrochloride on treatment with

57

ammonia gave S-allyl-D-cysteine. This was oxidized with hydrogen peroxide as before and when the resulting sulphoxide was fractionally crystallized from aqueous acetone separation into (−)-S-allyl-D-cysteine sulphoxide (which separated first) and (+)-S-allyl-D-cysteine-sulphoxide was achieved.

Stoll and Seebeck have reviewed the pharmacology of garlic and the products obtained from it and the general chemistry of alliin[99]. It may be interesting to compare the stereochemical work just described with that of Lavine[30] and of Moore and Stein[32] (see pp. 38, 40) on the separation of the diastereoisomers of methionine sulphoxide and of Schöberl[100] on the optically active cystathionines and allocystathionines. Blackburn[101] has also studied the diastereoisomers of lanthionine.

(see pp. 38, 40)

DJENKOLIC ACID

For at least fifty years it has been known that the natives of the East Indies often suffer from more or less severe damage to the urinary tract through eating the djenkol bean (*Pithecolobium lobatum*). This resembles a chestnut in appearance and is about 15 g. in weight. The susceptibility of different individuals varies greatly. The urine of the patients contains epithelial cells, blood and albumen and also sharp needle-shaped insoluble crystals, often in considerable quantity. On keeping the urine, however, these frequently disappear. The damage to the ureters is presumably due to mechanical irritation by the sharp crystals, which occasionally accumulate and cause an obstruction. The urine has an intensely unpleasant odour which is stated to resemble that of an organic sulphide or mercaptan and also that of a mustard oil. A similar odour is produced when the bean is allowed to germinate either by being placed in water or buried in the earth. There has been some discussion as to whether germination through burying increases or diminishes the toxicity of the bean.

Isolation of djenkolic acid—The first scientific investigation of 'djenkol sickness' and its cause was carried out by van Veen and Hyman[102–104] in Batavia, Java. They examined the crystals deposited from the urine of both men and monkeys and found them to be acidic and to contain carbon, hydrogen, oxygen, nitrogen and sulphur. The name djenkolic acid was given to the new substance. Earlier work had indicated that the bean contains a complex which on hydrolysis gave djenkolic and phenylacetic acids. An investigation of the other ingredients of the djenkol bean would furnish interesting results.

The method used for the isolation of djenkolic acid was as follows:

Shelled grated beans were treated with water and excess of baryta, allowed to stand, the mixture filtered, acidified with dilute sulphuric acid, filtered, brought to pH 5–6 and concentrated in a stream of carbon dioxide under diminished pressure. Djenkolic acid then separated. 10–16 g. were obtained from 1 kg. of beans and crystallized from much boiling water.

Constitution of djenkolic acid—The analysis of the acid and of its monohydrochloride indicated the empirical formula $C_7H_{14}O_4N_2S_2$. Treatment with sodium nitroprusside proved the absence of an —SH or —S—S— group, no purple colour being obtained in absence or in presence of potassium cyanide, with which —S—S— groups react to produce —SK and —SCN[105].

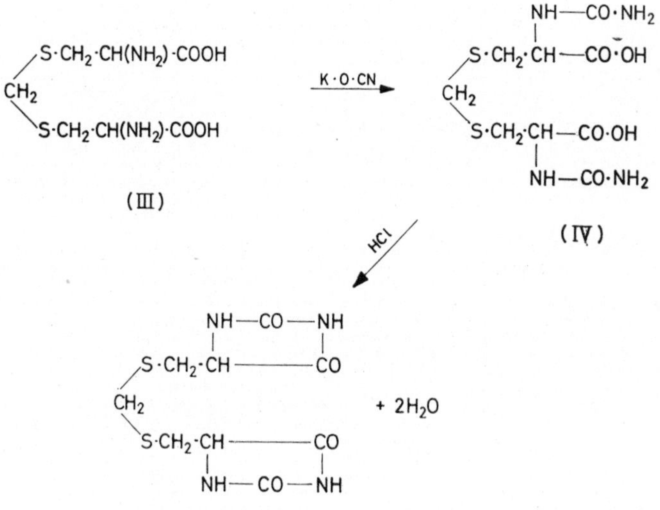

It was soluble in both acid and alkali. This explains the use of soda-water or of an aqueous extract of the ashes of rice-straw in the treatment of 'djenkol sickness' by the natives, the deposited crystals being dissolved. An infusion of the upper leaves of the kapok tree is also used successfully. The gradual disappearance of the deposit of djenkolic acid from the pathological urine may be due to the production of alkalinity on standing. Djenkolic acid gave a strong ninhydrin reaction. These observations suggested an amino-acid structure which was confirmed by the formation of a dihydantoin (V) with potassium cyanate. A dibenzoyl derivative was also formed. The presence of two amino-acid residues therefore seemed probable. On warming with sulphuric acid at 120°–140°C in an atmosphere of carbon dioxide, pouring on ice, neutralizing with baryta, filtering and evaporating in a vacuum, a crystalline residue resulted which was identified as cystine.

These results suggested that two cysteine residues might be present and be linked to a central carbon atom through the sulphur atoms. Consequently djenkolic acid was warmed with aqueous sulphuric acid (about 1 : 1) and phloroglucinol[105], and the precipitated solid separated. Its weight corresponded to the presence of one —CH$_2$— group in djenkolic acid and its analysis to that of the condensation product of phloroglucinol and formaldehyde. The structure (III) was therefore assigned to djenkolic acid. Its dihydantoin (V) is also shown on p. 59. The intermediate ureido-acid (IV) was not isolated.

van Veen and Hyman suggested that djenkolic acid might be formed in the plant by the condensation of formaldehyde and cysteine, a suggestion which was welcomed by the author and his co-workers[63,106], who almost simultaneously with van Veen and Hymans' publication, had suggested that methylation of sulphur in nature might occur by condensation of mercaptans and formaldehyde RSH + CH$_2$O → R·S·CH$_2$·OH → R·S·CH$_3$.

The condensation of aldehydes and ketones with cysteine gives either an addition compound (VI) or a thiazolidinecarboxylic acid (VII). Ratner and Clarke[107] studied the reaction with formaldehyde between pH 1·5 and 12 and obtained thiazolidine-4-carboxylic acid (VIII). Similar results had been reported by Schubert[108].

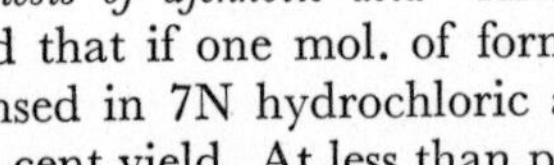

(VI) 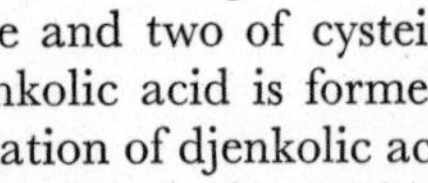   (VII)

Synthesis of djenkolic acid—Armstrong and du Vigneaud[109], then showed that if one mol. of formaldehyde and two of cysteine are condensed in 7N hydrochloric acid, djenkolic acid is formed in a 68 per cent yield. At less than pH 5 formation of djenkolic acid was negligible. When equimolecular proportions of cysteine and formaldehyde interact in 6N hydrochloric acid, Armstrong and du Vigneaud[110] also found that the main product was thiazolidine-4-carboxylic acid. With excess of cysteine the main product is djenkolic acid. The intermediate hemithioacetal (IX) in hydrochloric acid may lose water to give thiazolidine-4-carboxylic acid, or react with a second molecule of cysteine to give djenkolic acid according to the experimental conditions.

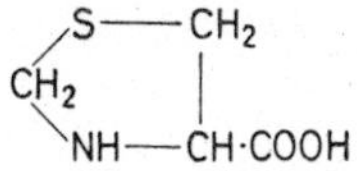

$$HO \cdot CH_2S \cdot CH_2CH(NH_2) \cdot COOH$$

(VIII)   (IX)

This synthesis of djenkolic acid was confirmed by formation of the monohydrochloride, the dibenzoyl derivative and the dihydantoin. Armstrong and du Vigneaud have submitted the reaction between L-cysteine and aldehydes and ketones in 6N hydrochloric acid at room temperature to a further study.

du Vigneaud and Patterson[111] also synthesized djenkolic acid from methylene chloride and 2 molecular proportions of L-cysteine in liquid ammonia.

The suggestion that formaldehyde was involved in the biological synthesis of djenkolic acid did not postulate the intervention of free formaldehyde. The development of the idea of the 'formaldehyde equivalent' by Robinson had rendered such an assumption unnecessary. Later work by Sakami, Arnstein, Kisliuk and others on one-carbon fragments and on 'active formaldehyde', which is discussed in Chapter 5 and in reviews by the author[112] and by Verly[113], has indicated the lines along which reaction with 'formaldehyde' may occur.

It is possible that the formaldehyde is carried as one of the 'active formaldehydes' which have been suggested from time to time, e.g. as N-hydroxymethyl glycine $HO \cdot CH_2 \cdot NH \cdot CH_2 \cdot COOH$ or as 5-N-hydroxymethyltetrahydropteroylglutamic acid[113].

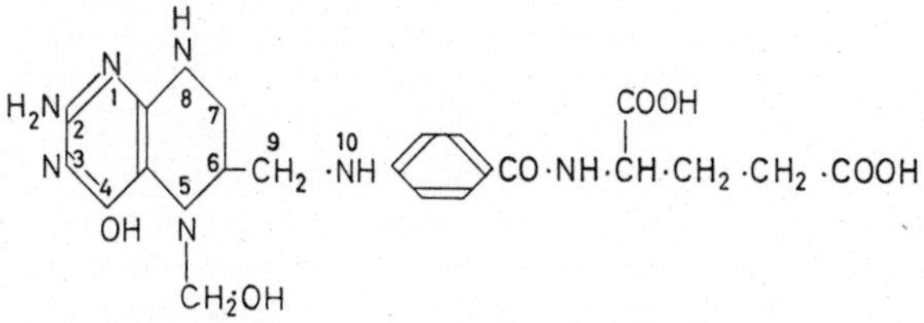

In that case the reaction with cysteine might be represented thus:

$$> N \cdot CH_2 \cdot \boxed{OH + H} \cdot S \cdot CH_2 \cdot CH(NH_2) \cdot COOH \longrightarrow$$

$$> N \cdot CH_2 \cdot S \cdot CH_2 \cdot CH(NH_2) \cdot COOH \xrightarrow{\ HOH\ }$$

$$> NH + HO \cdot CH_2 \cdot S \cdot CH_2 \cdot CH(NH_2) \cdot COOH$$

61

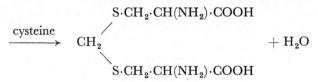

cysteine

In the relations set out above $>$NH represents tetrahydropteroyl-glutamic acid which is regenerated and later reformylated and reduced to 'active formaldehyde'.

FELININE, AN AMINO ACID CONTAINING SULPHUR FROM CATS' URINE

In 1951 Datta and Harris[114] reported that the urine of cats and of the ocelot contained a substance which gave a ninhydrin reaction. This compound was investigated by Westall[115]. It was found to overlap with leucine and isoleucine on two-dimensional paper chromatograms run with phenol-ammonia and collidine-lutidine. By a one-dimensional process using tertiary butyl alcohol it could be obtained as an individual spot which, on treatment with hydrogen peroxide no longer appeared in its original position. It seemed possible that the new amino acid contained sulphur and, if so, the disappearance of the spot would be due to oxidation to a sulphoxide or more probably a sulphone. Consequently several amino acids containing sulphur were examined under the same conditions but in no case did the resulting ninhydrin spot coincide with that obtained by oxidation of the new amino-acid. This eliminated homocysteine, homomethionine, lanthionine, $\beta\beta$-dimethylcysteine and the corresponding cystine derivative, and the S-alkylcysteines (n-CH$_3$ to n-C$_5$H$_{11}$).

The new amino acid was finally isolated by fractionation on ion-exchange resins, another unknown amino acid being removed by a Zeo-Karb 215 column at 65°C. Precipitation with acetone from aqueous-alcoholic solution yielded the new compound. Analysis indicated the empirical formula C$_8$H$_{17}$O$_3$NS. The content of amino-nitrogen was the same as the total nitrogen. The molecular weight in aqueous solution agreed with the formula given above. The substance was retained in quantity by both cation and anion exchange resins. On two-dimensional chromatograms in the presence of copper carbonate a copper complex was formed and no ninhydrin spot was obtainable. All the evidence, therefore, suggested that the new compound—felinine—was an amino acid. On oxidation with hydrogen peroxide two atoms of oxygen were taken up by felinine and the resulting product was almost certainly a sulphone, as suggested by the chromatographic evidence already outlined.

Desulphurization of felinine with Raney nickel—Distillation of felinine with water and Raney nickel gave nickel sulphide and a volatile oil, immiscible with water which was identified as *iso*amyl alcohol $(CH_3)_2 \cdot CH \cdot CH_2 \cdot CH_2 \cdot OH$ by formation of the 3 : 5-dinitrobenzoate. Careful oxidation of the oil with dilute chromic acid gave *iso*valeraldehyde which was characterized as the 2 : 4-dinitrophenyl-hydrazone. Concentration of the original aqueous reaction mixture gave an amino acid which was identified as alanine by analysis after separation on a column. Paper chromatography of the eluate showed that no other amino acid was present.

The structure of felinine—From these results Westall suggested the provisional formula

$$HO \cdot CH_2 \cdot CH_2 \cdot C(CH_3)_2 \cdot S \cdot CH_2 \cdot CH(NH_2) \cdot COOH$$

The point of attachment of the sulphur atom to the five-carbon chain was not ascertained. Thus, a structure such as

$$\begin{array}{c} HC(CH_3)_2 \\ | \\ HO \cdot CH_2 \cdot CH \cdot S \cdot CH_2 \cdot CH(NH_2) \cdot COOH \end{array}$$

was not excluded. The occurrence of the $(CH_3)_2C$—S—C linkage in penicillin (X) suggests that this system may be found in other natural products.

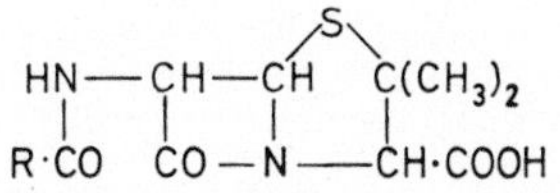

(X)

The synthesis of ($\pm$)—*felinine*—The structure tentatively assigned to felinine by Westall was confirmed by Trippett[116] by addition of toluene-ω-thiol (benzyl mercaptan) to β-methylcrotonaldehyde (prepared from β-methylcrotonic acid by reduction with lithium aluminium hydride, followed by oxidation with manganese dioxide) in presence of piperidine, followed by heating the mixture at 100°C β-Benzylthio*iso*valeraldehyde was obtained,

$$(CH_3)_2C = CH \cdot CHO + HS \cdot CH_2 \cdot C_6H_5 \longrightarrow$$

$$(CH_3)_2C \Big\langle \begin{array}{l} CH_2 \cdot CHO \\ \\ S \cdot CH_2 \cdot C_6H_5 \end{array}$$

This, on reduction with lithium aluminium hydride in ether followed by acidification, yielded the corresponding β-benzylthio*iso*amyl alcohol. When this was dissolved in liquid ammonia and treated with sodium the benzyl group was removed by hydrogenolysis and replaced by sodium. Without removing the ammonia α-amino-β-chloropropionic acid was added and the ammonia then allowed to evaporate. The residue was dissolved in water and passed down a column of Dowex 50 ion-exchange resin (H^+ form) and washed with water. When the effluent was neutral the amino acid was eluted with ammonia. Evaporation of the eluate and crystallization from aqueous ethanol gave ($\pm$)-felinine, S-3-hydroxy-1 : 1-dimethyl-propyl-cysteine:

$$HO \cdot CH_2 \cdot CH_2 \cdot (CH_3)_2 C \cdot SNa + Cl \cdot CH_2 \cdot CH(NH_2)COOH \longrightarrow$$
$$HO \cdot CH_2 \cdot CH_2 \cdot (CH_3)_2 C \cdot S \cdot CH_2 \cdot CH(NH_2)COOH$$

Felinine

The product behaved on paper chromatography in five different solvents exactly as did the natural amino acid. On treatment with 2 : 4-dinitrofluorobenzene the N-2 : 4-dinitrophenyl-derivative was obtained. Its infra-red spectrum in acetonitrile-chloroform was identical with that of the analogous derivative from natural felinine.

Felinine undergoes an interesting decomposition on heating with 5N-hydrochloric acid at 105°C. The products are cystine, a small amount of a volatile oil, unchanged felinine and a new amino acid $C_{11}H_{22}O_4N_2S_2$ which on paper chromatography formed a ninhydrin spot in the alanine region. Natural felinine behaved in the same way. This decomposition of felinine by acid was noticed by Westall[115] but was not studied in detail. Trippett suggests the structure $COOH \cdot CH(NH_2) \cdot CH_2 \cdot S \cdot CH_2 \cdot CH_2 \cdot C(CH_3)_2 \cdot S \cdot CH_2 \cdot CH(NH_2) \cdot COOH$ for the new amino acid. It may be formed by the interaction of felinine with cysteine resulting from its own decomposition.

THE OCCURRENCE OF DERIVATIVES OF THIOPHEN IN NATURE

PYROGENIC FORMATION OF THIOPHEN AND RELATED COMPOUNDS

Since the original isolation of thiophen from coal-tar benzene by Victor Meyer[117] in 1882 much research has been carried out, especially since 1914, on the formation of this compound and its derivatives. This work is so well-known that only a few key references need be given[118-125].

It has long been known that by passing thiophen through a hot tube a mixture of isomeric dithienyls, e.g. (XI) is formed which can be partially separated by crystallization[126].

During a study of the isomeric thiophthens[122-124] formed by the action of acetylene on boiling sulphur attention was paid to the fractions boiling higher than the thiophthens. That of b.p. 120°–140°C at 15 mm. deposited a pale yellow solid. On distillation in steam and crystallization the m.p. was 98°–104°C. It did not form a picrate and was shown to be a mixture of isomeric dithienyls[127].

Polythienyls containing from 2–6 thienyl residues linked presumably on the α-positions have been obtained from α-iodothiophen and metallic copper, free radicals being involved in the synthesis[128].

Natural Polyacetylene Derivatives, Possible Sources of Thiophen Compounds in Nature

The work described above was regarded at the time as having a purely experimental and theoretical interest. It was most surprising therefore that in 1947 Sease and Zechmeister[129] isolated α-terthienyl (XII) from a methanol extract of the flowers of the Indian marigold (*Tagetes erecta*, Nat. Order *Compositae*). It was separated by chromatographic adsorption from petroleum ether first on a column of calcium hydroxide and then on alumina, followed by elution with ether. The compound is a solid of m.p. 94°–95.5°C, with a blue fluorescence.

Until this discovery the only thiophen derivative which had been found in nature was the growth factor known as biotin which consists of a tetrahydrothiophen nucleus carrying a —$(CH_2)_4COOH$ side chain and condensed in the 3 : 4 position with a urea residue (XIII).

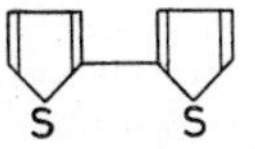

(XI) 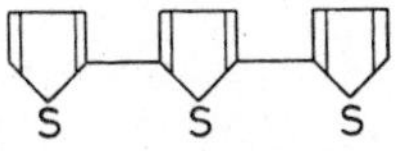   (XII) 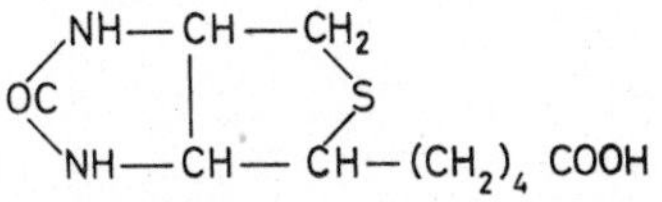   (XIII)

Many members of the *Compositae* contain polyacetylene derivatives e.g. Sorensen and Stene isolated the diolefinic diacetylene $CH_3 \cdot CH : CH \cdot C \vdots C \cdot C \vdots C \cdot CH : CH \cdot CO \cdot O \cdot CH_3$ from *Matricaria inodora* a plant closely allied to the common camomile[130]. The corresponding dihydro-derivative $CH_3 \cdot CH_2 \cdot CH_2 \cdot C \vdots C \cdot C \vdots C \cdot CH : CH \cdot CO \cdot O \cdot CH_3$ occurs in *Lachnophyllum gossypinum*[131]. Carlina oxide (benzyl-2-furyl-acetylene) is found in the oil obtained from the roots of *Carlina acaulis* (*Circium acaulos*)[132].

The author pointed out[133] that it may be more than a coincidence that the only instance so far recorded of the occurrence of a true thiophen derivative in plants should be found in a family, so many members of which contain polyacetylenes. He suggested that α-terthienyl may be formed by interaction of hydrogen sulphide (possibly arising from cysteine) with a straight chain compound containing an acetylenic or an acetylenic-olefinic system, possibly also some methylene groups, as in the dihydro compound cited on p. 66. Oxidation, decarboxylation or dehydrogenation might also be involved. Possibly a long chain paraffin or fatty acid might serve equally well as the starting point. Ring closure would, however, undoubtedly be facilitated by the presence of olefinic and acetylenic linkages.

The suggested mechanism may be represented by some such scheme as the following:

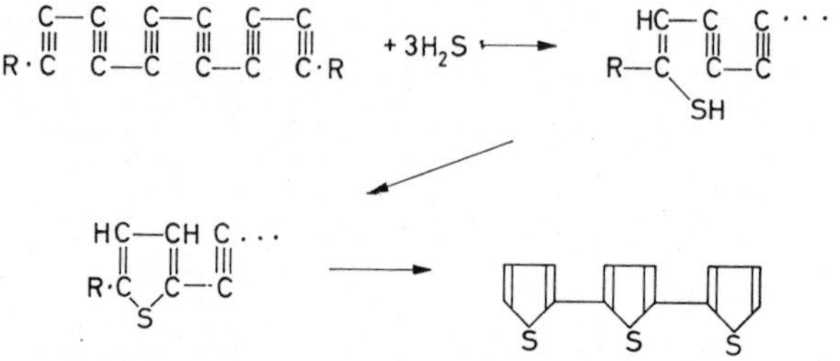

Nevertheless polyacetylenes are not confined to the *Compositae*, e.g. tariric acid $CH_3(CH_2)_{10}C : C \cdot (CH_2)_4 COOH$ occurs as a glyceride in the fruits of varieties of *Picramnia* and erythrogenic acid, which can be isolated from the seeds of *Ungokea klaineana*, Pierre has the structure $CH_2 : CH \cdot C : C \cdot (CH_2)_4 C : C \cdot (CH_2)_7 \cdot COOH$ or possibly $CH_2 : CH \cdot (CH_2)_4 C : C \cdot C : C \cdot (CH_2)_7 COOH$. Both the heterocyclic ring and the $-(CH_2)_4 COOH$ side-chain of biotin may arise from an acid of this type. Sörensen refers to an ester which is a dehydro-derivative of the ester previously isolated from the root of *Matricaria inodora* (the scentless mayweed)—*see* p. 65. This is spectrally closely related to $CH_3 \cdot C : C \cdot C : C \cdot C : C \cdot CH : CH \cdot COOCH_3$ which has been synthesized. Another triacetylenic ester occurs in the root of *Artemisia vulgaris* along with a ketone and a hydrocarbon both containing three adjacent acetylene linkages[134]. The natural occurrence of these polyacetylenes with so low a content of hydrogen affords some further support to the suggestion as to the origin of the α-terthienyl of *Tagetes erecta* put forward above, and possibly

66

simplifies the assumptions involved. Polyacetylene derivatives have recently been isolated by Lythgoe and his co-workers[135,136] from the *Umbelliferae*.

THE OCCURRENCE OF AN ACETYLENIC DERIVATIVE OF THIOPHEN IN A WOOD-DESTROYING FUNGUS

The suggestion[133] as to the biogenesis of α-terthienyl was put forward in 1953. Two years later Birkinshaw and Chaplen[137] described their work on some metabolic products of the wood-destroying fungus *Daedalena juniperina*, Murr. which infests the East African cedar *Juniperus procera* Hochst.

This fungus was grown mainly upon a medium containing glucose, inorganic salts and a trace of 'Marmite' as a source of vitamin B_{12}. The contents of the culture flasks were distilled in steam. Extraction of the distillate with ether yielded an oil which, with light petroleum gave a crystalline compound C_8H_6OS. This exhibited aldehyde reactions and formed a 2 : 4-dinitrophenylhydrazone.

It was oxidized by aqueous alkaline potassium mercuric iodide (the Doeuvre reagent) to a monobasic acid $C_7H_5S \cdot COOH$. The original aldehyde was named junipal and the formula $C_7H_5S \cdot CHO$ assigned to it. The methyl ester of the monobasic acid (juniperic acid) with cold potassium permanganate gave the monomethyl ester of a dibasic acid $C_4H_2S \begin{cases} COOH \\ COOCH_3 \end{cases}$. The corresponding dimethyl ester was identical with the dimethyl ester of thiophen-2 : 5-dicarboxylic acid (XIV) synthesized for comparison. Oxidation of juniperic acid by potassium permanganate in acetone gave the free thiophen-2 : 5-dicarboxylic acid. The second carboxyl group must have arisen from the oxidation of a C_3H_3 group in juniperic acid or its methyl ester. A Kuhn–Roth oxidation showed junipal to contain one CH_3—C group. Consequently the C_3H_3 side-chain must be $CH_3C \equiv C$—. The presence of an acetylenic linking was confirmed by infra-red spectroscopy. Junipal has therefore the constitution (XV).

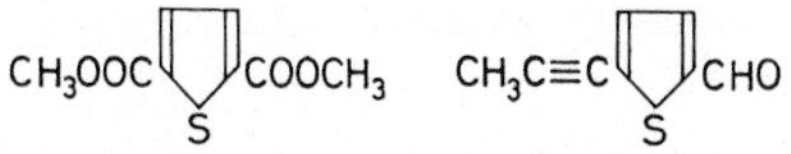

$$CH_3OOC \underset{S}{\bigcup} COOCH_3 \qquad CH_3C \equiv C \underset{S}{\bigcup} CHO$$

(XIV)　　　　　　　(XV)

Birkinshaw and Chaplen refer to the suggestion of Challenger and Holmes[133], that the α-terthienyl of *Tagetes erecta* arises from an acetylene derivative. They remark: 'this hypothesis is considerably strengthened by the isolation of junipal as a product of fungal metabolism, since both the acetylenic linkage and the thiophen nucleus are present in the same molecule.'

They also point out that derivatives of acetylene occur among the metabolic products of fungi. Several very unstable substances isolated from Basidiomycetes were recognized through their ultra-violet absorption spectra as acetylenic derivatives[138],[139]. Celmer and Solomons[140] have shown that the crystalline antibiotic mycomycin isolated from an Actinomycete by Johnson and Burdon[141] is 3 : 5 : 7 : 8-tridecatetraene-10 : 12- diynoic acid.

$$HC \equiv C \cdot C \equiv C \cdot CH = C = CH \cdot C = C \cdot C = C \cdot CH_2 \cdot COOH$$

A summary of some of the earlier work on natural derivatives of acetylene has been published by Birkinshaw[142]. We may look forward with some confidence to the detection of other derivatives of thiophen in natural products.

REFERENCES

[1] Haas, P., *Biochem. J.* **15** (1921) 469
[2] Haas, P. and Russell-Wells, Miss B., *ibid.* **23** (1929) 425
[3] Haas, P. and Hill, T. G., *ibid.* **25** (1931) 1472
[4] Haas, P. and Bird, Miss M. G., *ibid.* **25** (1931) 403
[5] Haas, P. and Russell-Wells, Miss B., *ibid.* **17** (1923) 696
[6] Haas, P., *ibid.* **29** (1935) 1258
[7] Blackburn, S. and Challenger, F., *J. chem. Soc.* (1938) 1872
[8] Birkinshaw, J. H., Findlay, W. P. K. and Webb, R. A., *Biochem. J.* **36** (1942) 526
[9] Challenger, F. and Charlton, P. T., *J. chem. Soc.* (1947) 424
[10] Cromwell, B. T., *Biochem. J.* **45** (1949) 84; **46** (1950) 578
[11] Challenger, F. and Simpson, Miss M. I., *J. chem. Soc.* (1948) 1591
[12] Cantoni, G. L. and Anderson, D., *Conférences et Rapports 3ème Congrès International de Biochimie, Bruxelles* (1955) 236
[13] Cantoni, G. L., *Conférences et Rapports 3ème Congrès International de Biochimie, Bruxelles* (1955) 236
[14] Challenger, F., *Conférences et Rapports 3ème Congrès International de Biochimie, Bruxelles* (1955) 239
[15] Woolley, D. W., *Nature, Lond.* **171** (1953) 323
[16] Ericson, L. E. and Carlson, B., *Ark. Kemi* **6** (1953) 511
[17] Cantoni, G. L., Personal communication
[18] Bywood, R., *Thesis*, Univ. of Leeds (1953)
[19] Challenger, F. and Liu, Y. C., *Rec. Trav. chim. Pays-Bas* **69** (1950) 334

[20] Cantoni, G. L., *J. biol. Chem.* **204** (1953) 403

[21] Leaver, D. and Challenger, F., *J. chem. Soc.* (1957) 39

[22] Bywood, R. and Challenger, F., *Biochem. J.* **53** (1953) XXVI

[23] Nicolai, Miss E. and Preston, R. D., *Nature, Lond.* **171** (1953) 752

[24] Challenger, F., Bywood, R., Thomas, Mrs. P. and Hayward, Miss B. J., *Arch. Biochem. Biophys.* **69** (1957) 514

[25] Karrer, P. and Eugster, C. H., *Helv. chim. acta* **32** (1949) 957, 2397

[26] Bywood, R., Challenger, F., Leaver, D. and Whitaker, Mrs. M. I., *Biochem. J.* **48** (1951) XXX

[27] Smythe, C. V., *J. biol. Chem.* **142** (1942) 387

[28] Synge, R. L. M. and Wood, J. C., *Biochem. J.* **64** (1956) 252

[29] Synge, R. L. M., *ibid.* **49** (1951) 642

[30] Lavine, T. F., *J. biol. Chem.* **169** (1947) 477

[31] Stoll, A. and Seebeck, E., *Advanc. Enzymol.* **11** (1951) 379

[32] Moore, S. and Stein, W. H., *J. biol. Chem.* **211** (1954) 893, 907

[33] Morris, C. J. and Thompson, J. F., *Chem. & Ind.* (1955) 951; *J. Amer. chem. Soc.* **78** (1956) 1605

[34] Thompson, J. F., Morris, C. J. and Zacharius, R. M., *Nature, Lond.* **178** (1956) 593

[35] Melville, D. B., *J. biol. Chem.* **208** (1954) 495

[36] Melville, D. B., Genghof, D. S. and Lee, J. M., *ibid.* **208** (1954) 503

[37] Wright, L. D. and Cresson, E. L., *J. Amer. chem. Soc.* **76** (1954) 4156

[38] Wright, L. D., Cresson, E. L., Valiant, J., Wolf, D. E. and Folkers, K., *ibid.* **76** (1954) 4160, 4163

[39] Wright, L. D. and Driscoll, C. A., *ibid.* **76** (1954) 4999

[40] Westall, R. G., *Biochem. J.* **55** (1953) 244

[41] Trippett, S., *J. chem. Soc.* (1957) 1929

[42] Toennies, G. and Kolb, J. J., *J. biol. Chem.* **128** (1939) 399

[43] Mellanby, E., *Brit. med. J.* **2** (1946) 885

[44] Bentley, H. R., McDermott, E. E., Moran, T., Pace, J. and Whitehead, J. K., *Proc. roy. Soc.* **137B** (1950) 402

[45] Bentley, H. R., McDermott, E. E. and Whitehead, J. K., *ibid.* **138B** (1951) 265

[46] Misani, F., Fair, T. W. and Reiner, L., *J. Amer. chem. Soc.* **73** (1951) 459

[47] Abel, R., *Z. physiol. Chem.* **20** (1894) 253

[48] Neuberg, C. and Grosser, P., *Centralblatt Physiol.* **19** (1905–6) 316

[49] Ingold, C. K. and Kuriyan, K. L., *J. chem. Soc.* (1933) 991

[50] Nencki, L., *Arch. exp. Path. Pharmak.* **28** (1891) 206

[51] Allison, A. C., Personal communication

[52] Jansen, D. F., *J. biol. Chem.* **176** (1948) 657

[53] Allison, A. C. and McWhirter, K. G., *Nature, Lond.* **178** (1956) 748

[54] Challenger, F. and Hayward, Miss B. J., *Chem. & Ind.* (1954) 729

[55] McRorie, R. A., Sutherland, G. L., Lewis, M. S., Burton, A. D., Glazener, M. R. and Shive, W., *J. Amer. chem. Soc.* **76** (1954) 115

[56] Challenger, F. and Charlton, P. T., *J. chem. Soc.* (1947) 424

[57] Stahl, W. H., McQue, B., Mandels, G. R. and Siu, R. G. H., *Arch. Biochem.* **20** (1949) 422

[58] Challenger, F. and Walshe, J. M., *Biochem. J.* **59** (1955) 372

[59] Challenger, F. and Walshe, J. M., *Lancet* (1955) 1239

[60] Dransfield, P. B. and Challenger, F., *J. chem. Soc.* (1955) 1153

[61] Niemann, F., *Arch. Hyg.* **19** (1893) 126

[62] Rubner, N., *ibid.* **19** (1893) 136

[63] For references see Challenger, F. and Rawlings, A. A., *J. chem. Soc.* (1937) 868

[64] Zwergal, A., *Die Pharmacie* **6** (1951) 245

[65] Blackburn, S. and Challenger, F., *J. chem. Soc.* (1938) 1872

[66] Nakamura, N., *Biochem. Z.* **164** (1925) 31

[67] Schmid, H. and Karrer, P., *Helv. chim. acta* **31** (1948) 1017, 1087, 1497

[68] Koolhaas, D. R., *Biochem. Z.* **230** (1931) 446

[69] Challenger, F. and North, H. E., *J. chem. Soc.* (1934) 68

[70] Dransfield, P. B., *Thesis*, Univ. of Leeds (1953)

[71] Salkowski, E., *Z. physiol. Chem.* **89** (1914) 485

[72] Salkowski, E., *ibid.* **92** (1914) 89

[73] Schiff, L., *The Differential Diagnosis of Jaundice*, 1st ed. The Year Book Publishers, Chicago

[74] Himsworth, H. P., *Lectures on the Liver and its Diseases*, 1st ed. Blackwell, Oxford

[75] Davidson, L. S. P., *Lancet* **2** (1949) 197

[76] Lichtman, S. S., *Diseases of the Liver, Gall-bladder and Bile Ducts*, 2nd ed. Kimpton, London

[77] Blackburn, S. and Challenger, F., *J. chem. Soc.* (1938) 1872

[78] Challenger, F. and Charlton, P. T., *ibid.* (1947) 424

[79] Binkley, F., *J. biol. Chem.* **186** (1950) 287

[80] Walshe, J. M., *Quart. J. Med.* **22** (1953) 483

[81] Dent, C. E., *Biochem. J.* **41** (1947) 240

[82] Challenger, F. and Liu, Y. C., *Rec. Trav. chim. Pays-Bas* **69** (1950) 334

[83] Astwood, E. B., *J. Pharm.* **78** (1943) 79

[84] Astwood, E. B., *J. Amer. med. Ass.* **122** (1943) 78

[85] Himsworth, H. P., *Lancet* **2** (1943) 465

[86] Pohl, F., *Arch. exp. Path. Pharmak.* **51** (1904) 341

[87] Challenger, F. and Greenwood, D., *Biochem. J.* **44** (1949) 87

[88] Walker, J. C., Lindegren, C. C. and Bachmann, F. M., *J. agric. Res.* **30** (1925) 175

[89] Kohmann, E. F., *Science* **106** (1947) 625

[90] Schöberl, A., *Liebig's Ann.* **507** (1933) 111; **522** (1936) 97

[91] Thomas, M. Personal communication

[92] Cavallito, C. J. and Bailey, J. H., *J. Amer. chem. Soc.* **66** (1944) 1950

[93] Cavallito, C. J., Buck, J. S. and Suter, C. M., *ibid.* **66** (1944) 1952

[94] Cavallito, C. J., Bailey, J. H. and Buck, J. S., *ibid.* **67** (1945) 1032

[95] Stoll, A. and Seebeck, E., *Helv. chim. acta* **32** (1949) 197, 866

[96] Stoll, A. and Seebeck, E., *ibid.* **31** (1948) 189

[97] Stoll, A. and Seebeck, E., *Sci. pharm.* **18** (1950) 61

[98] Stoll, A. and Seebeck, E., *Helv. chim. acta* **34** (1951) 481

[99] Stoll, A. and Seebeck, E., *Advanc. Enzymol.* **11** (1951) 377

[100] Schöberl, A., *Liebig's Ann.* **599** (1956) 23

[101] Blackburn, S. and Lee, G. R., *Analyst* **80** (1955) 875

[102] van Veen, A. G. and Hyman, A. J., *Geneesk. Tijdschr. Nederl. Indie* **73** (1933) 991

[103] van Veen, A. G. and Hyman, A. J., *Rec. Trav. chim. Pays-Bas* **54** (1935) 493

[104] Hyman, A. J. and van Veen, A. G., *Geneesk. Tijdschr. Nederl. Indie* **76** (1936) 840

[105] Clowes, *Ber. dtsch. chem. Ges.* **32** (1899) 2841

[106] Challenger, F. and Higginbottom, Miss C., *Biochem. J.* **29** (1935) 1757

[107] Ratner, S. and Clarke, H. T., *J. Amer. chem. Soc.* **59** (1937) 200

[108] Schubert, M. P., *J. Biol. Chem.* **114** (1936) 341

[109] Armstrong, M. D. and du Vigneaud, V., *ibid.* **168** (1947) 373

[110] Armstrong, M. D. and du Vigneaud, V., *ibid.* **173** (1948) 749

[111] du Vigneaud, V. and Patterson, W. I., *ibid.*, **114** (1936) 533

[112] Challenger, F., *Quart. Rev. chem. Soc.* **9** (1955) 271, 279

[113] Verly, W. G., *Arch. Internat. Physiol. Biochem.* **64** (1956) 309

[114] Datta, S. P. and Harris, H., *J. Physiol.* **114** (1951) 39 P

[115] Westall, R. G., *Biochem. J.* **55** (1953) 244

[116] Trippett, S., *J. chem. Soc.* (1957) 1929

[117] Meyer, V., *Ber. dtsch. chem. Ges.* **16** (1883) 1465

[118] Meyer, V., *Die Thiophen Gruppe*, Vieweg und Sohn, Braunschweig, 1888

[119] Steinkopf, W., *Die Chemie des Thiophens*, Steinkopf, Leipzig, 1941

[120] Hartough, H. D., *Thiophene and its Derivatives*, Interscience, New York and London, 1952

[121] Challenger, F., Haslam, J., Bramhall, R. J. and Walkden, J., *J. Inst. Petrol.* **12** (1926) 106

[122] Challenger, F. and Harrison, J. B., *ibid.* **21** (1935) 135

[123] Challenger, F. and Emmott, R., *ibid.* **37** (1951) 396

[124] Challenger, F. and Fishwick, B., *ibid.* **39** (1953) 220

[125] Hartough, H. D., *op. cit.* p. 55. Ref. 120

[126] Hartough, H. D., *op. cit.* p. 460. Ref. 120

[127] Bruce, J., Challenger, F., Gibson, H. B. and Allenby, W. E., *J. Inst. Petrol* **34** (1948) 226

[128] Steinkopf, W., Hofmann, K. H. and Leitsmann, R., *Annalen* **546** (1941) 180

[129] Sease, J. W. and Zechmeister, L., *J. Amer. chem. Soc.* **69** (1947) 270, 273

[130] Sörensen, N. A. and Steene, J., *Annalen* **549** (1941) 80

[131] Wiljams, W. W., Smirnow, V. S. and Goljmow, V. P., *J. gen. Chem. U.S.S.R.* (A) **5** (1935) 1195

[132] Pfau, A. S., Picktet, J., Plattner, P. and Susz, B., *Helv. chim. acta* **18** (1935) 935

[133] Challenger, F. and Holmes, J. L., *J. chem. Soc.* (1953) 1837

[134] Sörensen, N. A., *Chem. Soc. Symposium*, 5 Feb. 1953

[135] Anet, E. F. L. J., Lythgoe, B., Silk, M. H. and Trippett, S., *J. chem. Soc.* (1953) 309

[136] Hill, Miss B. E., Lythgoe, B., Mirvish, S. and Trippett S., *ibid.* (1955) 1770

[137] Birkinshaw, J. H. and Chaplen, P., *Biochem. J.* **60** (1955) 255
[138] Anchel, M., Polatnick, J. and Kavanagh, F. *Arch. Biochem.* **25** (1950) 208
[139] Anchel, M., *J. Amer. chem. Soc.* **74** (1952) 1588
[140] Celmer, W. D. and Solomons, I. A., *ibid.* **74** (1952) 1870
[141] Johnson, E. A. and Burdon, K. L., *J. Bact.* **54** (1947) 281
[142] Birkinshaw, J. H., *Anu. Rev. Biochem.* **22** (1953) 372

3

THE SULPHUR COMPOUNDS OF PETROLEUM AND OTHER MINERAL OILS

SOME broad definition of the term 'mineral oils' is desirable at the outset. In its widest sense, the term includes all oils which have been produced by the action of heat on organic matter, whether this heat has been applied naturally during geological changes, as in the formation of petroleum (where the effect of pressure has also to be considered) or in modern technical processes such as the distillation of coal, oil-shale, lignite or peat. In this chapter the term mineral oil will therefore be interpreted broadly.

Much work has been carried out during the last sixty years on the ingredients of mineral oils[1] and it is clear that the sulphur compounds which these oils contain are of very similar types, although the proportions in which each type is present may vary considerably. Consequently it is not possible to separate the study of one kind of mineral oil from that of another. Thiophen (I), for example, and its 2-methyl derivative (II) occur in certain petroleums and also in distillates from coal-tar, shale and lignite[1].

Between 1891 and 1906 Mabery[2,3] extracted various fractions of American petroleum with sulphuric acid and isolated dimethyl-, diethyl- and di-n-butyl sulphides by dilution of the resulting 'acid sludge' with water. The dilution of 'acid sludge' obtained during the refining of petroleum distillates will frequently be mentioned. The liberation of sulphides by this process depends on the hydrolysis of the sulphonium hydrogen sulphates of various open-chain and cyclic saturated sulphides, e.g. $\left[R_2\overset{+}{S}H\right]\cdot\bar{O}\cdot SO_2OH$, which are formed by co-ordination of the hydrogen ion of sulphuric acid by the unshared electrons of the sulphur atom. These sulphonium salts are stable in strong sulphuric acid but not in the dilute acid. The solubility of ether which forms an oxonium sulphate and of diethyl sulphide in sulphuric acid, accompanied by loss of odour and reappearance on dilution, is well known.

Thierry[4] in 1925 obtained results similar to those of Mabery. By dilution of an acid sludge from a Persian petroleum he isolated methyl ethyl sulphide, tetrahydrothiophen (tetramethylene sulphide or thia*cyclo*pentane) (III) and pentamethylene sulphide (or thia*cyclo*hexane) (IV). These compounds were identified by the

73

formation of derivatives such as the mercurichloride, $R_2\overset{+}{S}\text{-}\overline{H}gCl_2$ (V), the mercuri-iodide, the sulphone, the methylsulphonium chloride and iodide and the methylsulphonium mercuri-iodide, $\left[R_2\overset{+}{S}\cdot CH_3\right]\overline{H}gI_3$ or $\left[R_2\overset{+}{S}\cdot CH_3\right]_2\overline{H}gI_4$.

About the same time Birch and Norris[5] detected ethyl-, *iso*propyl and *iso*amyl mercaptans in a low-boiling fraction of Persian oil. The oil was washed with sodium hydroxide, and the alkaline extract separated, and slowly distilled. Hydrolysis of the sodium mercaptides $R\cdot S\cdot Na$ occurred and an oil came over from which mercaptans were removed by alkali; the alkaline extract was acidified and the mercaptans fractionated. The *iso*propyl mercaptan was characterized as the mercury derivative, $(CH_3)_2CH\cdot S\cdot Hg\cdot S\cdot CH(CH_3)_2$, as the chloromercury compound, $(CH_3)_2CH\cdot S\cdot HgCl$, obtained with mercuric oxide and mercuric chloride respectively, and as *p*-nitrobenzyl *iso*propyl sulphide, $NO_2\cdot C_6H_4\cdot CH_2\cdot S\cdot CH(CH_3)_2$. These mercaptans were oxidized by nitric acid to the sulphonic acids and analysed as the barium salts. *Iso*butyl mercaptan also yielded a chloromercury derivative, $(CH_3)_2CH\cdot CH_2\cdot S\cdot HgCl$.

This investigation, the first of a long series of researches by Birch on the organic sulphur compounds of petroleum, is still in progress and has added greatly to our knowledge of these compounds.

Mabery's Thiophanes from Canadian Oil

Mabery[6], who was a pioneer in the study of the sulphur compounds of petroleum, had also examined many years previously a large number of compounds of the general formula $C_nH_{2n}S$ separated from the 'acid sludge' from Canadian petroleum. These he called thiophanes but did not prove that they contained the thiophane (tetrahydrothiophen, III) ring system.

The oil so obtained was repeatedly distilled and the fractions separately heated with alcoholic mercuric chloride solution in order to precipitate the sulphur compounds as co-ordinated addition compounds of type (V) and leave most hydrocarbons unattacked. The viscous precipitates were then decomposed with hydrogen sulphide to regenerate the sulphur compound. Apparently this did not cause any complication due to the formation of new sulphur linkages arising from the hydrogen sulphide. In general, however, treatment of unknown sulphur compounds with hydrogen sulphide is to be avoided wherever possible. Co-ordination compounds of type (V) can usually be decomposed by alkali or dilute acid and even if the mercury has entered an aromatic or heterocyclic nucleus by mercuration (VI, VII), hot dilute acid will regenerate the parent compound. Most organic sulphides, including thiophen derivatives, are stable to hot dilute acids and alkali.

Mabery's regenerated sulphur compounds were separately fractionated and products obtained which, from the b.p., the sulphur content and the molecular refraction, he regarded as homogeneous. This was probably true in some but not in all cases. Mabery's sulphides $C_nH_{2n}S$ had many of the properties of the dialkyl sulphides, R_2S ($R = C_nH_{2n+1}$) and formed sulphones $C_nH_{2n}SO_2$, methiodides, $\left[C_nH_{2n}\overset{+}{S}\cdot CH_3\right]\bar{I}$, and combined with mercuric chloride. Their densities were, however, higher than those of the dialkyl sulphides but the sulphides were certainly not homologues of thiophen. Mabery regarded them as polymethylene sulphides containing five, six or seven methylene groups either unsubstituted or containing numerous or long side-chains. Apart from Victor Meyer's classical work on the occurrence of thiophen and its homologues in coal tar this was almost the first systematic study of the sulphur compounds occurring in mineral oils and it was not until after 1920 that any further considerable work was carried out on this subject.

THE SULPHUR COMPOUNDS OF COAL TAR, LIGNITE TAR AND SHALE OIL

The next advances came from investigations of the oils obtained by distillation of coal, oil-shale and lignite.

Coal Tar and Lignite Tar

Boes[7] obtained thionaphthen (VIII) and diphenylene sulphide (2 : 3-benzothionaphthen IX) from lignite tar and coal tar respectively and Weissgerber and Krüber[8] found both of them in coal tar. They isolated both compounds as the sulphone, and the thionaphthen also as the picrate and the mercurated derivative naphthienyl mercury acetate. Krüber[9] several years later isolated 6 : 7-benzothionaphthen (X), and 4 : 5-benzothionaphthen (XI) from coal tar. The synthesis of these compounds has recently been reported by Carruthers[10]. He has also described[11] the isolation of 1 : 8-dimethyl diphenylene sulphide (XII) from a fraction of Kuwait oil of b.p. 330°–350°C by distillation under reduced pressure, removal of aromatic compounds by extraction with furfuraldehyde, formation of the picrate, decomposition with sodium hydroxide and separation on a column of alumina. Its ultra-violet spectrum supports the suggested structure (XII). Like 1-methyldiphenylene sulphide it is not desulphurized by Raney nickel, probably due to the presence of a substituent or substituents in close proximity to the sulphur atom. It is identical with a product isolated from coal tar by Krüber and Raeithel[12] which was also inert to Raney nickel.

Low Temperature Coal Tar Distillates

In 1927 Weissgerber[13] examined low-temperature tar obtained by distillation of coal in a rotating furnace. The fraction of b.p. 187°–201°C was first freed from coumarones and indenes with 2 per cent of sulphuric acid and was then extracted with 90 per cent sulphuric acid at 15°–20°C. The separated acid on dilution with water gave an oil. Ketones were removed from this by phenylhydrazine and nitriles by hot sodium hydroxide. The residual oil was systematically

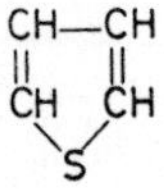

$$(I) \qquad (II) \qquad (III) \qquad (IV)$$

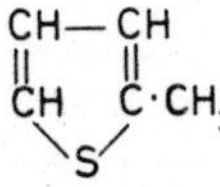

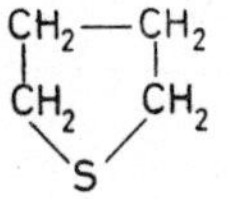

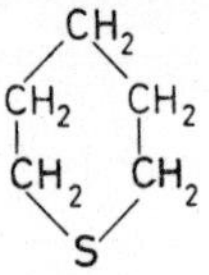

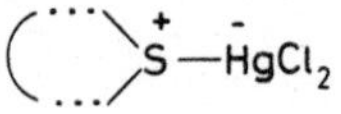

$$(V) \qquad (VI) \qquad (VII)$$

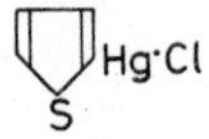

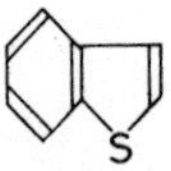

$$(VIII) \qquad (IX) \qquad (X) \qquad (XI)$$

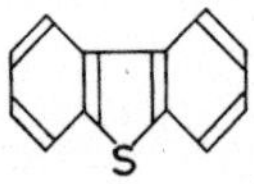

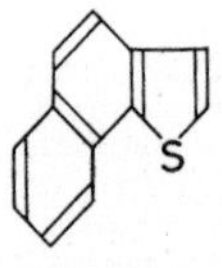

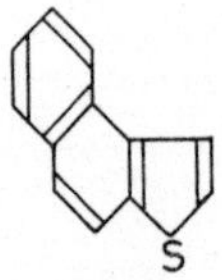

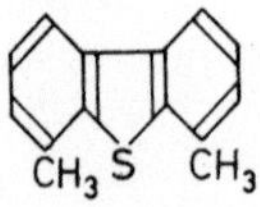

$$(XII) \qquad (XIII) \qquad (XIV) \qquad (XV)$$

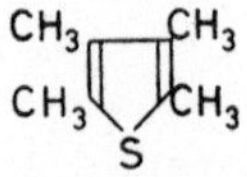

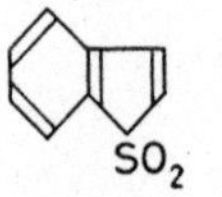

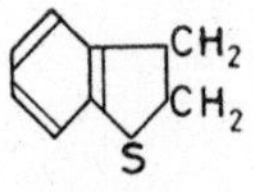

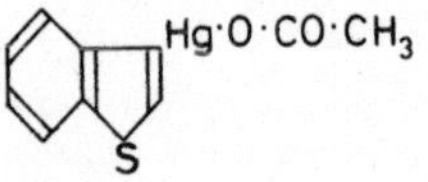

$$(XVI)$$

76

treated with sulphuric acid whereby some insoluble hydrocarbons were removed. The remainder was precipitated from the acid by water and represented 0·76 per cent of the original oil. Its density was very high (0·96), its b.p. 190°–200°C, its odour rather unpleasant and the sulphur content in different fractions 16 to 19 per cent. Alkyl sulphates (so often produced during the refining of hydrocarbons containing olefines) and thiols were shown to be absent and the usual tests for sulphides failed. The stability to sulphuric acid pointed to the presence of tetra-substituted thiophen derivatives; oxidizing agents gave sulphuric acid and no nuclear mercurichloride could be obtained, i.e. no mercuration was possible, this being further evidence of the absence of nuclear hydrogen atoms.

Tetramethylthiophen (XIII) was not available for comparison but dimethyldiethylthiophen was specially prepared. It boiled at 214°–217°C, had density 0·9573, was soluble without change in sulphuric acid and gave sulphuric acid on oxidation.

Weissgerber showed that 2 : 4-dimethylthiophen gave thiophen and methylthiophens on passage through a heated tin-lined iron tube. Application of this method of pyrolysis to the supposed tetramethylthiophen, at 650°–675°C, gave a mixture in which thiophen (as tetrabromo-derivative), 1-methylthiophen and 2 : 3-dimethylthiophen (as mercurichloride compounds) were identified. A mercurichloride apparently derived from trimethylthiophen was also isolated. These mercurichlorides contained a C—HgCl linkage, being obtained by substitution of a hydrogen of the thiophen nucleus.

The identification of the stable sulphur compound as tetramethylthiophen appears, therefore, to be justified. Many years later Birch[14] described the isolation of tetramethylthiophen and of 2 : 3 : 4-trimethyl-5-ethylthiophen from an 'acid sludge' obtained in the refining of a Persian oil (see p. 82).

Shale Oil

Scheibler[15] in 1915 detected what appeared to be a propylthiophen in shale oil from the Tyrol and the South of France, though the possibility that the compound might be a trimethyl- or a methylethylthiophen was not excluded. Pfaff and Kreutzer[1] then identified 2-methylthiophen in lignite oil. These substituted thiophens were isolated as the methylketones obtained by the Friedel–Crafts reaction. The author and his students[16,17] then showed that thiophen, 2-methylthiophen, 2-ethylthiophen, 2 : 3-dimethylthiophen, tetrahydrothiophen and thionaphthen were present in the Kimmeridge shale oil of Dorset.

The thionaphthen was detected in the fraction of b.p. 210° 230°C

Picric acid yielded a crude picrate which on decomposition with alkali gave an oil. On boiling with methylalcoholic mercuric acetate this gave a solid mercurated derivative which with acid again liberated an oil. This, with hydrogen peroxide, yielded thionaphthen sulphone (XIV).

The thiophen and its homologues were separated from appropriate fractions of the steam distillate from the crude Kimmeridge oil by treatment with aqueous mercuric acetate, when nuclear mercuration occurred. When separated and demercurated by distillation with hydrochloric acid these solids yielded oils which, by fractional distillation, fractional crystallization of the mercurichlorides to constant m.p. (nuclear mercuration, e.g. $CH_3CH_2 \cdot C_4H_2S \cdot HgCl$) and final decomposition with acid, yielded the pure thiophen homologues. Dodonow and Sochestwenskaja[18] also detected thiophen, 2-methylthiophen and 2 : 3-dimethylthiophen in a Russian shale oil by very similar methods.

The tetrahydrothiophen (tetramethylene sulphide) in the Kimmeridge shale oil was detected in the aqueous filtrate from the mercuric acetate precipitate (*see* above), where it was present as a soluble co-ordinated mercuriacetate. Addition of common salt to this filtrate gave an insoluble, co-ordinated mercuric *chloride* addition product. With alkali this liberated the cyclic sulphide which was then characterized as the sulphone, as the mercuric chloride addition product ($C_4H_8\overset{+}{S}\!\!-\!\!\overset{=}{Hg}Cl_2$) and as the methiodide. Higher fractions of the steam distillate contained analogous, presumably homologous, sulphides, which were, however, not identified. This process, depending on the differing behaviour of thiophen homologues and polymethylene sulphides (and also dialkyl sulphides) towards mercuric acetate and on the differing solubilities of the products, was clearly established as a method for separation of the two classes of compounds. Conversely by addition of aqueous mercuric chloride to the same mixture the thiophen derivative reacts very slowly (in absence of sodium acetate), whereas the polymethylene sulphide readily forms the insoluble co-ordinated mercuric chloride addition product (V). By this method the presence of tetrahydrothiophen in the fraction of b.p. 109°–117°C was confirmed.

DEVELOPMENT OF THE MERCURIC ACETATE METHOD FOR THE SEPARATION OF ORGANIC SULPHIDES

The mercuric acetate method of separation of thiophens and cyclic sulphides is fully described in a comprehensive publication by Birch and McAllan[19], who have considerably developed the process and find it to be of very general application. Their independent discovery of this method dates back to 1924 and was simultaneous with, or even somewhat prior to, its use by the author[17]. Extraction of a sulphide fraction with aqueous mercuric acetate can also separate dialkyl sulphides from cyclic sulphides, the latter being preferentially extracted. In some, but not all cases, mixtures of cyclic sulphides (but not mixtures of dialkyl sulphides) can also be separated in this way.

Separation of Open-chain and Cyclic Sulphides

Birch and McAllan give details of the separation of an equimolecular mixture of ethyl *n*-propyl sulphide (16 g.) $n_D^{20} = 1.4461$ and tetrahydrothiophen (thia*cyclo*pentane, 13 g.) $n_D^{20} = 1.5047$. The light petroleum solution of the sulphides was washed with mercuric acetate solution in batches (20 per cent of an equimolecular equivalent) until no further precipitate was obtained on addition of sodium chloride. The separate precipitates were refluxed with dilute acid, and the sulphide from each was dried and filtered. The total sulphide recovery (23 g.) was 80 per cent. The refractive index of the mixture was 1.4691; that of each of 5 successive regenerated sulphides 1.4961, 1.4804, 1.4519, 1.4469 and 1.4463. It is clear that a considerable separation had been effected and that the tetrahydrothiophen reacted more quickly than the open chain sulphide.

Similar results were obtained with a mixture of ethyl-*n*-butyl sulphide and tetrahydrothiophen. Application of this method to an unknown sulphide fraction of b.p. 141°C and $n_D^{20} = 1.4930$ obtained from a 'sulphuric acid sludge' from a Persian oil, enabled pentamethylene sulphide [thia*cyclo*hexane (IV)] to be separated in two fractions $n_D^{20} = 1.5050$ and 1.5040. Thia*cyclo*hexane has b.p. 141.6°C and $n_D^{20} = 1.5067$.

When the sulphides were removed by mercuric acetate from a light petroleum solution of another sulphide fraction from the same sludge the residual solution yielded on evaporation methyl-*n*-amyl ketone, $CH_3 \cdot CO \cdot (CH_2)_4 CH_3$. Birch suggests that ketones in petroleum oils might possibly be formed from thioketones $R_2C : S$.

Separation of Different Cyclic Sulphides

Birch and McAllan also separated thia*cyclo*pentane from its 3-methyl derivative in light petroleum solution by mercuric acetate. The recovery was 80 per cent. The refractive indexes of the two sulphides are $n_D^{20} = 1.5047$ and 1.4924. Five successive regenerated sulphide fractions had $n_D^{20} = 1.5004$, 1.4984, 1.4954, 1.4926 and 1.4924. The original mixture had $n_D^{20} = 1.4982$.

79

Thia*cyclo*hexane was also separated from admixture with 3-methyl-thia*cyclo*pentane by the same process.

The difference in the behaviour to aqueous mercuric acetate of thiophen and tetrahydrothiophen (or dialkyl sulphides, which closely resemble the cyclic sulphides)—to take the simplest example— is only a single instance of the fundamental change in properties which accompanies the hydrogenation of a ring system of aromatic type. Tetrahydrothiophen (tetramethylene sulphide) forms a methiodide, a mercurichloride (co-ordinated) and a sulphone, and has an unpleasant odour. Thiophen smells rather like benzene and does not form compounds of the first two types. Its sulphone is extremely unstable[20]. The well-known indophenin reaction is given by thiophen and its incompletely substituted homologues, but not by their hydrogenated derivatives.

BEHAVIOUR OF THIONAPHTHEN AND ITS 2 : 3-DIHYDRODERIVATIVE WITH MERCURIC ACETATE

The behaviour of thionaphthen and its dihydroderivative (XV) in Birch and McAllan's experiments is of interest. Thionaphthen is a thiophen derivative of aromatic type and would not be expected to form co-ordinated compounds with mercuric acetate, but rather to undergo mercuration in the thiophen nucleus. This was shown by Weissgerber and Krüber[8] and by Challenger and Miller[21] to occur slowly in cold methylalcoholic solution giving the mono-mercuriacetate and some dimercuriacetate, which was readily produced with the boiling reagent. The mono-mercurated compound has the structure (XVI), mercuration occurring in position 3 (S = 1) and following the normal course of electrophilic substitution in thionaphthen.

In agreement with these considerations Birch and McAllan found that thionaphthen was not removed from solution in light petroleum by aqueous mercuric acetate but was recovered unchanged. 2 : 3-dihydrothionaphthen, however, in which the hydrogenated thiophen ring has no aromatic properties but resembles a cyclic sulphide, is slowly removed by mercuric acetate, presumably as a co-ordinated compound though only to the extent of 40 per cent.

DISULPHIDES AND AQUEOUS MERCURIC ACETATE. SEPARATION FROM OPEN-CHAIN MONOSULPHIDES

Since disulphides occur in petroleum distillates, especially when mercaptans are also present, Birch and McAllan examined the behaviour of diethyl disulphide to aqueous mercuric acetate. On washing its solution in light petroleum six times with the mercuric salt 50 per cent of the disulphide remained in the solvent. The extracts gave precipitates with sodium chloride which were refluxed with dilute hydrochloric acid giving ethanethiol. The precipitates were regarded by Birch and McAllan as chloromercury ethanethiol, $C_2H_5 \cdot S \cdot HgCl$, derived from the corresponding soluble acetate $C_2H_5 \cdot S \cdot HgO \cdot COCH_3$. The reaction is clearly analogous to that of mercuric chloride on dialkyl disulphides $R \cdot S \cdot S \cdot R$ which was shown by the author with Rawlings[22] and Blackburn[23] (*see* p. 15), to give $R \cdot S \cdot HgCl$, $R \cdot S \cdot HgCl \cdot HgCl_2$ and $R \cdot SO_2H$ (*see* Chapter 1, p. 18). The structure of the second compound is probably $C_2H_5 \cdot S \cdot HgCl$.

$$HgCl_2$$

The molecule of mercuric chloride is presumably co-ordinated as it is lost on boiling with water, giving $C_2H_5 \cdot S \cdot HgCl$ in which the mercury is firmly fixed. This compound re-combines with mercuric chloride when shaken with excess of the reagent.

The reaction of diethyl disulphide with mercuric acetate gives a soluble mercury compound. Birch and McAllan showed that this method afforded a separation of diethyl disulphide and ethyl *iso*butyl sulphide. After 3 extractions of the mixture with aqueous mercuric acetate 83 per cent of the disulphide was recovered from the light petroleum used as solvent. Acidification and distillation of the extracts gave slightly impure ethyl *iso*butyl sulphide.

BEHAVIOUR OF TRISULPHIDES WITH AQUEOUS MERCURIC ACETATE

Diethyl trisulphide, $C_2H_5 \cdot S \cdot S \cdot S \cdot C_2H_5$, in light petroleum reacted very slowly on extraction with aqueous mercuric acetate and about 85 per cent was recovered unchanged. A white solid separated in small amount and from this, and the aqueous extracts, traces of ethanethiol were obtained on acidification. Challenger and Blackburn[23] found that dimethyl trisulphide and aqueous mercuric chloride slowly gave a mixture of chloromercurymethanethiol, $CH_3 \cdot S \cdot HgCl$, containing some co-ordinated mercuric chloride and a compound of mercuric sulphide and mercuric chloride, probably $HgCl_2 \cdot 2HgS$. Probably fission occurred on either side of the central sulphur atom of the trisulphide group, assuming the structure $CH_3 \cdot S \cdot S \cdot S \cdot CH_3$ for dimethyl trisulphide. The results of Birch and McAllan with mercuric acetate appear very similar. Their 'white precipitate' may have contained a double compound of mercuric sulphide and mercuric acetate as well as a mercury derivative of ethanethiol.

Di-*n*-butyl tetrasulphide, $CH_3 \cdot (CH_2)_3 \cdot S \cdot S \cdot S \cdot S \cdot (CH_2)_3 \cdot CH_3$, was unaffected by Birch and McAllan's procedure.

SULPHUR COMPOUNDS IN 'SULPHURIC ACID SLUDGE' OBTAINED
FROM A PERSIAN OIL

By the use of the mercuric acetate method for the separation of
organic sulphides very interesting results were obtained by Birch[14].
He studied the sulphur compounds in the sludge produced during
the refining with sulphuric acid of a liquid sulphur dioxide extract
of the kerosene fraction (b.p. 180°–250°C) of Agha Jari (Persian)
oil. Dilution of the sludge gave a mixture of sulphides which on
repeated fractionation yielded several mixtures of compounds of
similar boiling point.

Fractional extraction with aqueous mercuric acetate left two
tetra-substituted thiophens (2 : 3 : 4 : 5-tetramethylthiophen and
2 : 3 : 4-trimethyl-5-ethylthiophen) unattacked and removed two
trialkylthiophens as C-mercurated compounds which were soluble
in the oil. After separation these were decomposed by hydrochloric acid yielding 2 : 3 : 4-trimethylthiophen, and 2 : 3-
dimethyl-4-ethylthiophen. The mercuriacetates of these compounds
had the structures (XVII) and (XVIII).

(XVII)   (XVIII)   (XIX)

The mercuric acetate treatment also effected a partial separation of
a few open-chain sulphides. The main bulk, however, consisted of
cyclic sulphides which were identified, usually without separation,
by an ingenious combination of modern organic- and physico-
chemical operations. Treatment with Raney nickel eliminated the
sulphur as nickel sulphide and completely hydrogenated the carbon
atoms previously attached to it. Thus, a compound R·S·R′ gave
RH + NiS + R′H, whereas a cyclic sulphide (XIX) gave
$CH_3(CH_2)_nCH_3$ + NiS. The resulting hydrocarbon or mixture of
hydrocarbons was then fractionated, if necessary with a micro-
column, and the compounds identified spectroscopically. The
constitution of the parent sulphides could often be readily deduced.
Birch gives a list of fifteen monocyclic sulphides which he identified
in Agha Jari oil, usually by the Raney nickel procedure. Among
them are tetramethylene sulphide (thia*cyclo*pentane), its 2- and 3-
methyl derivatives, pentamethylene sulphide and its 2-, 3- and
4-methyl compounds. The presence of the last four compounds in

Canadian oil was suggested by Mabery. None of Birch and Mc-Allan's sulphides contained ring systems larger than pentamethylene sulphide (thia*cyclo*hexane). In the case of five of the sulphides it was uncertain whether the ring system was thia*cyclo*pentane or thia*cyclo*hexane containing in each case alkyl substituents.

Certain higher fractions appeared to be almost homogeneous and with Raney nickel they gave substituted *cyclo*pentanes and *cyclo*hexanes. It was concluded that these hydrocarbons had arisen from bicyclic sulphides containing fused five- and six-membered polymethylene rings, a conclusion already rendered probable by the high boiling point and refractive index of the original sulphide fractions. Four alkyl*cyclo*pentanes—the ethyl, *n*-propyl, *iso*-propyl and *sec*-butyl-derivatives—and also ethyl*cyclo*hexane were obtained by desulphurization with nickel. These could have arisen from eight different bicyclic sulphides; thus a compound of structure (**XX**)

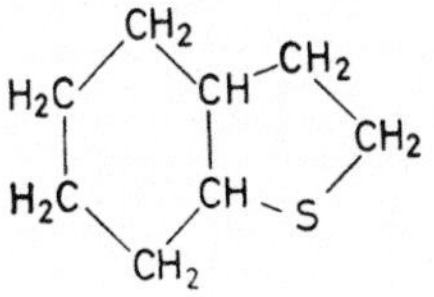

(XX)

would yield ethyl*cyclo*hexane. Birch remarks that 'complete identification of these bicyclic compounds was not easy, as the parent sulphur compound could rarely be obtained in a sufficiently pure state, with the result that the hydrocarbons obtained by desulphurization were mixtures of naphthenes difficult to analyse. Identification was rendered more difficult by the presence of geometrical isomers, few of which, particularly di-substituted *cyclo*pentanes, were available for comparison. Yet a further complication was the possibility that, during desulphurization, ring expansion, which almost invariably takes place when the *cyclo*pentylmethyl radical is involved, had occurred'.

Birch found, however, that desulphurization of compounds such as di*cyclo*pentylmethyl sulphide (**XXI**) and *cis*- and *trans*-2-thiadecalin (*cis*- and *trans*-2-thiadecahydronaphthalene **XXII**, **XXIII**) provided

83

no evidence that isomerization involving ring expansion or *cis/trans* rearrangement occurs under the conditions employed.

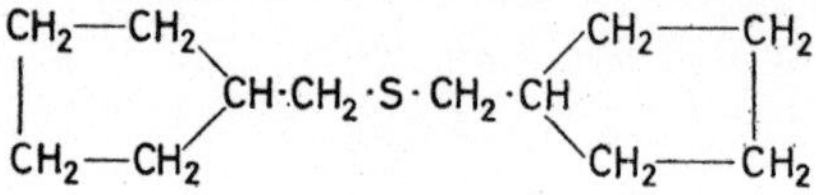

$$CH_2-CH_2 \diagdown \atop CH_2-CH_2 \diagup CH \cdot CH_2 \cdot S \cdot CH_2 \cdot CH \diagdown \atop CH_2-CH_2 \diagup CH_2-CH_2$$

(XXI)

$$CH_2-CH-CH_2 \atop CH_2 \diagdown S \atop CH_2-CH-CH_2$$

(XXII )　　　　(XXIII 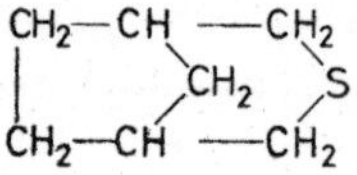)　　　　(XXIV)

Birch refers to the probability that bicyclic sulphides are present in which a *cyclo*pentane ring is fused to a thia*cyclo*pentane or thia-*cyclo*hexane ring and that ring expansion occurs during their desulphurization. One such compound, 6-thia [1 : 2 : 3] -bi*cyclo*-octane (XXIV), was prepared by Birch and Dean, *see* p. 90. Mass spectrographic examination of the high-boiling sulphides from a West Texas oil by Brown and Meyerson[24] also suggested the presence of bicyclic sulphides.

Birch's work gives an insight into the probable nature of many of Mabery's 'thiophanes' which were also characterized by high density and refractive index. His views on their structure would appear to be partly correct. Mabery envisaged, however, the possible presence of heptamethylene sulphide but so far no single ring system containing sulphur and more than five atoms of carbon has been detected by Birch, a result which is in agreement with some work on a crude American petroleum, now to be described.

THE SULPHUR COMPOUNDS OF THE CRUDE OIL OF WASSON, TEXAS

The sulphur compounds in this oil were carefully examined[25] and 40 were isolated or detected by physico-chemical methods such as mass spectrography. They included many aliphatic mercaptans and sulphides and also tetra- and pentamethylene sulphides (thia*cyclo*pentane and thia*cyclo*hexane) and several of their methyl derivatives. Neither hexamethylene sulphide nor heptamethylene sulphide (thia*cyclo*heptane and thia*cyclo*octane) were detected. *Cyclo*pentanethiol and *cyclo*hexanethiol were also present.

These mass spectrographic studies of Wasson crude oil have

yielded other interesting results[25]. The volatile ingredients were removed by heating to about 150°C and the 'asphaltenes' by subsequent extraction with pentane. The residual crude oil was chromatographed on alumina, and pentane, mixed amylenes, benzene, and benzene–methanol were used as developers. Nine fractions were so obtained varying in colour from water-white to black. The mass spectra afforded for the first time a picture of the sulphur compounds in a crude, *undistilled* oil, disturbing effects due to decomposition of the ingredients or to their reaction with sulphur or sulphur compounds being eliminated. The sulphur compounds represent 15 per cent of the crude oil of b.p. above 150°C and 65–80 per cent of these compounds contain thiophen rings either alkylated or, more often, condensed with one or more aromatic rings. The remaining sulphur compounds are chiefly cyclic sulphides, mainly benzothiophens containing one, two, three or more aromatic rings. Here reference may be made to the work of Krüber and of Carruthers on the isolation of benzothionaphthens from coal tar and Kuwait oil (*see* p. 75).

Thiadamantane

A remarkable volatile cyclic sulphide, $C_9H_{14}S$, of high melting point was isolated by Birch[14] during the fractionation of his sulphides. It formed a deposit at the top of the column and gave a sulphone and a mercurichloride. Desulphurization with Raney nickel yielded 1 : 3 : 3-bi*cyclo*nonane (XXV) and it appears that the new sulphide is the tricyclic compound (XXVI) corresponding to the hydrocarbon adamantane (XXVII) isolated many years previously from a Yugoslavian naphtha[26]. The name thiadamantane has been given to the new sulphide. No doubt much more will be heard of this compound in future and also of the parent adamantane[27].

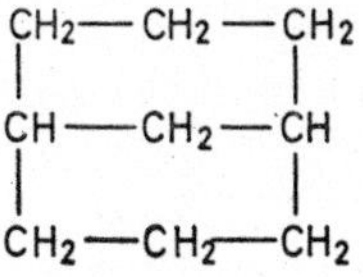

(XXV) 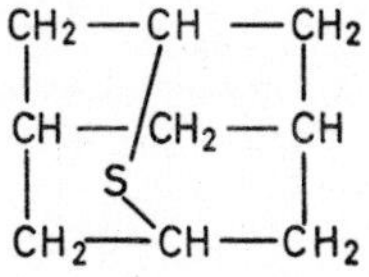   (XXVI) 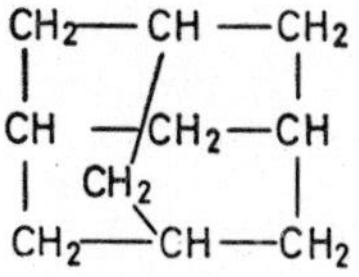   (XXVII)

Cyclic Sulphides in Kuwait Oil

In 1953 Emmott[28] described a study of the sulphur compounds removed by liquid sulphur dioxide from middle (kerosene) distillates of Texas, Iraq and Kuwait oils. The sulphides of Kuwait oil were separated from hydrocarbons by aqueous mercuric acetate which, in the case of the fractions of higher boiling point, was acidified with acetic acid, thereby increasing the ease of reaction. The soluble mercury derivatives were decomposed by sodium sulphide and the liberated sulphides distilled in steam. Emmott showed that an alkyl sulphide of high molecular weight such as dicapryl sulphide, $(C_6H_{13})_2S$, was readily extracted from its solution in kerosene by acidified mercuric acetate. Diphenyl sulphide was unaffected and phenyl ethyl sulphide, $C_6H_5 \cdot S \cdot CH_2CH_3$, was only partially and very slowly removed. The unshared electrons of aromatic sulphides are less reactive than those of their aliphatic or polymethylene analogues. Fractional distillation of the regenerated mixed sulphides, followed by attempted separation through their co-ordination compounds with mercuric chloride did not yield any pure compounds. The refractive indexes suggested that the sulphides consisted almost entirely of alkyl substituted cyclic sulphides. This conclusion was based on the observation that 3-n-butylpentamethylene sulphide possesses physical properties very similar to those of the lower sulphide fractions. The solubility of its mercurichloride in alcohol is, moreover, very similar to that of the mercurichlorides of the Kuwait sulphides investigated by Birch. The mercurichloride of penta-methylene sulphide, on the other hand, is almost insoluble in alcohol. In 1953, when Birch published his work, no pure compound of the alkylpolymethylene sulphide type had been isolated from petroleum. In 1954 the crude Wasson oil of Texas[25] was shown to contain pentamethylene sulphide and its 2-, 3-, and 4-methyl derivatives, a result which strengthens Emmott's conclusions.

All the sulphur dioxide extracts of Emmott's oil contained residual sulphides which were not removed by mercuric acetate nor ad-sorbed on silica gel or alumina. Their refractive indexes suggested the presence of bicyclic compounds, as in Birch's experiments, but no homogeneous product was isolated. Emmott's results are very similar to Mabery's and, though less comprehensive, to those of Birch. In all three cases the mixture of sulphides was non-separable by distillation.

Isolation of Thionaphthen from a Crude Petroleum

Thionaphthen was not separated from petroleum until 1956 when Richter et al.[28a] obtained it from the crude oil of Santa Maria. The oil was distilled through a nine ft. column and the fraction of b.p. 104°–134°C at 50 mm. collected. Bases and phenols were removed as usual and the purified distillate passed through silica gel moistened with pentane under nitrogen. The column was then eluted with methyl alcohol and the eluate treated with common salt and extracted with pentane. This on evaporation left an oil which was fractionated. The appropriate portion was treated with picric acid when a deposit was formed. This, on decomposition with alkali, gave an oil which on mercuration gave a mercuriacetate, thereby removing much naphthalene. Decomposition of the mercuration product with acid gave thionaphthen, which was recognized by its m.p. and infra-red spectrum.

The picrates of thionaphthen and naphthalene are isomorphous and, according to Meyer and Meyer[28b], non-separable by crystallization. The solubilities of the two picrates in 25 per cent ethanol at 30°C are 37 and 13 grams per litre respectively. In preliminary experiments it was found that addition of picric acid to an alcoholic solution containing 1 part of thionaphthen and 99 parts of naphthalene gave a 90 per cent recovery of thionaphthen whereas only 18 per cent of naphthalene was precipitated. In the absence of naphthalene 30 times as much thionaphthen would have been needed to secure the same recovery. In the separation just described the adsorption on the silica gel was carried out in nitrogen. During such operations, especially when dealing with reactive sulphur compounds containing either ethylenic or 'aromatic' double bonds, it is often desirable not only to exclude air, but also light.

RECENT AMERICAN WORK ON THE SULPHUR COMPOUNDS
OF MINERAL OILS

The researches of the American Petroleum Institute[29,30] and the United States Bureau of Mines, in the last 20 years, have greatly augmented our knowledge of the ingredients of mineral oils. The work of Kinney, Smith and Ball[31] has added greatly to our detailed knowledge of the thiophen homologues in shale oil. Kinney and Cook[32] describe a method for the identification of aromatic hydrocarbons and thiophen homologues, in which mass spectral correlations are used for the recognition of structural groups in previously unknown compounds. The authors point out that the use of mass spectra in the qualitative identification of unknown compounds has ordinarily been limited to comparison of the spectra of the compounds with those of reference samples. They remark: 'No prior mass spectral data for the unknown compounds are necessary for identification.' The fundamental relations on which the identification of unknown compounds is based were obtained from a consideration of the mass spectra of suitably chosen benzene and thiophen homologues. The available mass spectral data relating to thiophen and its homologues have been summarized by Hartough[33].

In devising a method for the identification of homologues of thiophen the authors have combined this technique with some chemical reactions of the unknown thiophen homologues, e.g. formation of nuclear mercuriacetates,

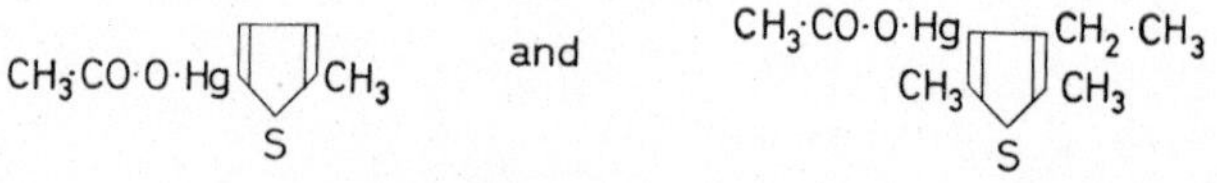

$$CH_3CO \cdot O \cdot Hg \underset{S}{\bigcirc} CH_3 \qquad \text{and} \qquad CH_3 \cdot CO \cdot O \cdot Hg \underset{S}{\bigcirc} \begin{smallmatrix} CH_2 \cdot CH_3 \\ CH_3 \end{smallmatrix}$$

the desulphurization with Raney nickel giving alkyl-*n*-butanes, or the introduction of a —CHO group followed by reduction of this to —CH₃. In this last method the position of the new methyl group is then determined by mass spectrography. Kinney and Cook can therefore identify any thiophen homologue with a molecular weight within the range 126 to 154 by determining the number of side chains and their relative positions in the nucleus. These results will greatly simplify the identification of the thiophen derivatives in shale oil fractions of high boiling point.

Formation of mercuriacetates from thiophen homologues—The number of —Hg·O·CO·CH₃ groups which can be introduced into the nucleus of different types of thiophen homologues is shown below, where R is an alkyl group and 'mono-', 'di-', etc. indicate the type of mercurated derivative produced. The mercuration was carried out with mercuric acetate in aqueous 50 per cent acetic acid by a slight modification of the method of Steinkopf and Killingstad[34], and its general applicability tested with a number of thiophen homologues at 25° and 60°C. At 60°C all unsubstituted nuclear hydrogen atoms are replaced by the mercuriacetate residue.

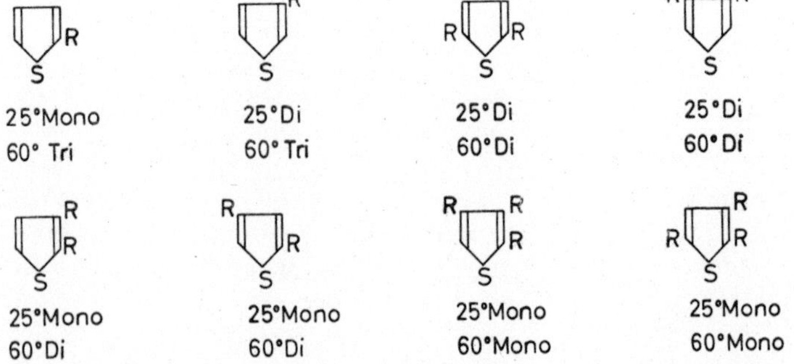

25°Mono	25°Di	25°Di	25°Di
60° Tri	60° Tri	60°Di	60°Di

25°Mono	25°Mono	25°Mono	25°Mono
60°Di	60°Di	60°Mono	60°Mono

At 25°C the reaction is allowed to proceed for 15 minutes only and the amount of mercuric acetate is 2 molecular proportions. At 60°C not more than the amount theoretically required to form a tri-derivative is employed. If no solid separates at 60°C a fresh experiment with 2 molecular proportions is set up and if necessary a third, using only one. This procedure is desirable since some mono-mercuriacetates are soluble in excess of the reagent. Determination of mercury or sulphur will indicate the type of mercuriacetate which is formed. It will be noted that in the cases of the 2 : 3- and the 2 : 4-dialkyl derivatives the extra substitution at 60°C is concerned with the 4- and the 3- positions respectively and, moreover, this method does not distinguish between these isomers. It is, therefore, necessary to desulphurize the thiophen derivative with Raney nickel and identify the resulting alkane by mass spectrography, e.g. 2-methyl-3-ethylthiophen and 2-methyl-4-ethylthiophen would give $CH_3CH_2 \cdot CH \cdot (C_2H_5) \cdot CH_2 \cdot CH_3$ and $CH_3 \cdot CH_2 \cdot CH_2 \cdot CH \cdot (C_2H_5) \cdot CH_3$ respectively.

In order to distinguish between a 2 : 5- and a 3 : 4-dialkyl thiophen a methyl group is introduced by first inserting a —CHO group and then reducing this to CH_3 as described below. Mass spectrographic examination of the resulting trisubstituted thiophen will show where the methyl group has been inserted and, therefore, whether the two free positions were adjacent to or remote from the sulphur atom. The formyl group is introduced into thiophen or its homologues by interaction with N-methylformanilide:

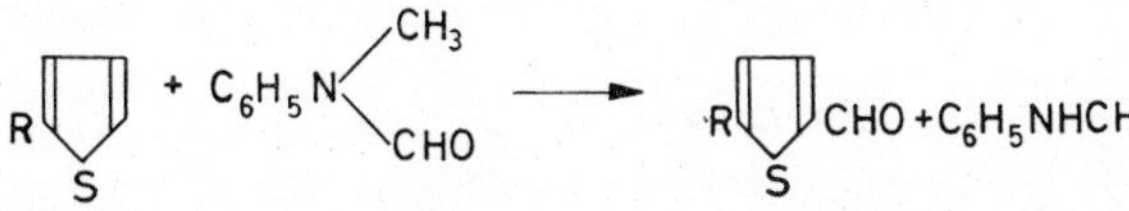

The reaction has been extensively studied by King and Nord[35], who have also converted thiophen aldehydes to the corresponding methylthiophens by heating the semicarbazones with potassium hydroxide at 100°–250°C in nitrogen (the Wolff–Kishner reaction[36]).

By these methods seventeen homologues of thiophen were identified in a fraction of Colorado shale oil of b.p. up to 210°C from which phenols and thiols had been removed by alkali and heterocyclic bases and some pyrroles by acid. The oil was then re-distilled and the fractions treated with 0·5N silver nitrate to remove any remaining thiols and with powdered mercurous nitrate to remove sulphides. Adsorption on 'florisil' followed by elution with pentane yielded first olefines and alkanes (which were neglected) and then a mixture of aromatic hydrocarbons and thiophen homologues which was distilled. Suitable fractions were treated with mercuric acetate in 50 per cent acetic acid at 60°C and the resulting solid mercurated compounds decomposed by hot acid, yielding

89

thiophen homologues which, after a second mercuration and decomposition with acid, usually contained less than 10 per cent of hydrocarbons.

These were examined by mass spectrography and by one or more of the three chemical methods already described. Conclusions were usually checked by synthesis of the appropriate homologue and direct comparison by the mass spectrograph and by formation of derivatives. The m.p. of mercuriacetate or mercurichloride (formed from the mercuriacetate and hot aqueous sodium chloride— direct mercuration of thiophen homologues with mercuric chloride and sodium acetate buffer also yields the mercurichlorides) were frequently used as confirmation. Mixtures of thiophen homologues were sometimes separated by boiling the mercurichlorides with alcohol in which mono-derivatives are soluble but di-derivatives are not.

The compounds identified by Kinney, Smith and Ball contained the methyl, ethyl, *n*-propyl, *iso*-propyl, *n*-butyl and *sec*-butyl groups and included several trialkylthiophens. Substitution in the 2-position was more frequently encountered than in the 3-position and 2 : 5-di-derivatives predominated over other di-substituted homologues, and 2 : 3 : 5-derivatives over the 2 : 3 : 4 compounds, in agreement with the known preferential reactivity of the 2- and 5-positions in thiophen.

THE COURSE OF DESULPHURIZATION BY RANEY NICKEL

On p. 84 reference was made to the synthesis in Birch's laboratory of a thiabi*cyclo*octane (XXIV). It was during experiments on the desulphurization of this bicyclic sulphide with Raney nickel that conclusive evidence was first obtained that such a reaction can proceed abnormally. The synthesis of the sulphide may first be described briefly.

Norbornylene, [2 : 2 : 1]-bi*cyclo*heptene-2 (XXVIII), was obtained by the condensation of ethylene and *cyclo*pentadiene at 190°–200°C and 400 atmospheres. Oxidation of its solution in *iso*octane by aqueous sodium permanganate in a stream of CO_2, to avoid too great alkalinity, gave *cyclo*pentane *cis*-1 : 3-di-carboxylic acid (XXIX). This was esterified with ethanol and the diethyl ester reduced with lithium aluminium hydride in ether to *cis*-1 : 3-bishydroxymethyl*cyclo*pentane (XXX). When the di-*p*-toluenesulphonyl derivative (XXXI) was heated with sodium sulphide in aqueous ethanol and the mixture then distilled a solid volatile sulphide was obtained. This was purified by formation of its co-ordination compound with mercuric chloride and regeneration with dilute hydrochloric acid. 6-Thia-(1 : 2 : 3)-bi*cyclo*octane (**XXXII** and **XXIV**) is a wax-like solid with an odour resembling that of camphor, and melts at 174°–175°C. When left in alcoholic solution with excess of Raney nickel for 12 hours and then heated under reflux desulphurization occurred and a hydrocarbon C_7H_{14} was obtained. This was saturated (the olefine content, by bromine titration, was less than 0·25 per cent) and from its physical properties and infra-red spectrum appeared to be identical with *cis*-1 : 3-dimethyl*cyclo*pentane (**XXXIII**).

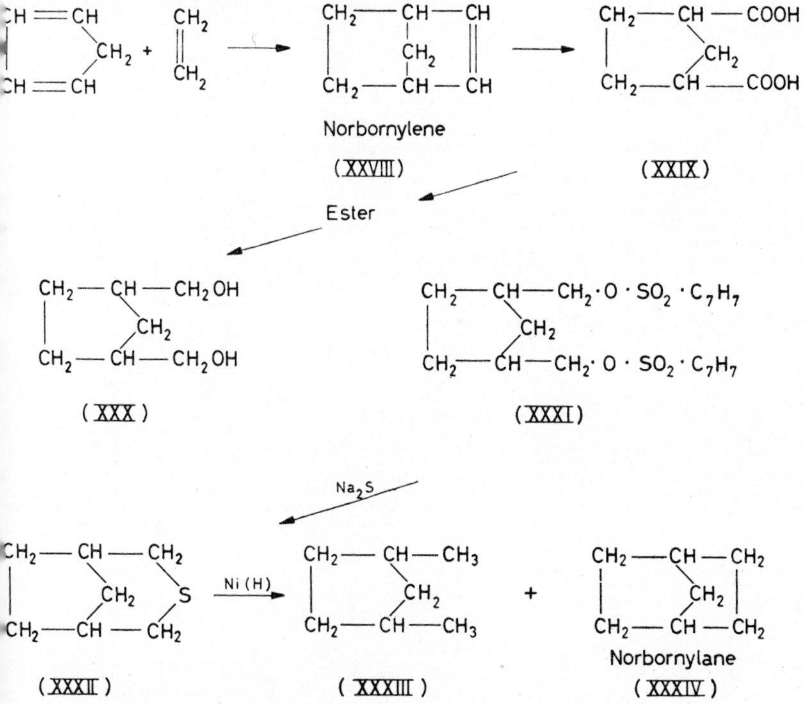

CH=CH / CH₂ + CH₂=CH₂ (||CH₂) → CH₂—CH—CH / CH₂ || CH₂—CH—CH

Norbornylene

(**XXVIII**)

→ CH₂—CH—COOH / CH₂ / CH₂—CH—COOH

(**XXIX**)

Ester →

CH₂—CH—CH₂OH / CH₂ / CH₂—CH—CH₂OH

(**XXX**)

CH₂—CH—CH₂·O·SO₂·C₇H₇ / CH₂ / CH₂—CH—CH₂·O·SO₂·C₇H₇

(**XXXI**)

Na₂S →

CH₂—CH—CH₂ / CH₂ S / CH₂—CH—CH₂

(**XXXII**)

Ni(H) →

CH₂—CH—CH₃ / CH₂ / CH₂—CH—CH₃

(**XXXIII**)

+ CH₂—CH—CH₂ / CH₂ | / CH₂—CH—CH₂

Norbornylane

(**XXXIV**)

Separation on a silica gel column gave fractions which all had a refractive index $n_D^{20} = 1·4098$, which was too high for that of pure *cis*-1 : 3-dimethyl*cyclo*pentane ($n_D^{20} = 1·40894$). Mass spectrography detected the presence of a second hydrocarbon containing two atoms of hydrogen fewer. This was finally isolated by very efficient fractional distillation as a crystalline volatile solid which was identified as 1 : 2 : 2-bi*cyclo*heptane (norbornylane, **XXXIV**) by mass spectrographic examination, mixed m.p. and odour. The main product of the reaction was, as expected, *cis*-1 : 3-dimethyl*cyclo*-pentane, but about 5 per cent of impurity was present which caused a slightly higher refractive index. It was believed to be due to formation of some *trans*-isomer during the desulphurization.

The removal of sulphur from thia*cyclo*hexane (pentamethylene sulphide) similarly yields pentane, but the reaction is slow and here again a small amount of *cyclo*pentane is formed; the reaction is analogous to that observed with 6-thia-(1 : 2 : 3)-bi*cyclo*octane. It appeared possible that the abnormal side-reactions in these desulphurization experiments might be due to a deficiency of hydrogen in the Raney nickel so that the di-radical, presumably resulting from the loss of sulphur, underwent ring-closure instead of reduction. However, by using Raney nickel in which some of the occluded hydrogen had been removed by long boiling with alcohol, no increase in the yield of *cyclo*pentane from thia*cyclo*pentane was observed, though the formation of olefine was increased from 3 per cent to 11 per cent. Birch and Dean consider that the olefine arises from a dismutation (disproportionation) of the free radical first formed.

Catalytic Hydrogenation of Sulphur Compounds without Desulphurization

Hydrogenation in presence of palladium–charcoal—In 1945 Mozingo and his colleagues[37] showed that thiophen derivatives could be hydrogenated at 2–3 atmospheres pressure to the tetrahydro-compounds, in presence of a palladium–charcoal catalyst. The presence or absence of mineral acid is immaterial. Thus, 2-thienyl-valeric acid (**XXXV**) yields the tetrahydro-compound; 2 : 5-dibromo-3 : 4-diaminothiophen gives 3 : 4-diaminothiophen without hydrogenation, and 2-bromothiophen gives tetrahydrothiophen, bromine again being eliminated. A dihydro-derivative of the thiophen (**XXXVI**) obtained during the synthesis of biotin is converted to the tetrahydro-compound.

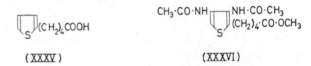

$$\text{(XXXV)} \qquad\qquad\qquad \text{(XXXVI)}$$

Hydrogenation in presence of rhenium sulphides—The heptasulphide of rhenium, Re_2S_7, and to a lesser extent the disulphide, ReS_2, have been applied recently[38] to the hydrogenation of olefines, nitro-compounds, unsaturated alkyl sulphides, thiophens and to the fission of disulphides. The sulphides are remarkably unsusceptible to the usual catalyst poisons. Large quantities of hydrogen sulphide or thiols can be added to nitrobenzene or to styrene without interfering with their reduction to aniline and ethylbenzene. The reaction proceeds at 150°–250°C and under 1,500–4,000 lb./sq. in. A special advantage is that desulphurization does not occur except under very drastic conditions. With Re_2S_7 phenyl allyl sulphide gives phenyl n-propyl sulphide, diphenyl disulphide and thiophenol at 165°–195°C. Only above 300°C and at 3,600 lb./sq. in. does fission of the carbon–sulphur link in the disulphide occur giving benzene, *cyclo*hexane and thiophenol. At 200°–260°C and 2,000 lb./sq. in. thiophen is converted to its tetrahydro-compound.

Less information is available about rhenium disulphide. It seems to be a less powerful catalyst. At 240°C and 2,300 lb./sq. in. phenyl allyl sulphide is converted to phenyl n-propyl sulphide.

Rhenium heptasulphide is prepared by passing hydrogen sulphide into potassium per-rhenate, $KReO_4$, in hydrochloric acid. The mixture is boiled, and the precipitated sulphide washed with hydrochloric acid, then with water and dried. Broadbent and his colleagues[38] have compared these rhenium sulphides with cobalt sulphide and similar catalysts. Cobalt polysulphide cleaves phenyl allyl sulphide at 250°C and 3,000 lb./sq. in., giving thiophenol. It has the disadvantage of giving much hydrogen sulphide when used in hydrogenations. The rhenium sulphides never behave in this manner and they are unattacked by concentrated, non-oxidizing mineral acids.

THE DESULPHURIZATION OF ORGANIC COMPOUNDS BY RANEY NICKEL

Desulphurization by Raney nickel has played an important part in many of the researches discussed in this chapter. The course of the reaction and particularly the formation of by-products may depend on the mode of preparation of the nickel and on its content of adsorbed hydrogen. Usually no attempt is made to remove this, but the results of some work in which this was done are outlined on p. 96.

Raney nickel is obtained as a microcrystalline powder by heating a nickel–aluminium alloy containing 33–50 per cent of nickel with aqueous sodium hydroxide. After solution of the aluminium the nickel is washed thoroughly with water and kept under alcohol. The product, which contains much adsorbed hydrogen, is comparable in hydrogenating activity with palladium–charcoal. Sometimes it is used as a catalyst in hydrogenations carried out with gaseous hydrogen, but the following discussion is not concerned with such applications of the reagent.

Some of the earliest applications of Raney nickel as a desulphurizing agent were recorded by Bougault, Cattelain and Chabrier[39], who obtained acetic acid from thioacetic acid, $HS \cdot CH_2 \cdot COOH$, β-phenylpropionic acid from α-thiocinnamic acid, $C_6H_5CH : C(SH) \cdot COOH$, and acetanilide from $HS \cdot CH_2 \cdot CO \cdot NH \cdot C_6H_5$.

du Vigneaud and his colleagues[40,41] converted biotin (XXXVII) to its desthio-derivative (XXXVIII).

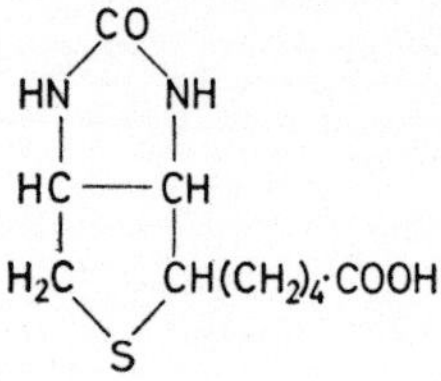

(XXXVII) 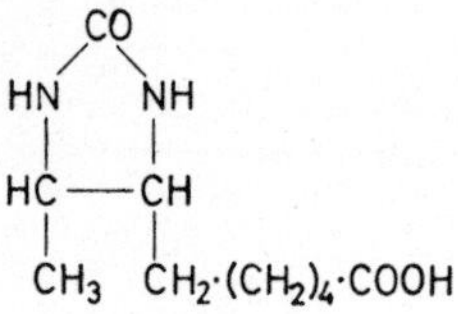   (XXXVIII)

The new amino-acid felinine, $HO \cdot CH_2 \cdot CH_2 \cdot C(CH_3)_2 \cdot S \cdot CH_2 \cdot CH(NH_2) \cdot COOH$, isolated from cats' urine by Westall, is readily desulphurized by Raney nickel in the cold giving alanine and isoamyl alcohol. The work is summarized in Chapter 2.

The behaviour of Raney nickel with methyl-2-thienyl ketone (2-acetylthiophen) was studied by Badger, Rodder and Sasse[42] and affords a good example of the varied reactions to which different specimens of this reagent can give rise. In boiling xylene it gives the expected hexan-2-one (methyl-n-butyl ketone) and also acetaldehyde and ethanol. With another specimen (designated W_6)* under slightly different conditions acetaldehyde and hexan-2-one are again obtained, but in addition dodecane-2 : 11-dione (XXXIX) is produced. With sample W_7* acetaldehyde and the dodecanedione are again obtained but no hexan-2-one was detected.

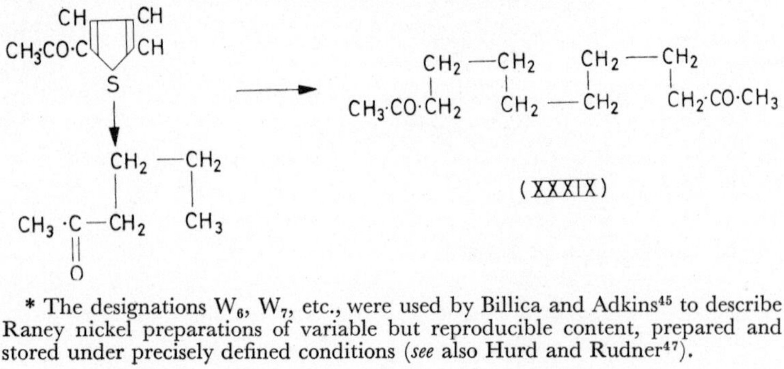

(XXXIX)

* The designations W_6, W_7, etc., were used by Billica and Adkins[45] to describe Raney nickel preparations of variable but reproducible content, prepared and stored under precisely defined conditions (*see* also Hurd and Rudner[47]).

The isolation of the dione points to the intermediate formation of the radical $CH_3CO \cdot CH_2 \cdot CH_2 \cdot CH_2 \cdot CH_2 \cdot$ and recalls the work of Hauptmann et al.[43,44] and of Birch and Dean (see p. 91). It also furnishes an example of the use of Raney nickel[45] in synthetic organic chemistry. Thienyl alkyl ketones are very accessible. They can be reduced by hydrazine hydrate to alkylthiophens which, with succinic anhydride and aluminium chloride, give alkylthenoylpropionic acids. These on reduction with hydrazine hydrate are converted to alkylthienylbutyric acids. Desulphurization with Raney nickel yields the desired fatty acid.

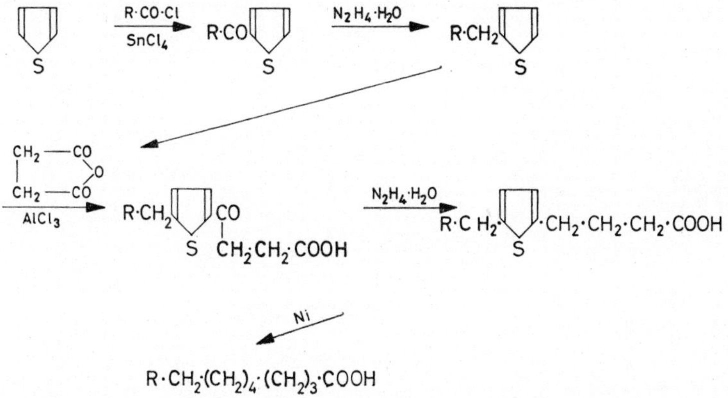

Many examples of this type of synthesis are given by Badger et al.

Challenger and Holmes[46] determined the structure of the methyl ketones (XL) and (XLI) derived from the two isomeric thiophthens (XLIa) and (XLIb) by reduction with Raney nickel in alcohol. With (XL) octan-2-one was obtained but the isomeric ketone gave the secondary alcohol and no ketone was detected.

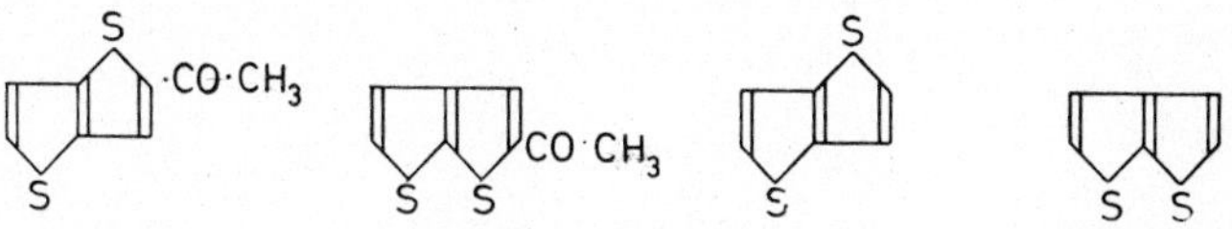

(XL)   (XLI)   (XLIa)   (XLIb)

Hurd and Rudner[47], by the use of a nickel catalyst prepared at a low temperature and not strictly comparable with Raney nickel, found that 2-amino-4-hydroxythiazole (XLII) in boiling ethanol loses sulphur and ammonia to give acetamide.

Using the same preparation and 2-mercapto-4-hydroxythiazole in boiling water the heterocyclic ring again underwent fission giving acetaldehyde and ammonia. No acetamide was obtained in this reaction.

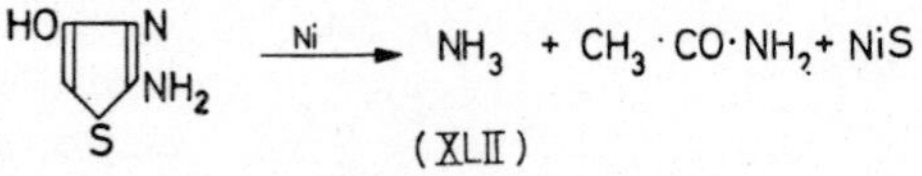

$$\text{(XLII)} \quad \xrightarrow{\text{Ni}} \quad NH_3 + CH_3 \cdot CO \cdot NH_2 + NiS$$

From thiobenzanilide, $C_6H_5CS \cdot NH \cdot C_6H_5$, with Raney nickel in boiling benzene, benzylaniline and a trace of benzanilide were obtained. 2-Mercaptobenzothiazole (XLIII) readily gave benzothiazole (XLIV), o-aminothiophenol and aniline with a Raney nickel specimen designated 'C' in boiling ethanol. With another nickel ('A') the products were o-aminothiophenol, the corresponding disulphide and aniline

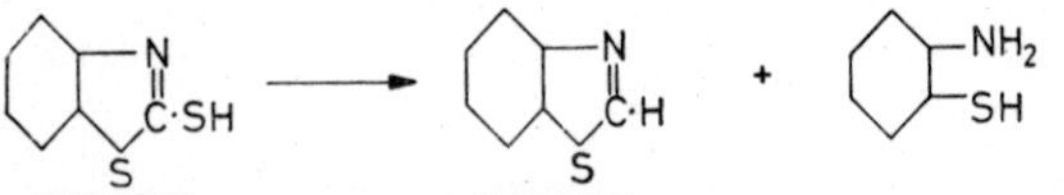

(XLIII)   (XLIV)

THE MECHANISM OF DESULPHURIZATION BY RANEY NICKEL

Hauptmann and Wladislaw[43,44] and their collaborators have investigated the effect of Raney nickel on diaryl disulphides, $R \cdot S \cdot S \cdot R'$ (where R and R' may be the same or different), on the ethyl and phenyl esters of thiobenzoic acid, $C_6H_5CO \cdot S \cdot R$, and the ethyl esters of α- and β-thionaphthoic acids, $C_{10}H_7 \cdot CO \cdot S \cdot C_2H_5$. The work was carried out with samples of Raney nickel which had been heated for 2 hours under 3 mm. pressure (a) at 100°C and (b) at 200°C. Heating under these conditions at 500°C produced samples which had the same properties as those prepared at 200°C. Process (a) gave a nickel containing 10–14 c.c. of hydrogen per gram, process (b) reduced the content of hydrogen to 1 c.c. per gram.

Desulphurization with nickel (a)—On heating this nickel in xylene solution with diphenyl disulphide or with formaldehyde diphenylmercaptal, $CH_2(S \cdot C_6H_5)_2$, diphenyl was obtained, though in the second case the yield was only 9 per cent. The diethyl- and diphenylmercaptals of benzaldehyde with nickel (a) gave stilbene, $(C_6H_5 \cdot CH : CH \cdot C_6H_5)$, in yields up to 37 per cent and acetophenone ethylene mercaptol,

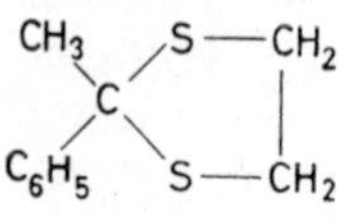

96

gave an 18 per cent yield of $C_6H_5 \cdot C(CH_3) = C(CH_3) \cdot C_6H_5$ dimethylstilbene. Ethane and ethylbenzene were presumably also produced. Dimethylstilbene was also obtained when an undescribed specimen of Raney nickel was heated with trithioacetophenone[48] (XLV):

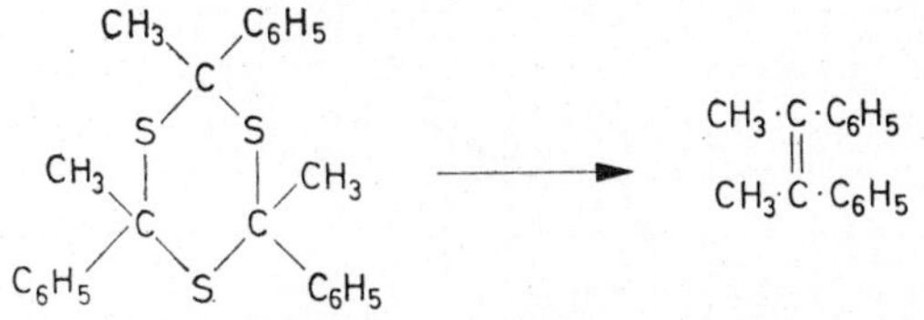

Some of the most useful results obtained by Hauptmann and his colleagues are concerned with the thiobenzoic esters $C_6H_5 \cdot CO \cdot S \cdot R$. The phenyl ester with nickel (*a*) gives benzene and if the hydrogen is lower than is usual with nickel (*a*), diphenyl is obtained. The reaction with nickel (*b*) is discussed in detail later.

Desulphurization with nickel (b)—Owing to the almost complete absence of hydrogen from the nickel and the use of boiling xylene as a solvent the course of the desulphurization reactions is different and, as will be seen later, is largely determined by the interaction of free radicals. Benzaldehyde diphenyl mercaptal $C_6H_5 \cdot CH(S \cdot C_6H_5)_2$ gave stilbene in 69 and diphenyl sulphide in 80 per cent yield. This result should be compared with the behaviour with nickel (*a*), described on p. 96. The three mercaptals of the type $CH_2(SR)_2$, where R is phenyl, *p*-tolyl or *β*-naphthyl give 70 per cent yields of the monosulphide $R \cdot S \cdot R$ (*see* below). The mercaptal $CH_2(S \cdot CH_2 \cdot C_6H_5)_2$, however, gave a quantitative yield of nickel sulphide and also stilbene and dibenzyl.

Desulphurization of esters of thiobenzoic acid—The esters of thiobenzoic or thionaphthoic acids when heated with Raney nickel previously heated to 200°C [i.e. nickel (*b*)] gave a mixture of three monosulphides with loss of carbon monoxide thus:

$$C_6H_5CO \cdot S \cdot C_{10}H_7 \rightarrow CO + C_6H_5 \cdot S \cdot C_6H_5 + C_{10}H_7 \cdot S \cdot C_{10}H_7 + C_6H_5 \cdot S \cdot C_{10}H_7$$

$$C_6H_5CO \cdot S \cdot C_2H_5 \rightarrow (C_6H_5)_2S + (C_2H_5)_2S + C_6H_5 \cdot S \cdot C_2H_5 + CO$$
$$(\alpha \text{ or } \beta) \quad C_{10}H_7 \cdot CO \cdot S \cdot C_2H_5 \rightarrow (C_{10}H_7)_2S + C_{10}H_7 \cdot S \cdot C_2H_5 + (C_2H_5)_2S + CO$$

In the last two experiments the diethyl sulphide was lost. The carbon monoxide was detected by removal in nitrogen and passage through a solution of palladium chloride, which was reduced to the metal.

In earlier experiments the same authors had shown that with nickel (*b*) disulphides R·S·S·R gave the monosulphides R·S·R in boiling xylene or in absence of a solvent at 140°–145°C. It seemed that investigation of this simpler reaction might throw some light on the results obtained with the thioesters. It seemed probable that this reaction involved the production of free RS· radicals. The action of nickel (*b*) on a mixture of two disulphides was therefore examined. Diphenyl disulphide and di-α-naphthyl disulphide were mixed and heated under reflux with nickel (*b*) in boiling xylene. The experiment clearly demonstrated the intermolecular nature of the reaction, the three possible monosulphides being obtained, of which the mixed phenyl α-naphthyl sulphide represented 33 per cent.

In a similar experiment the intermolecular nature of the decomposition of the thioesters (described on p. 97) was demonstrated. A mixture of phenyl thiobenzoate, $C_6H_5CO·S·C_6H_5$, and α-naphthyl thionaphthoate, $C_{10}H_7CO·S·C_{10}H_7$, was heated with nickel (*b*) in xylene. The products were diphenyl sulphide, di-α-naphthyl sulphide and phenyl-α-naphthyl sulphide, $C_6H_5·S·C_{10}H_7$. The mixed sulphide represented 50 per cent of the product. Phenyl mercaptan and nickel (*b*) gave diphenyl sulphide and, in admixture with α-naphthyl mercaptan, the three possible sulphides were again obtained, and in addition some naphthalene. This might have arisen through hydrogenation by the small amount of hydrogen still present in the nickel (*b*), but more probably by abstraction of hydrogen from an aromatic nucleus by the α-naphthyl radical.

The authors cite, in this connection, the well-known decomposition of lead mercaptides giving lead sulphide and an organic sulphide $Pb(SR)_2 = PbS + R·S·R$. Free radicals would appear to be involved in reactions of this type also. A nickel mercaptide $Ni(SR)_2$ could possibly be formed in reaction of nickel (*b*) with mercaptans, and it was found that nickel di-*p*-tolyl mercaptide, $Ni(S·C_6H_4·CH_3)_2$, heated with Raney nickel at 140°C gives di-*p*-tolyl sulphide. No mercaptide was, however, isolated in the reactions with Raney nickel described above. The formation of $CH_2 : CH·CH_2·S·$ radicals followed by formation and decomposition of $Zn(S·CH_2·CH : CH_2)_2$ was suggested by Challenger and Greenwood[49] to explain the conversion of diallyl disulphide to allyl sulphide on heating with zinc dust. On heating pure zinc allyl mercaptide at 100°C or in boiling benzene, allyl monosulphide and zinc sulphide were recognized by conversion to the sulphidimine and to hydrogen sulphide respectively.

The formation of free radicals by dissociation of disulphides is discussed in various publications by Schönberg[50].

Hauptmann, Wladislaw *et al.* point out that their results with Raney nickel and arylthioesters $R \cdot CO \cdot S \cdot R'$ need further consideration since one of the products is $R \cdot S \cdot R$ and the radical R is not attached to sulphur. They suggest that the first reaction which occurs on heating the thioester with Raney nickel is the formation of an $R \cdot CO \cdot$ and an $\cdot SR'$ radical and point out that the analogous reductive desulphurization of ethyl thiobenzoate, $C_6H_5CO \cdot S \cdot C_2H_5$, yields benzaldehyde, presumably by addition of a hydrogen atom to the benzoyl radical $C_6H_5CO \cdot$. The formation of carbon monoxide in their own experiments is ascribed to the breakdown of $C_6H_5CO \cdot$ to $CO + C_6H_5 \cdot$. They quote the photochemical decomposition of acetophenone and benzaldehyde in which carbon monoxide is eliminated. Many reactions of acid chlorides are known in which carbon monoxide is liberated. When *iso*valeryl chloride is passed over nickel at 400°C *iso*butylene and carbon monoxide are obtained[51]; other acid chlorides behave in a similar manner.

Disproportionation of Mixed Monosulphides with Raney Nickel

Assuming a primary fission of $R \cdot CO \cdot SR'$ to $R \cdot CO \cdot$ and $\cdot SR'$, how is $R \cdot S \cdot R$ produced? It seemed possible that the explanation might lie in the behaviour of the mixed sulphide $R \cdot S \cdot R'$ which is known to be formed. As already stated above, $C_6H_5CO \cdot S \cdot C_{10}H_7$ on heating with nickel (*b*) gives $(C_6H_5)_2S$, $(C_{10}H_7)_2S$ and also the mixed sulphide $C_6H_5 \cdot S \cdot C_{10}H_7$ presumably by union of the $C_6H_5 \cdot$ and $C_{10}H_7S \cdot$ radicals.

A number of mixed sulphides were therefore heated with nickel (*b*) in absence of a solvent and it was found that disproportionation occurred giving two simple sulphides:

$$2R \cdot S \cdot R' \rightarrow R \cdot S \cdot R + R' \cdot S \cdot R'$$

This was clearly demonstrated with ethyl phenyl sulphide, ethyl β-naphthyl sulphide, and phenyl α-naphthyl sulphide, the products being isolated as the corresponding sulphones by oxidation with hydrogen peroxide.

Inactivation of Raney nickel—Some interesting conclusions were drawn by Hauptmann *et al.* from their observation that *p-p'*-dinitrodiphenyl disulphide is almost completely unchanged after boiling for 15 hours with Raney nickel (*b*) in xylene. No monosulphide was detected. In a similar experiment with the phenyl ester of *p*-nitrothiobenzoic acid $NO_2 \cdot C_6H_4 \cdot CO \cdot S \cdot C_6H_5$ a recovery of 71·5 per cent was obtained, whereas the *p*-methoxy derivative $CH_3 \cdot O \cdot C_6H_4 \cdot CO \cdot S \cdot C_6H_5$ gave *p*-methoxydiphenyl sulphide in 63 per cent yield. Dissociation into radicals appears, therefore, to be hindered by the nitro-group but not by the methoxy-group. These results are, however, apparently not explicable on electron withdrawal from or accession to the sulphur atom due to the nitro- and methoxy-groups, since some nitrated aryl compounds dissociate more readily than the parent compound. Thus hexanitrohexaphenylethane is completely dissociated at room temperature, but hexaphenylethane only slightly so. *o-o'*-Dinitrodiphenyl disulphide reacts much more readily with mercury than does diphenyl disulphide.

Hauptmann considers that the effect is due to poisoning of the nickel by adsorption of the nitro-groups on its surface. In agreement with this view it was found that diphenyl disulphide, which normally gives an 82 per cent yield of the monosulphide with Raney nickel (*b*), is recovered unchanged to the extent of 80 per cent if dinitrodiphenyl is added to the reaction mixture. This probably explains why sulphur compounds do not interfere with the reduction of nitro-compounds by Raney nickel but are strong poisons for the catalytic reduction of ethylene by this metal.

Bonner (*see* p. 102) has suggested that the sulphone 2-phenyl-2-phenylsulphonylpropionamide can become attached to Raney nickel through its oxygen atoms and that radical dissociation is thereby hindered. The structure of the nitro-compounds exhibits a similarity to that of the sulphones,

$$\overset{\bar{O}}{\underset{\displaystyle \overset{\displaystyle \nearrow}{\underset{O}{\overset{+}{R \cdot N}}}}{}} \quad \text{and} \quad \overset{\bar{O}}{\underset{\displaystyle \overset{\displaystyle \nearrow}{\underset{O}{\overset{++}{R_2 S}}}}{}}$$

Reductive desulphurization with Raney nickel. The origin of the hydrogen —For many years there remained a doubt as to how the hydrogen was supplied by Raney nickel. It will be realized that in the majority of cases the nickel is used without the introduction of any gaseous hydrogen into the system. It is only with such cases that we are here concerned.

Examination of samples of Raney nickel prepared by the usual alkali treatment of an aluminium–nickel alloy showed that 1 gram contained from 40 to 120 c.c. of 'bound' or adsorbed hydrogen. This supported the view advanced by Mozingo and his colleagues[41] that this hydrogen, bound on the surface, acted as the reducing agent. This view and also the possible formation of free radicals was also mentioned by Kenner, Lythgoe and Todd[52] in the discussion of the desulphurization of a methylthiopyrimidine derivative. This compound also contained a dichlorobenzeneazo-group which by reductive fission of the —N=N— group gave an aminopyrimidine derivative.

Hauptmann's work, discussed on p. 97, suggests that the usual reaction which may be represented as (a), Ni(H) + R·S·R′ → RH + R′H + NiS, only occurs when this 'bound' hydrogen is present and that when this is removed by degassing at 100°–200°C *in vacuo* the reaction takes a different course, free radicals being involved, and that in xylene solution aromatic mercaptols $R_2C(SR')_2$, mercaptals $R·CH(SR')_2$, disulphides $R·S·S·R$ and thioesters $R·CO·SR'$ yield stilbenes, diaryls and diaryl sulphides rather than aromatic hydrocarbons, RH.

Wolfrom and Karabinos[53] put forward another suggestion based on the fact that Raney nickel can convert alcohols to aldehydes and ketones in presence of a hydrogen acceptor, such as an olefine. They considered that the source of the hydrogen in most reactions with Raney nickel was the alcohol used as solvent, which was thereby dehydrogenated to acetaldehyde [reaction (d)].

Acetaldehyde was actually detected by them when heptanal diethyl mercaptal $CH_3(CH_2)_5·CH(SC_2H_5)_2$ was converted in dilute alcoholic solution to n-heptane and ethane by Raney nickel. This acetaldehyde is probably the source of the ethyl groups of the N-ethylaniline obtained by Mozingo et al.[54] when azoxybenzene or hydrazobenzene is boiled with Raney nickel in alcohol. Aniline is presumably formed and reacts with acetaldehyde to give the Schiff's base $CH_3·CH : N·C_6H_5$ which is reduced to N-ethylaniline.

Bonner[55,56] has shown that the original explanation of Hauptmann is correct. β-Thionaphthol was refluxed in ethanol with Raney nickel in an air stream when a quantitative yield of naphthalene and 11 per cent of the acetaldehyde required by reaction (d) were obtained. Blank experiments, omitting the β-thionaphthol, gave the same yield of acetaldehyde, which was collected as the 2 : 4-dinitrophenylhydrazone. Moreover, naphthalene was again obtained in theoretical yield when the reaction was carried out in boiling benzene, under which circumstances reaction (d) was excluded. In order to obtain the maximum confirmation of his conclusions the thionaphthol was refluxed in ethanol with Raney nickel which had been degassed at 200°C *in vacuo*. Under these circumstances the same 11 per cent yield of acetaldehyde was obtained as in the blank experiment and, instead of naphthalene, β-β′-dinaphthyl disulphide was formed, obviously due to a deficiency of adsorbed hydrogen on the nickel. With the degassed nickel and the thiol in benzene the disulphide was again obtained.

The evidence so far adduced would appear conclusive but Bonner

carried out one further test. Conversion of β-thionaphthol to naphthalene or to the corresponding disulphide proceeds by abstraction
of hydrogen from the thiol group. It seemed conceivable that
in the reactions carried out in alcoholic solution this hydrogen might
have reduced the acetaldehyde arising through reaction (d), thus
lowering the yield to the observed value of 11 per cent. This was
disproved by replacing the β-thionaphthol by diethyl sulphide, when
the same amount of acetaldehyde was produced as before and, as
would be expected, nickel sulphide was formed. It is therefore clear
that ordinary Raney nickel carries out the desulphurization reactions
through its adsorbed hydrogen.

STEREOCHEMICAL CHANGES DURING DESULPHURIZATION WITH RANEY NICKEL

Bonner points out that the stereochemical course of reductive desulphurization by Raney nickel has not been established. The
reductive desulphurization of certain amino acids, of biotin and of
carbohydrate derivatives does not involve change in an asymmetric
centre if this is situated at some distance from the sulphur atom, and
references in support of this generalization are supplied. Some
experiments of Reichstein *et al.*[57] are cited in which the sulphur
atom which is removed is situated next to the asymmetric carbon
atom, as in the case of the carbohydrate derivative (XLVI)

$$
\begin{array}{l}
\text{H·C·OCH}_3 \\
\text{CH}_3\text{S·CH} \\
\text{H·C·OCH}_3 \\
\text{HC·O} \qquad \text{O} \\
\text{HC} \\
\text{CH}_2 \text{---O---CH·C}_6\text{H}_5
\end{array}
\qquad \text{(XLVI)}
$$

and similar compounds. Here the asymmetry of the carbon atom
adjoining the sulphur is lost on its conversion to a —CH$_2$— group.

Desulphurization of 2-phenyl-2-phenylthiopropionic acid derivatives—
Bonner synthesized the ester and amide of 2-phenyl-2-phenyl-
thiopropionic acid and also the corresponding sulphone.

The structure of the acid (XLVII) was confirmed by its reduction
and desulphurization with Raney nickel to 2-phenylpropionic acid
CH$_3$·CH(C$_6$H$_5$)·COOH and by a similar reaction with the amide

(XLVIII). This was found more suitable than the acid, which gave a certain amount of insoluble nickel salts. The acid was then resolved by the use of the $(+)$ and $(-)$ phenylethylamines $CH_3 \cdot CH(NH_2) \cdot C_6H_5$ and the enantiomorphs converted to the amides prior to desulphurization. On desulphurization with Raney nickel in boiling ethanol for 5 hours both the $(+)$ and the $(-)$ amide gave racemic 2-phenylpropionamide $CH_3 \cdot CH(C_6H_5) \cdot CO \cdot NH_2$.

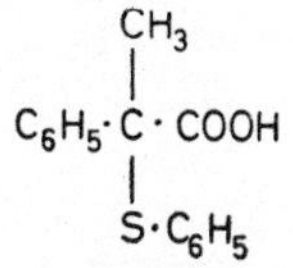

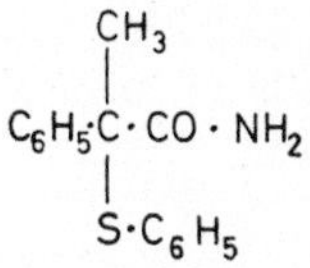

Desulphurization is therefore accompanied by a complete racemization. This racemization occurred during and not after the desulphurization because when $(-)$ -2-phenylpropionamide was treated with Raney nickel under the same conditions it was recovered unchanged in rotation.

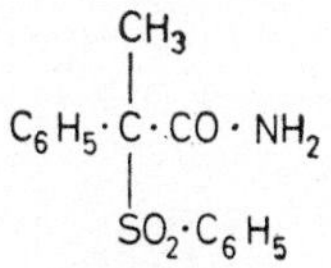

Desulphurization of derivatives of 2-phenyl-2-benzenesulphonylpropionic acid—The two optically active amides were then oxidized to the corresponding sulphones (XLIX) and these were submitted to desulphurization as before. The resulting 2-phenylpropionamides were optically active and enantiomorphic and their specific rotations showed that only about 10 per cent had undergone racemization in each case. Clearly, the desulphurization of the sulphone cannot proceed through the intermediate formation of the sulphide.

The authors at first considered the possibility that the sulphone might exist in the form of structures such as (L) or (LI) containing hydrogen bonds but this was disproved when it was shown that the $(-)$ ester (LII) of the sulphone also retained its rotation with only about 10 per cent diminution when desulphurized as before. The structure of the sulphone-ester does not permit of hydrogen bond formation.

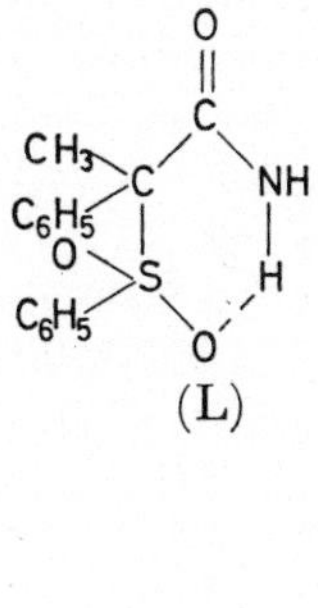

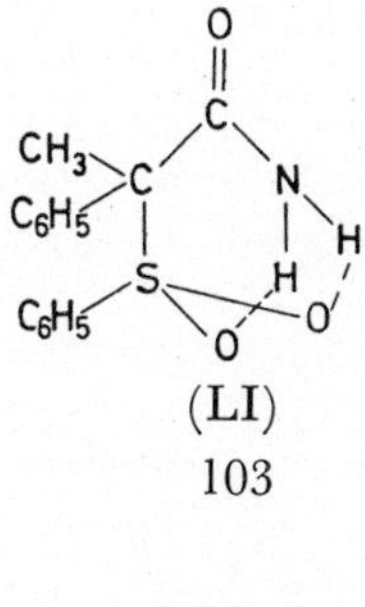

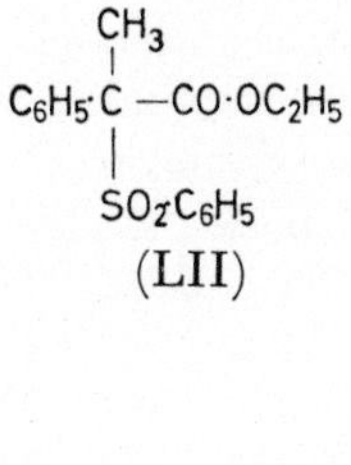

Bonner, in discussing these results, refers to the work of Hauptmann and Wladislaw[43,44] already described. He accepts their view of the formation of free radicals during desulphurization with Raney nickel. They postulated an adsorption of the sulphur compound on the surface of the metal, probably through the unshared electrons of the sulphur atom. This presumably weakens the C—S bond and consequently a free radical is eliminated which is reduced to a hydrocarbon by the adsorbed hydrogen on the surface of the nickel as shown by Bonner (*see* p. 100). If adsorbed hydrogen is absent as in 'degassed' Raney nickel the radicals combine with each other to form other products as already explained. There is much evidence to show that free radicals are optically unstable and that racemization accompanies their formation from an optically active compound[58,59]. Consequently the racemization observed by Bonner during the desulphurization of 2-phenyl-2-phenylthiopropionic ethyl ester and the corresponding amide is readily explicable if, e.g. the radical

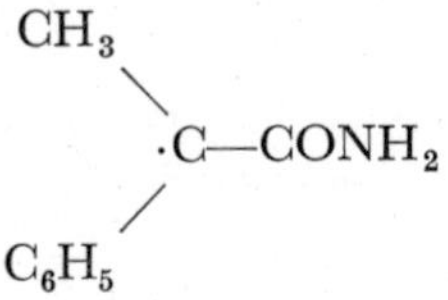

$$\underset{\displaystyle C_6H_5}{\overset{\displaystyle CH_3}{\diagdown \ \diagup}} \cdot C\!\!-\!\!CONH_2$$

is an intermediate product.

It seems clear that the desulphurization of the corresponding sulphone during which the optical activity is retained cannot be a free radical reaction of the type discussed above. Moreover, since there are no unshared electrons on the sulphur atom of the sulphones, adsorption on the nickel surface might take place through the oxygen

of the $-\overset{\displaystyle |}{\underset{\displaystyle |}{C}}-\overset{\displaystyle \bar{O}}{\underset{\displaystyle \underline{O}}{\overset{++}{S}}}\diagup$ group. The adsorbed molecule might then react

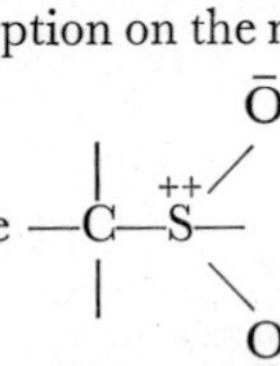

with an adjacent adsorbed hydrogen atom to break the sulphur-carbon bond so that an optically active reduction product is simultaneously formed. Bonner believes that this desulphurization is accompanied by optical inversion. This conclusion is based on Freudenberg's principle[60] of 'uniform rotational trends' and finds some support in a consideration of the rotations of the amide, esters, acid chloride and acid containing the $-SC_6H_5$ and $-SO_2 \cdot C_6H_5$ groups mentioned above, and of the corresponding compounds produced from them by reductive desulphurization, during which the sulphur atom is replaced by hydrogen.

Desulphurization of 2-phenyl-2-benzenesulphinylpropionic acid derivatives
—The unexpected results described in the preceding section suggested the study of the corresponding sulphoxide under analogous conditions, it being remembered that the formation of the sulphoxide group introduces a second centre of asymmetry.

Two crystalline enantiomorphs of 2-phenyl-2-benzenesulphinyl-propionamides (LIII) were prepared by the oxidation of the corresponding (+)- and (−)-2-phenyl-2-phenylthiopropionamides with hydrogen peroxide in acetic acid. These were dextro-rotatory $\left(\left[\alpha\right]_D^{20} = +187°\right)$ and laevo-rotatory $\left(\left[\alpha\right]_D^{25} = -207°\right)$ with m.p.'s 120°C and 120°C respectively. The first $\left(\begin{smallmatrix}+c\\+s\end{smallmatrix}\right)$ was slightly less optically pure than the second $\left(\begin{smallmatrix}-c\\-s\end{smallmatrix}\right)$. The mother liquors from these preparations gave syrupy, optically impure diastereoisomerides of the above sulphoxides of rotations $\left(\left[\alpha\right]_D^{25} = +55°\right)$ and $\left(\left[\alpha\right]_D^{25} = -53.2°\right)$—the $\left(\begin{smallmatrix}+c\\-s\end{smallmatrix}\right)$ and $\left(\begin{smallmatrix}-c\\+s\end{smallmatrix}\right)$ derivatives.

A preliminary desulphurization was carried out on the racemic sulphoxide. After boiling in ethanol with Raney nickel for three hours the product was shown to be 2-phenylpropionamide. This procedure was then employed in the desulphurization of the two crystalline and the two syrupy optically active sulphoxides, i.e. four experiments in all. The results were identical. Good yields of pure 2-phenylpropionamide were obtained and in each case the product was completely optically inactive.

$$CH_3 \qquad\qquad CH_3 \qquad\qquad CH_3$$
$$C_6H_5 \cdot C \cdot CONH_2 \longrightarrow C_6H_5 \cdot C \cdot CONH_2 \longrightarrow C_6H_5 \cdot C \cdot CONH_2$$
$$C_6H_5 \cdot S \qquad\qquad C_6H_5 \cdot SO \qquad\qquad H$$

(LIII)

Desulphurization of the sulphoxide therefore resembles stereochemically that of the sulphide and not that of the sulphone and it would appear that free radicals are involved in the process. It is possible that the sulphoxide may be reduced to the sulphide before desulphurization. It is well known that sulphoxides are readily reduced to sulphides whereas the similar reduction of sulphones is difficult (*see* Chapter 2, pp. 37, 49 and 54).

Desulphurization by Raney nickel in carbohydrate chemistry—Wolfrom and Karabinos[61] have employed Raney nickel in a convenient method for the conversion of carbonyl groups to methylene groups. By condensation with a mercaptan, a mercaptol or mercaptal is produced and this with Raney nickel in dilute alcoholic solution undergoes hydrogenolysis. Thus, benzophenone gives diphenylmethane

$$(C_6H_5)_2C = O \rightarrow (C_6H_5)_2C(SR)_2 \rightarrow C_6H_5CH_2C_6H_5$$

and D-galactose diethylmercaptal penta-acetate (LIV) gives 1-deoxy-D-galactitol penta-acetate (Ac = CO·CH$_3$) [62] (LV).

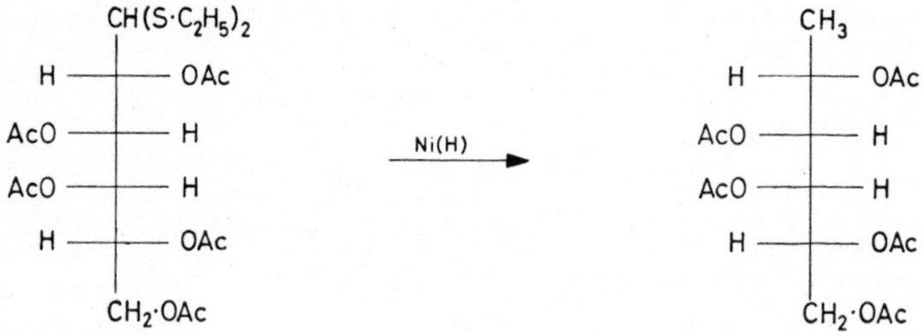

(LIV)   (LV)

Care is necessary in the interpretation of these reactions as one example is recorded where, during the formation of the diethylthioacetal from the penta-acetate of D-psicose (a ketose), an acetyl group on C-5 was replaced by —S·C$_2$H$_5$; reaction, therefore, occurs at two points in the molecule (C-2 and C-5) with final formation of two —CH$_2$ groups instead of one[62].

Raney nickel may also be used in the conversion of an acetobromohexose into a hexitol anhydride[63]. One further example of the use of desulphurization by Raney nickel in carbohydrate chemistry may be cited[64]. It was desired to convert the iodide (LVI; R = I)

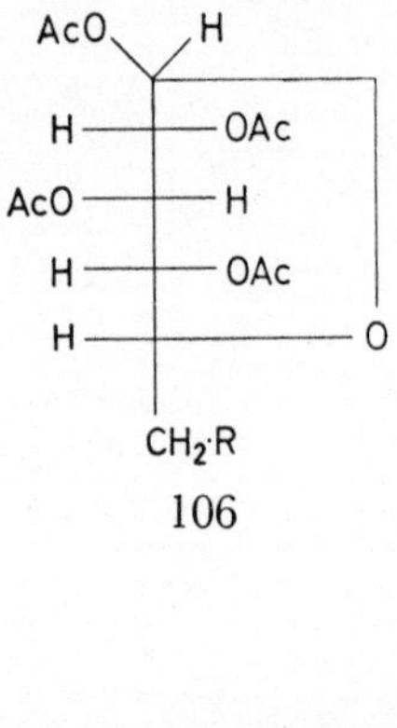

(LVI)

106

to the corresponding deoxy compound (LVI; R = H). The direct reductive displacement of the iodine by hydrogen was found to be difficult but by converting (LVI; R = I) to the hydriodide of the thiouronium salt (LVI; R = —S·C(: NH)·NH₂, HI) and treating with Raney nickel a good yield of the required deoxy compound (LVI; R = H) was obtained

Desulphurization by Raney nickel in sterol chemistry—The method of Wolfrom and Karabinos has been used to convert keto-steroids to the corresponding hydrocarbon derivatives[65].

Further work on the use of Raney nickel in the study of organic sulphides from mineral oils—Birch and his associates[66] have published a valuable review of their work on the sulphur compounds in the kerosene fraction of Persian oil of mixed origin. It includes much further information and a chart showing the treatment undergone by the mixture of sulphides resulting from dilution of the 'sulphuric acid sludge' with water. A careful fractionation with a very efficient column preceded the mercuric acetate treatment. Another table gives a full list of the saturated cyclic sulphides and the alkylated thiophens which have been isolated or detected, and the methods of identification. In this paper Birch *et al.* point out that not only does the mercuric acetate method enable a partial separation of open chain and cyclic sulphides to be effected, but it is of great assistance in concentrating mono- and bicyclic sulphides in different fractions. The order of extraction by the aqueous mercuric acetate from the mixture of sulphides is tricyclic sulphides > bicyclic > monocyclic > dialkyl sulphides. Regeneration from the mercuric acetate complex follows the reverse order. By a simple steam distillation of the extract the less stable mercury acetate compounds (i.e. those of the alkyl and monocyclic sulphides) are first decomposed giving sulphides which are designated A. Those sulphides which are only regenerated in acid solution are distinguished as B sulphides.

The authors emphasize that attempts to identify a sulphide through the hydrocarbon obtained by desulphurization have the disadvantage that no indication of the point of attachment of the sulphur atom to the carbon skeleton is afforded. Several alternatives may be possible, e.g. the hydrocarbon $CH_3 \cdot CH_2 \cdot CH_2 \cdot (CH_2)_4 \cdot CH_3$ might be formed either from a *n*-propylthia*cyclo*hexane or a *n*-butylthia*cyclo*pentane.

Birch *et al.* have assumed that the simple ring systems involved contain five or six members. Simple rings of four or seven atoms have not yet been identified in mineral oils. An excellent example of the interpretation of the results of a desulphurization experiment from the physical properties of the product and related compounds is given on p. 109.

An examination of the B sulphides obtained from the fraction of b.p. 187°–191°C (fraction XII) furnished interesting results. On repeated partial extraction with mercuric acetate and fractional regeneration a solid, volatile sulphide (m.p. 172°C in a sealed tube) was obtained. Its analysis and that of the sulphone and mercurichloride indicated the formula $C_7H_{12}S$ and on desulphurization with Raney nickel *cyclo*heptane was obtained and identified spectroscopically and by gas chromatography, thus leading to the identification of the sulphide as 8-thiabi*cyclo*- [3 : 2 : 1] octane.

In addition to *cyclo*heptane, methyl*cyclo*hexane and ethyl*cyclo*pentane were identified among the products of desulphurization of the B sulphides. The problems involved in an attempt to determine the origin of the methyl*cyclo*hexane may be indicated as they afford a good example of the mode of attack developed by Birch. It seemed possible at first that 3-thiabi*cyclo*-[3 : 3 : 0]-octane (LVII) was one of the sulphides present and that during its desulphurization ring expansion had occurred giving methyl*cyclo*hexane, thus:

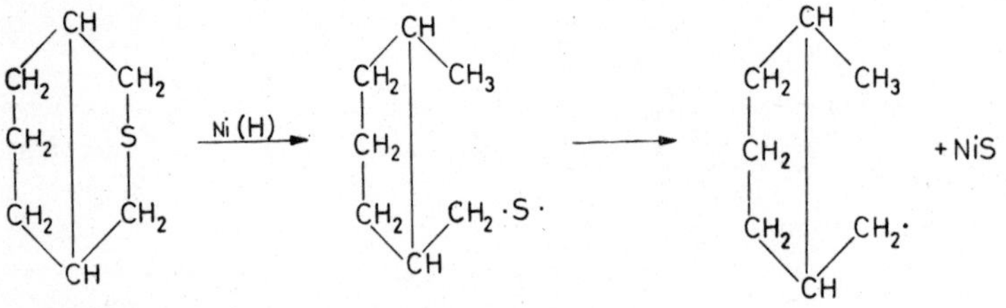

(LVII)

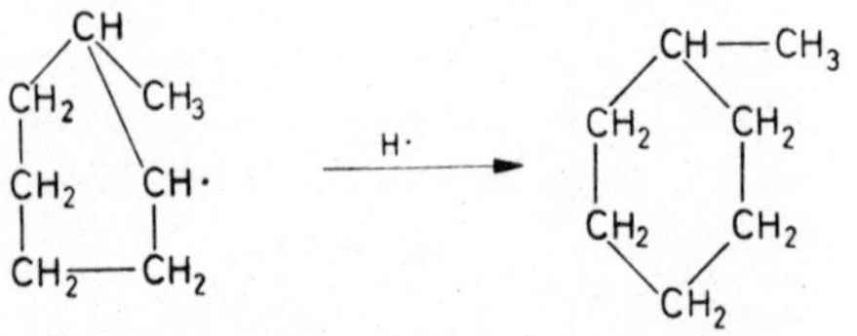

No such reaction was, however, detected on desulphurization of *trans*-3-thiabi*cyclo* -[3 : 3 : 0]- octane, *cyclo*pentylmethanethiol or di-(*cyclo*pentylmethyl) sulphide (*see* p. 84). No ring contraction with formation of methyl*cyclo*pentane could be detected during the desulphurization of methyl*cyclo*hexyl sulphide. It seems probable therefore that the methyl*cyclo*hexane was formed from a bridged bicyclic sulphide having one of the first two structures shown below:

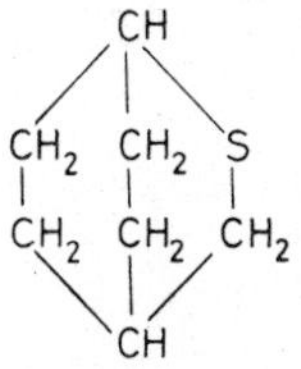

2 -Thiabi*cyclo* -
[2:2:2] octane

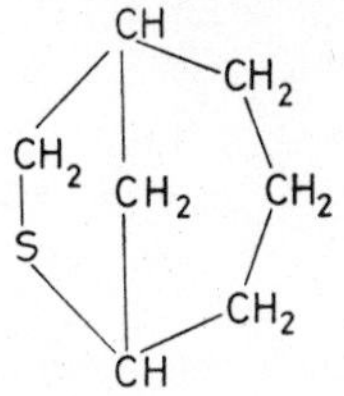

6 -Thiabi*cyclo* -
[3:2:1] octane

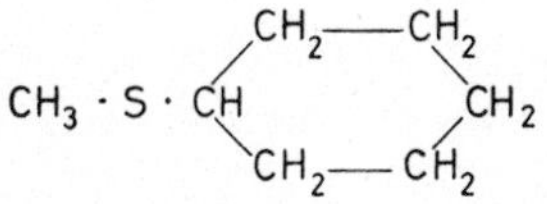

The examination of fraction VI b.p. 156°C involved the use both of Raney nickel for desulphurization and of a new reagent— diphenyl disulphide—for dehydrogenation. Raney nickel yielded mainly 3-methylhexane. This could arise from three different alkylated thia*cyclo*hexanes but all these should boil above 156°C

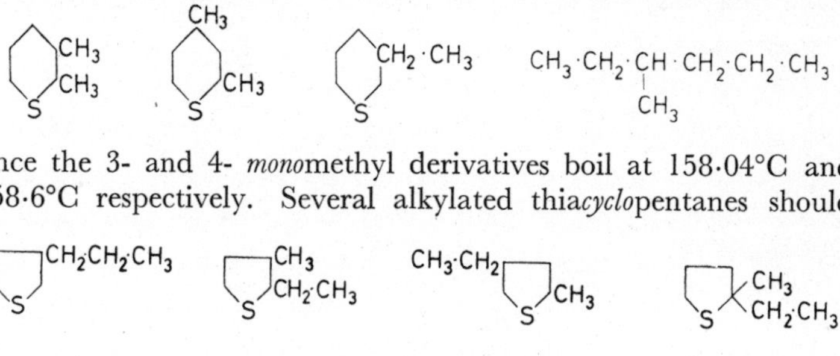

since the 3- and 4- *mono*methyl derivatives boil at 158·04°C and 158·6°C respectively. Several alkylated thia*cyclo*pentanes should

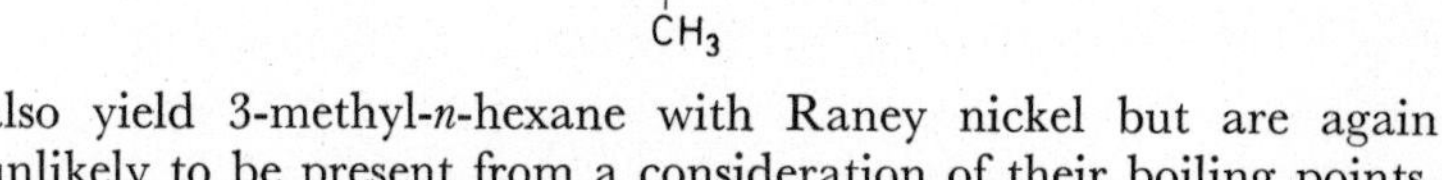

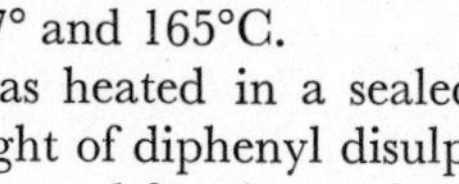

also yield 3-methyl-*n*-hexane with Raney nickel but are again unlikely to be present from a consideration of their boiling points. The first boils at 187°C and the *mono*derivatives, 2- and 3-ethylthia-*cyclo*pentanes boil at 157° and 165°C.

When fraction VI was heated in a sealed tube at 300°–310°C with three times its weight of diphenyl disulphide for 11 hours, the product distilled in steam and fractionated, an oil was obtained. In pentane with aqueous mercuric acetate this gave an oil which solidified and was shown by its m.p. and mixed m.p. to be 4-acetoxymercury-2 : 3 : 5-trimethylthiophen, arising by dehydrogenation of 2 : 3 : 5-trimethylthia*cyclo*pentane, which on desulphurization with Raney nickel would also yield 3-methyl-*n*-hexane.

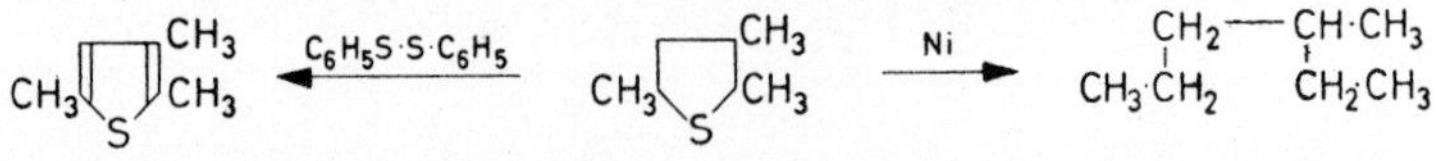

The fraction of b.p. 206°–210°C (fraction XIX) yielded important results. By comparison of the infra-red spectra of the B sulphides with those of pure synthetic *cis*- and *trans*-1-thiahydrindane (LVIII and LIX) the presence of both these compounds was definitely established. They are probably responsible for the ethyl*cyclo*hexane obtained on desulphurization of fraction XIX by Raney nickel. That portion of the same fraction which was unattacked by aqueous mercuric acetate was shown to contain naphthalene.

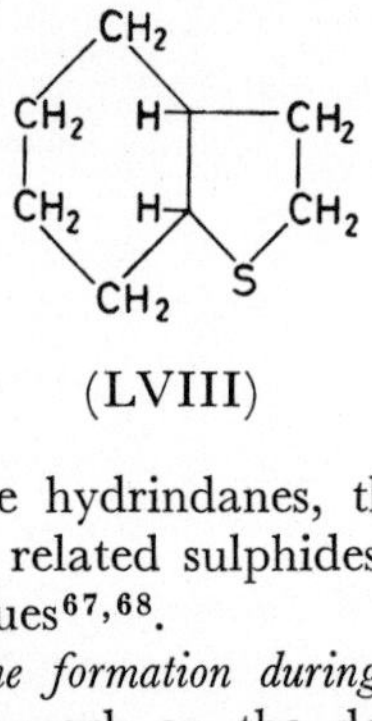

(LVIII) 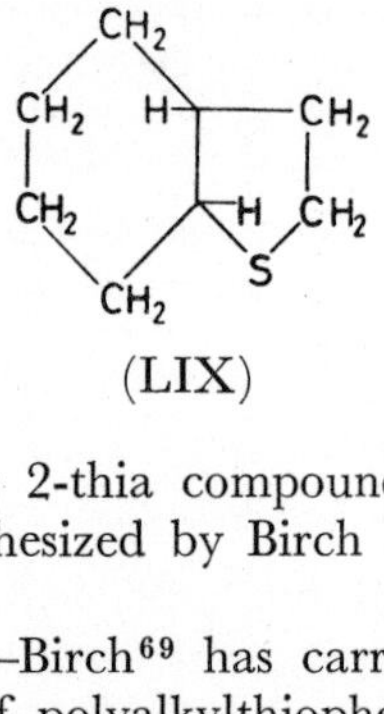   (LIX)

These hydrindanes, the corresponding 2-thia compounds, and several related sulphides have been synthesized by Birch and his colleagues[67,68].

Olefine formation during desulphurization—Birch[69] has carried out further work on the desulphurization of polyalkylthiophens and various unidentified bi- and tricyclic sulphides obtained on addition of water to the sulphuric acid sludge already mentioned.

The hydrocarbons obtained on desulphurization of these sulphides are often accompanied by 10–33 per cent of olefine, and for the hydrocarbons from the polycyclic sulphides this figure may rise to 60 per cent. The causes of this olefine formation are not known. It is presumably a dehydrogenation and Birch and Dean (see p. 92) obtained a much larger yield of olefines from pentamethylene sulphide (thia*cyclo*hexane) by the use of Raney nickel which had been partly denuded of its adsorbed hydrogen. It is not known whether olefine formation occurs during desulphurization or by hydrogenation of the resulting hydrocarbon.

There may be some relation between the extent of olefine formation and the number of carbon atoms in the sulphide. For sulphides with 7, 8 and 9 carbon atoms the percentage of olefine formation was 10, 20 and 33 respectively. With the higher but unidentified sulphides the figure rose to 60 per cent. Here the number of carbon atoms would be 9–10. Carbon content alone would therefore appear not to be the only factor in determining olefine formation. Structural considerations are probably involved. That Raney nickel can cause fission of, at any rate, a 2-carbon chain was shown by Birch *et al.* who obtained methane on boiling the nickel with ethanol. Methane is also obtained from ethane-1 : 2-dithiol and Raney nickel.

CATALYTIC DESULPHURIZATION OF PETROLEUM DISTILLATES IN PRESENCE OF HYDROGEN—'HYDRODESULPHURIZATION'

A modern catalytic desulphurization–hydrogenation process has recently been described[70] in which the sulphur is removed as hydrogen sulphide and saturated or aromatic or even hydroaromatic hydrocarbons are produced, often accompanied by branching of the paraffin chain. Fission of the chain by 'cracking' followed by some hydrogenation of the resulting olefines may also occur. The alkylbenzothiophens [alkylthionaphthens (LX)] which are found in the fractions known as 'straight-run gas oils' or 'catalytically cracked cycle oils' give dialkylbenzenes, whereas the dibenzothiophens [diphenylene sulphides (LXI)] which occur in the higher fractions give, for example, diphenyl, which may undergo some hydrogenation. These reactions recall those observed by the use of Raney nickel. In

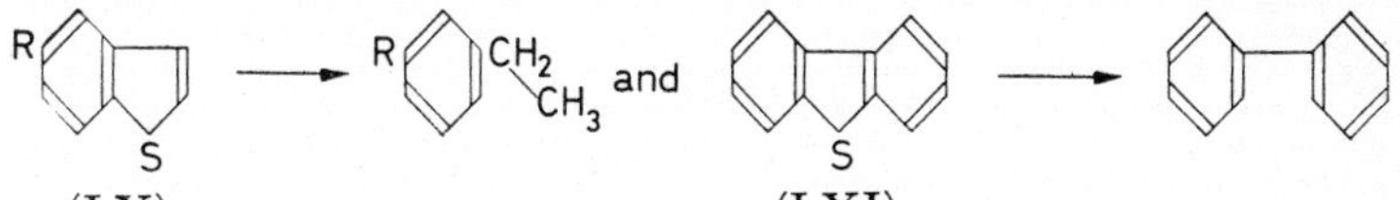

$$(LX) \qquad (LXI)$$

addition to possessing the properties usually desirable in catalytic processes the catalyst required for this type of desulphurization must be selective so that the hydrogenation of aromatic hydrocarbons is reduced to a minimum.

The oxides of cobalt, molybdenum or zinc possess such selectivity; cobalt and molybdenum oxides when suspended on bauxite or alumina were found to be specially suitable for this process.

PETROLEUM (OR 'NAPHTHENIC') ACIDS CONTAINING SULPHUR

'Naphthenic acids' is the name given to the acidic ingredients, other than phenols and mercaptans, i.e. carboxylic acids, which are found in petroleum and particularly in the 'kerosene' and 'light gas oil' fractions. These or their salts with various metals have been used as emulsifiers, preservatives for wood or textiles and as siccatives in the paint industry and for other purposes. An account has recently been published of the higher naphthenic acids isolated from a lubricating oil of Venezuelan origin[71].

The 'naphthenic' acids were purified on alumina and eluted with suitable solvents. They were then converted to the methyl esters by the usual methanol–hydrogen chloride process and fractionated in a molecular still. Reduction to the corresponding hydrocarbons was effected by reduction to the alcohols with lithium aluminium hydride, conversion to the iodides with hydriodic acid and reduction to the hydrocarbon with zinc and acetic acid.

The hydrocarbons were separated by alumina and by thermal diffusion into fractions of which the refractive indexes and ultra-violet absorption spectra were determined. The elementary analyses and the graphs showing the refractive indexes indicated the presence of hydrocarbons containing one or two aromatic nuclei, of saturated homocyclic compounds and also of dibenzothiophens. In all cases alkyl side chains were present. It is suggested that the term 'naphthenic acid' which suggests only derivatives of polymethylene hydrocarbons should be replaced by the more comprehensive designation 'petroleum acids'. It is considered, no doubt with reason, that the 'petroleum acids' from other oils will be shown to be of similar type to those of Venezuelan origin.

REFERENCES

[1] For the numerous early references *see* Challenger, F., Haslam, J., Bramhall, R. J. and Walkden, J., *J. Inst. Petrol.* **12** (1926) 24

[2] Mabery, C. F., *Amer. chem. J.* **13** (1891) 233; **17** (1895) 713; **18** (1896) 43

[3] Mabery, C. F., *J. Amer. chem. Soc.* **28** (1906) 419, 426

[4] Thierry, E. H., *J. chem. Soc.* **127** (1925) 2756

[5] Birch, S. F. and Norris, W. S. G. P., *ibid.* **127** (1925) 898, 1934

[6] Mabery, C. F. and Quayle, W. O., *Amer. chem. J.* **16** (1894) 92; **35** (1906) 404

[7] Boes, J., *Apotheker Zeitung* **17** (1902) 565, 638; *Cent. Blatt* (1902) II 804

[8] Weissgerber, R. and Krüber, O., *Ber. dtsch. chem. Ges.* **53** (1920) 1552, 1566

[9] Krüber, O. and Raeithel, A., *Chem. Ber.* **86** (1953) 366

[10] Carruthers, W., *J. chem. Soc.* (1953) 4186

[11] Carruthers, W., *Nature, Lond.* **176** (1955) 790

[12] Krüber, O. and Raeithel, A., *Chem. Ber.* **87** (1954) 1469

[13] Weissgerber, R., *Ber. dtsch. chem. Ges.* **61** (1928) 2111

14 Birch, S. F., *J. Inst. Petrol.* **39** (1953) 185
15 Scheibler, H., *Ber. dtsch. chem. Ges.* **48** (1915) 1815; **49** (1916) 2595; **52** (1919) 1903; *Arch. Pharm.* **258** (1920) 70; *Pharm. Monatshefte* **1** (1920) 148, 182
16 Challenger, F., Jinks, J. R. A. and Haslam, J., *J. chem. Soc.* **127** (1925) 162
17 Challenger, F., Haslam, J., Bramhall, R. J. and Walkden, J., *J. Inst. Petrol* **12** (1926) 24
18 Dodonow, J. and Sochestwenskaja, E., *Ber. dtsch. chem. Ges.* **59** (1926) 2202
19 Birch, S. F. and McAllan, D. T., *J. Inst. Petrol.* **37** (1951) 443
20 Melles, J. L., *Thesis,* Univ. of Groningen (1951) 62; Melles, J. L. and Backer, H. J., *Rec. Trav. chim. Pays-Bas* **72** (1953) 314, 492
21 Challenger, F. and Miller, S. A., *J. chem. Soc.* (1939) 1005
22 Challenger, F. and Rawlings, A. A., *ibid.* (1937) 868
23 Blackburn, S. and Challenger, F., *ibid.* (1939) 1872
24 Brown, R. H. and Meyerson, S., *Amer. chem. Soc. Meeting* Milwaukee, 1952
25 *Rep. Proc. Amer. Pet. Inst.,* **36** (1954) Vol. VI, 106
26 Landa, S. and Machacek, F., *Coll. trav. chem. Tshécoslav* **5** (1933) 1
27 Prelog, V. and Seiwerth, R., *Ber. dtsch. chem. Ges.* **74** (1941) 1644
28 Emmott, R., *J. Inst. Petrol.* **39** (1953) 695
28aRichter, F. P., Williams, A. L. and Meisel, S. L., *J. Amer. chem. Soc.* **78** (1956) 2166
28bMeyer, R. and Meyer, W., *Ber. dtsch. chem. Ges.* **52** (1919) 1249
29 Brooks, B. T., Kurtz, S. S., Boord, C. E. and Schmerling, L., *The Chemistry of Petroleum Hydrocarbons,* Reinhold, New York, 1954
30 Rossini, F. D., Mair, B. J. and Streif, A. J., *Hydrocarbons from Petroleum,* Reinhold, New York, 1953
31 Kinney, I. W., Smith, J. R. and Ball, J. S., *Anal. Chem.* **24** (1952) 1749
32 Kinney, I. W. and Cook, G. L., *ibid.* **24** (1952) 1391
33 Hartough, H. D., *Thiophene and its Derivatives,* Interscience, New York and London, 1952, p. 132
34 Steinkopf, W. and Killingstad, A., *Annalen* **532** (1937) 288
35 King, W. J. and Nord, F. F., *J. Org. Chem.* **13** (1948) 635; **14** (1949) 405, 638
36 *Organic Reactions,* John Wiley & Sons, New York, **4** (1948) 378
37 Mozingo, R., Harris, S. A., Wolf, D. E., Hoffhine, C. E., Easton, N. R. and Folkers, K., *J. Amer. chem. Soc.* **67** (1945) 2092
38 Broadbent, H. S., Slaugh, L. H. and Jarvis, N. L., *ibid.* **76** (1956) 1519
39 Bougault, J., Cattelain, E. and Chabrier, P., *Bull. soc. Chim.* **5** (1938) 1699; **7** (1940) 780
40 du Vigneaud, V., Melville, D. B., Folkers, K., Wolf, D. E., Mozingo, R., Keresztesy, J. C. and Harris, S. A., *J. biol. Chem.* **146** (1942) 475
41 Mozingo, R., Wolf, D. E., Harris, S. A. and Folkers, K., *J. Amer. chem. Soc.* **65** (1943) 1013
42 Badger, G. M., Rodda, H. J. and Sasse, W. H. F., *J. chem. Soc.* (1954) 4162
43 Hauptmann, H. and Wladislaw, B., *J. Amer. chem. Soc.* **72** (1950) 707, 710

[44] Hauptmann, H., Wladislaw, B., Nazario, L. L. and Walter, W. F., *Annalen* **576** (1952) 45

[45] Billica, H. R. and Adkins, H. *Org. Synth.* **29** (1949) 24

[46] Challenger, F. and Holmes, J. L., *J. chem. Soc.* (1953) 1837

[47] Hurd, C. D. and Rudner, B., *J. Amer. chem. Soc.* **73** (1951) 5157

[48] Cline, J. K., Campaigne, E. and Spies, J. W., *ibid.* **66** (1944) 1136

[49] Challenger, F. and Greenwood, D., *J. chem. Soc.* (1950) 26

[50] Schönberg, A., *Ber. dtsch. chem. Ges.* **68** (1935) 162; Schönberg, A. and Mustafa, A., *J. chem. Soc.* (1949) 889; Schönberg, A. and Barakat, M. Z. *ibid.* (1949) 892

[51] Mailhe, A., *Compt. rend.* **180** (1925) 1111

[52] Kenner, G. W., Lythgoe, B. and Todd, A. R., *J. chem. Soc.* (1948) 957

[53] Wolfrom, M. L. and Karabinos, J. V., *J. Amer. chem. Soc.* **66** (1944) 909; *see* also Fletcher, H. G. and Richtmeyer, N. K., *Advances in Carbohydrate Chemistry*, Academic Press, New York **5** (1950) p. 2

[54] Mozingo, R., Spencer, C. and Folkers, K., *J. Amer. chem. Soc.* **66** (1944) 1859

[55] Bonner, W. A., *ibid.* **74** (1952) 1033

[56] Bonner, W. A., *ibid.* **74** (1952) 5089

[57] Jeanloz, R., Prins, D. A. and Reichstein, T., *Helv. chim. acta* **29** (1946) 373; Maehly, A. C. and Reichstein, T. **30** (1947) 497; Gut, M., Prins, D. A. and Reichstein, T. **30** (1947) 743

[58] Mozingo, R., *Org. Synth.* **21** (1947) 15

[59] Gilman, H., *Organic Chemistry*, 2nd ed. John Wiley & Sons, New York, **1** (1943) p. 382; Wheland, C. W., *Advanced Organic Chemistry*, 2nd. ed. John Wiley & Sons, New York, (1949) p. 713

[60] Freudenberg, K., *Stereochemie*, F. Deuticke, Leipzig and Vienna, (1933) p. 695

[61] Wolfrom, M. L. and Karabinos, J. V., *J. Amer. chem. Soc.* **66** (1944) 909

[62] Wolfrom, M. L., Lew, B. W. and Goepp, R. M., *ibid.* **68** (1946) 1443

[63] Hudson, C. S. and Fletcher, H. G., *ibid.* **65** (1943) 1477

[64] Hardegger, E. and Montavon, R. M., *Helv. chim. acta* **29** (1946) 1129

[65] McOmie, J. F. W., *Ann. Rep. Chem. Soc.* **45** (1948) 201

[66] Birch, S. F., Cullum, T. V., Dean, R. A. and Denyer, R. L., *Industr. Engng Chem.* **47** (1955) 240

[67] Birch, S. F., Dean, R. A. and Whitehead, E. V., *J. org. Chem.* **19** (1954) 1449

[68] Birch, S. F., Dean, R. A., Hunter, N. J. and Whitehead, E. V., *ibid.* **20** (1955) 1178

[69] Birch, S. F., Hunter, N. J. and McAllan, D. T., *ibid.* **21** (1956) 970

[70] Storey, G. R., *Inst. Petrol. Rev.* **11** (1957) 35

[71] Knotnerus, J., *J. Inst. Petrol.* **43** (1957) 307

4

THE NATURAL MUSTARD OIL GLUCOSIDES AND THE RELATED *ISO*THIOCYANATES AND NITRILES

EARLY WORK ON MUSTARD SEEDS AND OIL OF MUSTARD

ALTHOUGH the Dutch scientist Boerhaave appears to have been the first to prepare oil of mustard and to describe its properties in 1732, it would seem that the formation of a volatile oil on distillation of mustard seeds with water was observed by Portas in 1608 and by Febure in Paris in 1660. The references, all to very inaccessible publications, are given by Gildemeister and Hofmann[1].

The conclusion that the pungent principle of mustard is not present in the free state in the seeds must have been reached by early users of the plant, and they can hardly have failed to notice that grinding with water is necessary before the odour is produced. However, Gildemeister and Hofmann place the date of publication of this second observation as late as 1825 and give four references, mainly to the *Journal de Pharmacie*. The presence of sulphur in the mustard oil was detected by Thiebierge in 1819 and an elementary analysis of the oil was carried out by Dumas and Pelouze[2] who also showed that with ammonia it was converted to thiosinamine (later shown to be allylthiourea $CH_2 : CH \cdot CH_2 \cdot NH \cdot CS \cdot NH_2$). This work must be regarded as the beginning of the modern investigations relating to mustard oil (allyl *iso*thiocyanate $CH_2 : CH \cdot CH_2 \cdot N : C : S$) and its production from the plant. Boutron and Fremy[3] made a significant step forward when, by extraction of black mustard seeds with *cold* alcohol, they obtained a solid substance which Bussy[4] named myrosin. (This was later shown to contain an enzyme.) If the seeds, after the extraction with alcohol, were pressed to remove fatty oil, treated with water and the aqueous extract treated with myrosin, oil of mustard was liberated. The substance left in the seeds after extraction of the myrosin (now named myrosinase) with cold alcohol, and which yields the mustard oil by action of the enzyme, was extracted with water, the extract concentrated, and protein precipitated with alcohol, finally yielding the potassium salt of a complex acid named myronic acid. This potassium myronate was later given the name sinigrin by which it is known today.

115

If the myrosinase in the seeds was decomposed by heating at 100°C, addition of water to the ground seeds produced no trace of oil of mustard. Potassium myronate (sinigrin) could then be extracted with water. The simultaneous presence of myrosinase and sinigrin in the seeds of black mustard was, therefore, clearly established by Bussy.

Chemical Properties of Oil of Mustard

Bussy also studied the chemical properties of the mustard oil while Will[5] and, simultaneously, Wertheim[6] suggested in 1844 that the oil was 'schwefelcyanallyl', C_3H_5CNS. This was, however, not a complete answer to the question of its nature as ideas on the structure of the CNS group were still rudimentary. Sixteen years later an important advance was made by Ludwig and Lange[7] who also obtained sinigrin from black mustard seed and showed that on 'fermentation' with myrosin, glucose, potassium hydrogen sulphate and allyl mustard oil were obtained. Further studies of this biological breakdown were carried out by Will and Körner[8] and are discussed in detail later. Here it need only be mentioned that had some of their observations and comments received sufficient attention and amplification a much earlier re-assessment of the structural formula (I) put forward for sinigrin by Gadamer[9] in 1895 would have been made.

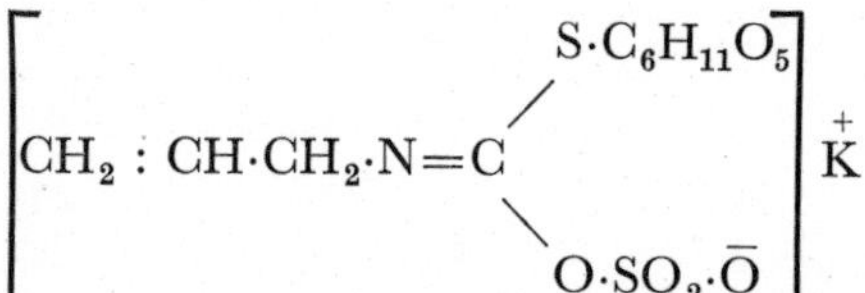

$$\left[CH_2 : CH \cdot CH_2 \cdot N = C \begin{array}{c} S \cdot C_6H_{11}O_5 \\ \diagup \\ \diagdown \\ O \cdot SO_2 \cdot \overline{O} \end{array} \right] \overset{+}{K}$$

(I)

This type of structure has been generally accepted as probably applying to all glucosides which yield a 'mustard oil' (an *iso*thiocyanate), potassium hydrogen sulphate or other sulphate, and glucose on enzymic hydrolysis. It remained unchallenged till 1956. It will be preferable, however, to discuss the whole question in chronological order.

The suggestion made in 1844 that allyl mustard oil (from sinigrin, i.e. potassium myronate) was 'schwefelcyanallyl' was much strengthened when Zinin[10] and almost simultaneously Berthelot and de Luca[11] synthesized the oil by heating allyl iodide with potassium thiocyanate and confirmed their synthesis by converting the mustard oil to thiosinamine, $C_3H_5 \cdot NH \cdot CS \cdot NH_2$, which exhibited all the properties characteristic of that prepared from the natural oil. This

116

led to the conclusion that allyl mustard oil was the allyl ester of thiocyanic acid, although Oeser[12] remarked that the other known esters of thiocyanic acid had properties which were very different from those of allyl mustard oil. He also pointed out that the formation of thiosinamine from mustard oil and ammonia is not analogous with the behaviour of ethyl thiocyanate with this reagent. The reaction with alkali was also different.

Hofmann[13], in a paper of fundamental importance, suggested in 1868 that in compounds of the mustard oil type the alkyl group was linked to nitrogen, but in the isomeric thiocyanates to sulphur. This view was later firmly established through a study of the products of reduction, oxidation and hydrolysis of the two isomeric types and by the interaction of the mustard oils with amines[14].

Further light was thrown on the properties and structure of thiocyanates and *iso*thiocyanates when it was shown by Billeter[15] and by Gerlich[16] that by the action of allyl bromide on potassium (or ammonium) thiocyanate in the cold the thiocyanate $CH_2 : CH \cdot CH_2 \cdot S \cdot C \vdots N$ is first formed and undergoes isomerization by heat giving the mustard oil. Gerlich's account of the experiment may be quoted:

'Erhitzt man das Rhodanallyl am Rückflusskühler, so sinkt der anfängliche Siedepunkt von 161° allmälig bei immer intensiver hervortretendem Senfölgeruch auf 148° bis 149° herab. Die Umwandlung ist dann vollendet, ein weiteres Sinken des Queck-silbers findet nicht statt. Für sich oder in alkoholischer Lösung möglichst bei Licht und Luftabschluss und mit Eis umgeben, hielt sich der Körper unverändert.'

Gerlich[17] gave directions for the preparation of reasonably pure allyl thiocyanate $CH_2 : CH \cdot CH_2 \cdot S \cdot C \equiv N$ from ammonium thio-cyanate and allyl bromide in 80–90 per cent alcohol at 0°C.

In view of Gerlich's work the question naturally arose whether allyl *iso*thiocyanate is the actual product liberated by myrosin from sinigrin or whether allyl thiocyanate is first formed and then iso-merized to the *iso*thiocyanate. Schmidt[18] carried out the enzymic fission of sinigrin at a low temperature (0°C) and he stated that although traces of allyl thiocyanate were formed the main and initial product was the *iso*thiocyanate.

Gadamer's Work on the Oils of Black and White Mustard

In a series of papers of which the most important was published in 1897 Gadamer discussed the structure of sinigrin and sinalbin, the glucosides of black and white mustard seeds. In that year he proposed a formula for sinigrin (potassium myronate) which satisfactorily explained its enzymic hydrolysis by myrosin giving allyl *iso*thiocyanate, glucose and potassium hydrogen sulphate. This structural formula which is given below (I) held the field for just under 60 years and seems never to have been seriously questioned, except by Semmler. In reviewing early work on sinigrin[19] he does not give Gadamer's formula and appears to have doubts as to the interpretation of Schmidt's low temperature hydrolysis of sinigrin *see* p. 117.

Gadamer's formula appears in most recent textbooks of organic chemistry along with the evidence on which it was based, which may briefly be summarized

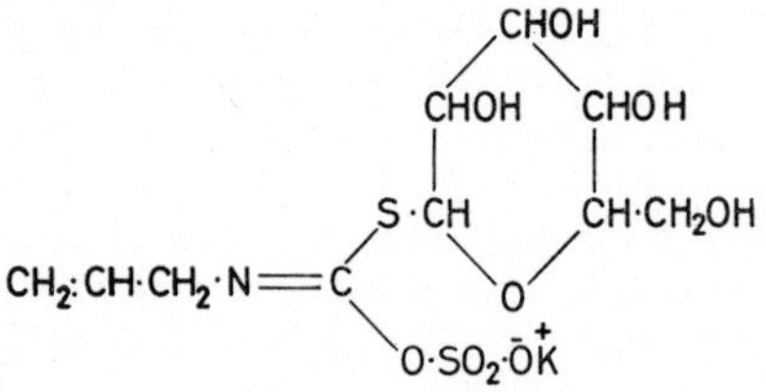

$$CH_2{:}CH{\cdot}CH_2{\cdot}N = C \quad \begin{array}{c} CHOH \\ CHOH \quad CHOH \\ S{\cdot}CH \quad\quad CH{\cdot}CH_2OH \\ O \\ O{\cdot}SO_2{\cdot}\bar{O}\overset{+}{K} \end{array}$$

(I)

(The stereochemical configuration of glucose is not represented.)

Meyer and Jacobson[14] only give the empirical formula for sinigrin and add significantly (after the equation showing its enzymic breakdown) 'infolge sekundäre Reaktionen enthält das ätherische Senföl auch kleine Mengen Allyl-cyanid und Schwefelkohlenstoff'.

The structure of sinigrin—We may now consider some early observations by Will and Körner[8] in 1863 and various facts which have emerged since then which suggest that not all the decompositions of sinigrin can readily be explained by Gadamer's formula (1897).

1. Will and Körner confirmed the liberation of free sulphur already reported by Ludwig and Lange[7] during the decomposition of sinigrin by myrosin, but experimental details were not given. As a consequence, however, they concluded that, in addition to glucose, allyl mustard oil and potassium hydrogen sulphate, another compound, free from sulphur, must be produced. Later on, in the same paper, they stated that this is allyl cyanide.

2. When aqueous potassium hydroxide of d. 1·28 is added to dry sinigrin the mixture boils and an odour of the mustard oil followed by those of allyl cyanide and ammonia is noticed. Ammonia is a product of the hydrolysis of nitriles but not of mustard oils.

3. When sinigrin is heated with aqueous baryta half its sulphur is

at once precipitated as barium sulphate. There is no odour of mustard oil but further heating again gives ammonia.

4. When sinigrin is boiled with barium chloride and hydrochloric acid, the barium sulphate removed and the filtrate made alkaline, ammonia is evolved and was characterized and analysed as ammonium platinichloride. Allylamine, which would be expected if sinigrin has the structure proposed by Gadamer, was not detected.

5. A very significant fact was recorded by Will and Körner as a result of their study of the action of aqueous silver nitrate on sinigrin. This eliminates glucose from the molecule and a silver compound is precipitated to which the formula

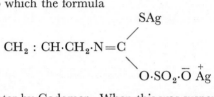

was assigned later by Gadamer. When this was suspended in water and treated with hydrogen sulphide, silver sulphide and sulphur were obtained in equivalent amounts; carbon disulphide removed half the sulphur from the precipitate. The aqueous filtrate, freed from hydrogen sulphide, had a leek-like odour and on distillation gave an oil. This was separated, and on fractionation gave allyl cyanide, b.p. 117°–118°C, an operation which was carefully checked. It was analysed and converted by alkali to ammonia and crotonic acid, m.p. 72°C. This formation of allyl cyanide will later be seen to be of fundamental importance.

6. Robiquet and Bussy[20] had already found that the oil of black mustard seeds contained, in addition to 'schwefelcyanallyl', a more volatile product lighter than water. Will and Körner by fractionation of two samples of natural oil of mustard found allyl cyanide, b.p. 118·3°C, in each; the last traces of allyl *iso*thiocyanate, b.p. 151°C, were removed from the nitrile by dilute cold aqueous ammonia which formed thiosinamine, allylthiourea.

7. Will and Körner remark in a paragraph which may be quoted in the original German that, in effect, the structure of sinigrin (potassium myronate) may be such as to allow the formation of allyl *iso*thiocyanate or allyl cyanide according to circumstances and that it is not certain that 'the mustard oil grouping' is 'ready formed' in the potassium myronate.

'Es scheint in der That keinem Zweifel zu unterliegen dass die Zucker und Schwefelsauregruppen fertig gebildet in der Verbindung vorhanden sind, für die Senfölgruppe ist dass weniger deutlich ausgesprochen. Das Verhalten des myronsauren Kalis bei der Gährung und beim Erhitzen mit Wasser so wie dass der Silberverbindung deutet vielmehr darauf hin, dass die Elemente des Schwefelcyanallyls in einer Anordnung neben einander liegen, dass bei einer Störung derselben ebensowohl Schwefelcyanallyl als Cyanallyl und freier Schwefel auftreten köhnen.

'Die Zersetzung des myronsauren Kalis unter dem Einfluss einer Ferments, des Myrosins, ist gleichsam eine aus beiden Fällen gemischte Reaktion, es bildet sich neben Schwefelcyanallyl gleichzeitig auch Cyanallyl und Schwefel, vorzugsweise aber ersteres.'

This conclusion, which we now know to be very near to the truth, and its possible implications seem to have been disregarded by all later workers on the subject for 93 years.

The presence of nitriles in natural mustard oils—The presence of allyl cyanide in mustard oil (allyl *iso*thiocyanate) is not the only case of the simultaneous occurrence of a nitrile and an *iso*thiocyanate in the same oil. In 1948 Schmid and Karrer[21] isolated sulphoraphene,

$$CH_3 \overset{+}{\underset{\overset{|}{\overset{-}{O}}}{S}} \cdot CH : CH \cdot CH_2 \cdot CH_2 \cdot N : C : S,$$ and the corresponding nitrile

from radish seeds. Here the glucoside was converted to a silver derivative with loss of glucose and the silver compound decomposed by sodium thiosulphate giving an oil. Enzymic decomposition of the glucoside was not employed, *see* p. 140.

A further example of this 'paired' occurrence is cited on p. 130. Doubtless further instances will be forthcoming and the results of Kjaer[22] and of Zwergal[23] are relevant. No one, since the time of Will and Körner's far-sighted but necessarily somewhat vague speculations, has suggested an explanation of this simultaneous natural occurrence of *iso*thiocyanate and nitrile, nor a simple mechanism whereby $R \cdot N : C : S$ might be converted to $R \cdot C : N$. The author stressed the obscurity of the position in a review[24] published in 1949 which may here be quoted. After summarizing the work of Schmid and Karrer on sulphoraphene and the analogous nitrile he stated:

'The *iso*thiocyanate, sulphoraphene, occurs in the seed as a glucoside of the usual type

$$R \cdot N {=} C \begin{array}{l} \diagup \;\; O \cdot SO_2 \cdot OK \\ \diagdown \;\; S \cdot C_6 H_{11} O_5 \end{array}$$

where $R = CH_3SO \cdot CH : CHCH_2CH_2$—; the silver compound is presumably $RN = C$—OSO_2OAg. The hydrolysis of such gluco-
　　　　　　　　　＼
　　　　　　　　　　SAg

sides to an *iso*thiocyanate, glucose and potassium hydrogen sulphate is well known. Schmid and Karrer consider that the nitrile also arises by decomposition or transformation of this glucoside; the mechanism is obscure. They point out that cases are already known in which *iso*thiocyanates and nitriles have been isolated from the same plant. Thus steam distillation of *Lepidium sativum* and *Tropaeolum majus* yields benzyl *iso*thiocyanate and benzyl cyanide, and from *Nasturtium officinale* phenylethyl *iso*thiocyanate and phenylethyl cyanide are obtained by the same process. Using the thoroughly disintegrated plant the *iso*thiocyanate predominates, otherwise the nitrile is the chief product. This would suggest the normal enzymic decomposition as a source of the *iso*thiocyanate, whereas steam distillation of the more or less intact plant may decompose the enzyme before it can react with the glucoside, which may then break down in a different manner. The simple conditions under which the nitrile and *iso*thiocyanate are produced in these three cases would suggest that the rather more drastic method of formation and decomposition of a silver salt in the experiments of Schmid and Karrer was not the cause of nitrile formation. A direct transformation of *iso*thiocyanate by loss of sulphur and isomerization of the resulting *iso*nitrile seems improbable, although *iso*nitriles are known to yield nitriles on heating.'

THE WORK OF ETTLINGER AND LUNDEEN ON SINIGRIN AND SINALBIN

THE STRUCTURE OF SINIGRIN

We must now consider the new formula for sinigrin and sinalbin put forward by Ettlinger and Lundeen[25] in the autumn of 1956, when it will be at once apparent that the new structure explains not only the formation of allyl cyanide in Will and Körner's experiments[8] and several new reactions of the two glucosides, but also the occurrence of nitriles and *iso*thiocyanates in the same essential oil. It will also be seen that Will and Körner's speculations (quoted in full above) were surprisingly near the truth. The revised formula for sinigrin (II) is shown on p. 122, that for sinalbin as well as the earlier formula is given later (*see* p. 125).

121

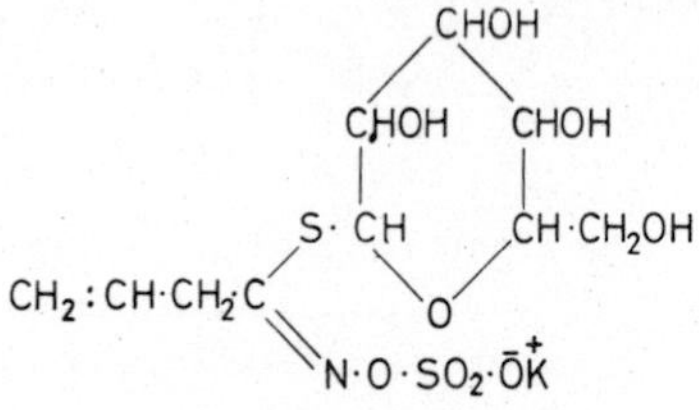

$$\text{CH}_2:\text{CH·CH}_2\text{C}\underset{\displaystyle \text{N·O·SO}_2\text{·}\bar{\text{O}}\overset{+}{\text{K}}}{\overset{\displaystyle \begin{array}{c}\text{CHOH}\\ \text{CHOH}\quad\text{CHOH}\\ \text{S·CH}\quad\text{CH·CH}_2\text{OH}\\ \text{O}\end{array}}{\diagdown\diagup}}$$

(II)

The most striking feature of this new formula is that it requires that the allyl group should migrate from carbon to nitrogen during enzymic hydrolysis. This will be discussed somewhat later. Ettlinger and Lundeen point out that Gadamer's formula (I) does not explain the direct chemical hydrolysis of sinigrin and of its analogue, sinalbin, to nitriles and carboxylic acids containing the same number of carbon atoms as the *iso*thiocyanate obtained by enzyme action.

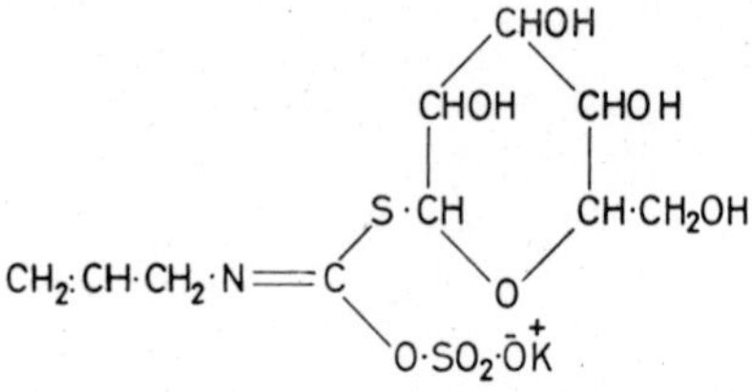

$$\text{CH}_2\text{:CH·CH}_2\text{·N}\!=\!\!\text{C}\underset{\displaystyle \text{O·SO}_2\text{·}\bar{\text{O}}\overset{+}{\text{K}}}{\overset{\displaystyle \begin{array}{c}\text{CHOH}\\ \text{CHOH}\quad\text{CHO H}\\ \text{S·CH}\quad\text{CH·CH}_2\text{OH}\\ \text{O}\end{array}}{\diagdown\diagup}}$$

(I)

On Gadamer's formula amines would be expected. The earliest evidence for this statement was provided by the work of Will and Körner which is discussed on p. 118 and particularly by that outlined in sections 2–5 and 7. The American authors remark that the formation of a nitrile (allyl cyanide) from sinigrin or from the silver sinigrinate (III) obtained from sinigrin and silver nitrate with loss of glucose recalls the

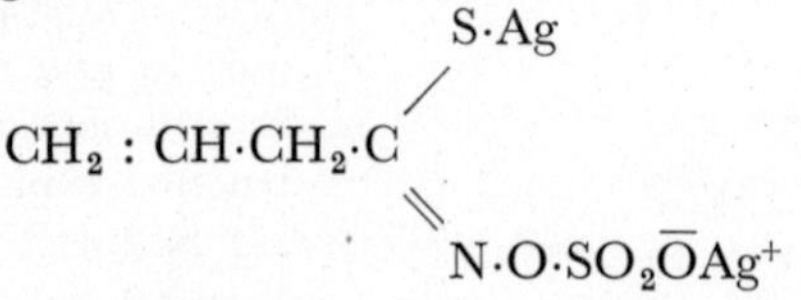

$$\text{CH}_2:\text{CH·CH}_2\text{·C}\underset{\displaystyle \text{N·O·SO}_2\bar{\text{O}}\text{Ag}^+}{\overset{\displaystyle \text{S·Ag}}{\diagup}}\qquad\qquad \text{R·C}\underset{\displaystyle \text{NOH}}{\overset{\displaystyle \text{SH}}{\diagup}}$$

(III) 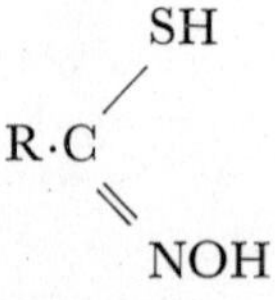   (IV)

behaviour of the analogous thiohydroxamic acids (IV) which were studied by Voltmer[26]. This author showed that when *iso*thiocyanates, mainly of aromatic type, react with hydroxylamine in aqueous solution addition takes place and compounds of the type R·NH·CS·

$$NHOH \quad \text{or} \quad R{\cdot}NH{\cdot}\overset{\displaystyle SH}{\overset{\diagup}{C}}{=}NOH$$

NHOH or R·NH·C=NOH are formed which are clearly of type (IV). When left for some time or heated in alcohol or at their m.p. these compounds lose elementary sulphur and water giving arylcyanamides R·NH·CN. This reaction is analogous with that in which, according to Will and Körner, free sulphur and allyl cyanide in addition to allyl *iso*thiocyanate are formed biologically from sinigrin and myrosin, or with the purely chemical reaction of hydrogen sulphide on silver sinigrinate.

With phenyl *iso*thiocyanate and O-ethylhydroxylamine the same reaction occurs on boiling the solutions of the addition product:

$$CH_3{\cdot}CH_2{\cdot}O{\cdot}NH_2 + C_6H_5N : C : S$$

$$\rightarrow C_6H_5NH{\cdot}CS{\cdot}NH{\cdot}O{\cdot}CH_2{\cdot}CH_3 \rightleftarrows C_6H_5NH{\cdot}\overset{\displaystyle SH}{\overset{\diagup}{C}} = N{\cdot}O{\cdot}CH_2{\cdot}CH_3$$

$$\rightarrow C_6H_5{\cdot}NH{\cdot}CN + S + CH_3{\cdot}CH_2{\cdot}OH$$

O-benzylhydroxylamine behaves in a similar manner and the reaction has been further exemplified by using *o*-tolyl or *α*-naphthyl *iso*thiocyanate and hydroxylamine or O-benzylhydroxylamine. With allyl *iso*thiocyanate and hydroxylamine no addition product could be isolated, but on warming in alcohol a vigorous reaction occurred, sulphur was deposited and an oil having the properties of allyl cyanamide was produced but was not characterized.

New Reactions of Sinigrin

With Raney nickel in water at room temperature sinigrin gives *n*-butylamine which was isolated as the *p*-nitrobenzoyl derivative in 47 per cent yield. Acid hydrolysis of sinigrin gave vinylacetic acid, $CH_2 : CH{\cdot}CH_2{\cdot}COOH$, presumably by way of the nitrile $CH_2 : CH{\cdot}CH_2{\cdot}CN$. These two reactions show the presence of a chain of 4 carbon atoms in sinigrin and that the allyl group is not linked to nitrogen. Alkaline hydrolysis of allyl cyanide gives crotonic acid $CH_3{\cdot}CH : CH{\cdot}COOH$ as was shown by Will and Körner (*see* p. 119) and others.

Acid hydrolysis of sinigrin yielded also hydroxylamine which was obtained in very good yield and identified as the oxime of fluorenone. It was determined as the ferric salt of benzhydroxamic acid

$$C_6H_5\overset{\displaystyle OH}{\underset{\displaystyle NOH}{\overset{\diagup}{\underset{\diagdown}{C}}}}$$

C₆H₅C and also by Yamada's method[27]. The hydroxylamine

was also detected by paper chromatography after liberation on the paper with a mixture of methanol and 6N-hydrochloric acid. This formation of hydroxylamine on hydrolysis of sinigrin is impossible to explain on Gadamer's formula but is readily accounted for by that of Ettlinger and Lundeen. Its formation is analogous to the hydrolysis of numerous aldoxime- and ketoxime-O-sulphonic acids $R_2C=N-O-SO_2-OH$ to which several references are cited by these authors. Thus, hydroxylamine sulphate and chloro-sulphonic acid give a hydroxylamine O-sulphonic acid which reacts with aldehydes and ketones to give the corresponding O-sulphonic acids of the oximes[28]

$$NH_2OH + Cl \cdot SO_2OH \rightarrow H_2N-O-SO_2 \cdot OH \rightarrow$$
$$RCH=N \cdot O \cdot SO_2 \cdot OH \text{ and } R_2C=N \cdot O \cdot SO_2 \cdot OH$$
$$(V) \qquad\qquad (VI)$$

The potassium salt of the aldoxime sulphonic acid (V) with hydro-chloric acid gives a nitrile and potassium hydrogen sulphate:

$$R \cdot CH=N-O-SO_2-OK \rightarrow RC{\equiv}N + HO \cdot SO_2 \cdot OK$$

Re-formation of aldehyde, sulphuric acid and hydroxylamine also occurs.

THE STRUCTURE OF SINALBIN

The results of Ettlinger and Lundeen have been confirmed by their analogous study of sinalbin, the glucoside occurring in the seeds of the white mustard. This has a more complex structure than sinigrin and instead of yielding potassium hydrogen sulphate on enzymic hydrolysis by myrosin it gives, in addition to glucose and the mustard oil, p-hydroxybenzyl isothiocyanate $HO \cdot C_6H_4 \cdot CH_2 \cdot N : C : S$, the hydrogen sulphate of a complex derivative of choline known as sinapin sulphate. This has the structure (VII)

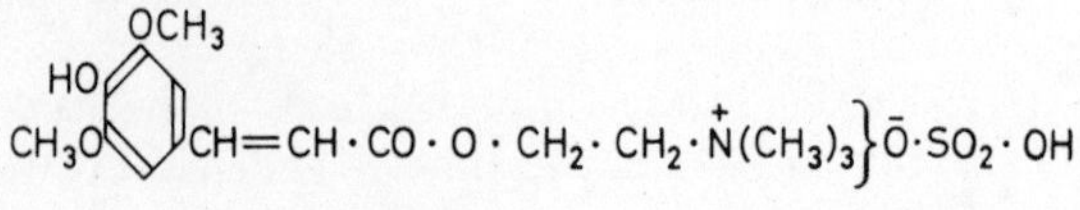

$$\text{CH}_3\text{O}\underset{\text{HO}}{\overset{\text{OCH}_3}{\bigcirc}}\text{CH}=\text{CH} \cdot \text{CO} \cdot \text{O} \cdot \text{CH}_2 \cdot \text{CH}_2 \cdot \overset{+}{\text{N}}(\text{CH}_3)_3\Big\}\bar{\text{O}} \cdot \text{SO}_2 \cdot \text{OH}$$

$$(VII)$$

as is shown by its hydrolysis by barium hydroxide giving barium sulphate, choline and sinapinic acid, 4-hydroxy-3 : 5-dimethoxy-cinnamic acid (VIII).

This is closely related to syringic acid (IX) which is a degradation product of many anthocyanins.

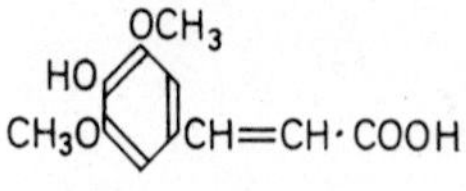

(VIII) 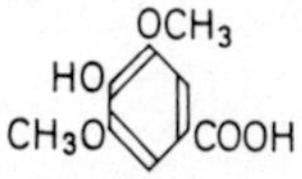   (IX)

A structure (X) analogous to that of sinigrin had been assigned to sinalbin by Gadamer and accepted without question. This is shown below along with the modified structure (XI) established by Ettlinger and Lundeen.

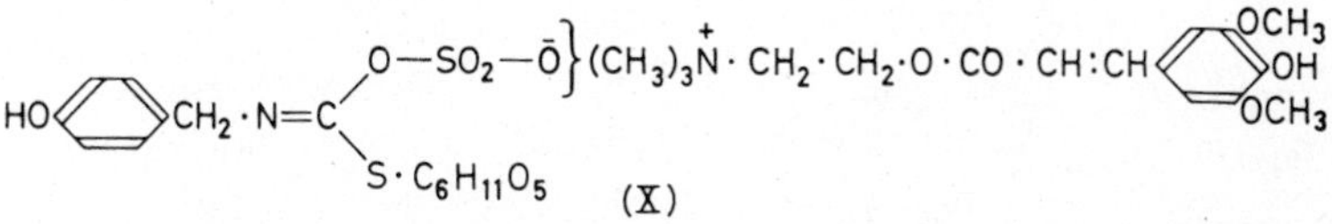

(X)

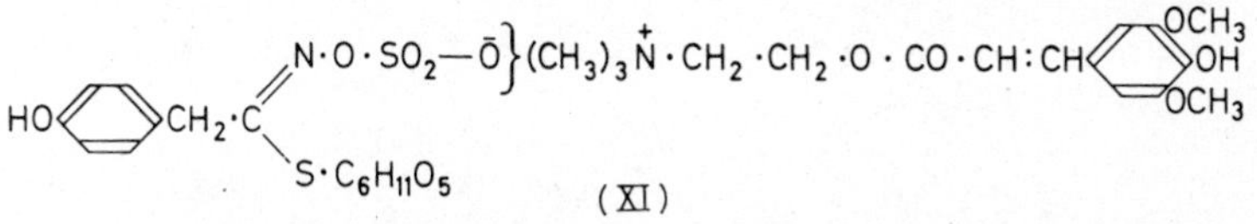

(XI)

The American authors found that sinalbin is reduced by Raney nickel to tyramine [p-hydroxyphenylethylamine (XII)], is hydrolysed to p-hydroxyphenylacetic acid (XIII) and also gives hydroxylamine with acid.

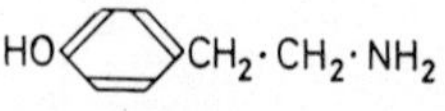

(XII) 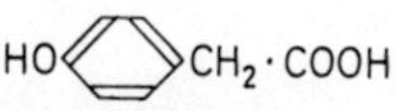   (XIII)

Its structure is therefore analogous to that of sinigrin and in both cases the enzymic hydrolysis gives rise to a migration from carbon to nitrogen which Ettlinger and Lundeen point out is similar to that observed in the Lossen rearrangement, in which an alkyl or an aryl group of a hydroxamic acid salt $R \cdot C \overset{\bar{O}}{\underset{N \cdot O \cdot CO \cdot R'}{\big/}}$ migrates from carbon to nitrogen

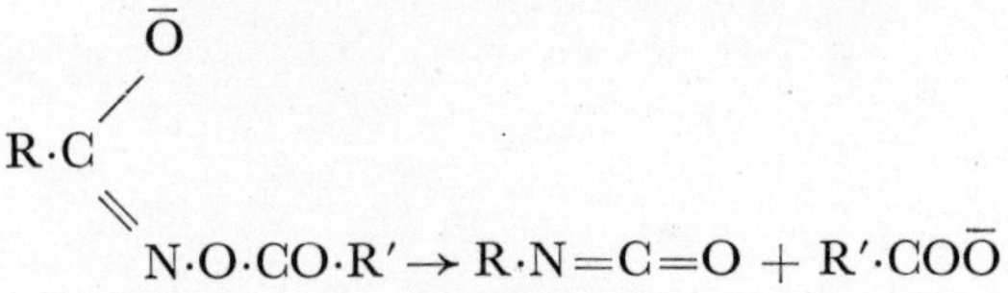

$$R \cdot C \overset{\overline{O}}{\underset{N \cdot O \cdot CO \cdot R'}{\diagup}} \to R \cdot N = C = O + R' \cdot CO\overline{O}$$

Ettlinger and Lundeen point out that an alternative formula for sinigrin in which the thioglucose residue is linked to nitrogen is highly improbable as a compound of this type

$$R \cdot C \cdot O \cdot SO_2 \cdot \overline{O}$$
$$\|$$
$$N \cdot S \cdot C_6 H_{11} O_5$$
(XIV)

could only yield the mustard oil $R \cdot N : C : S$ by an obscure double migration and should moreover yield ammonia on acid hydrolysis and not hydroxylamine, as it contains the sulphenamide group, $C_6 H_{11} O_5 \cdot S \cdot N\mathord{<}$, derived theoretically from the sulphenic acid $C_6 H_{11} O_5 \cdot S \cdot OH$. The properties of the sulphenic acids and their derivatives are well known and have been summarized by Kharasch[29].

Amplification by Later Workers of the Results of Will and Körner on the Decomposition of the Mustard Oil Glucosides and the Nature of the Products

Ettlinger and Lundeen's important conclusions concerning the structures of sinigrin and sinalbin have so far (May 1958) been published only in a short summary. Although enough information was presented by Will and Körner in 1865 to throw doubt on the formulae for sinigrin and sinalbin proposed by Gadamer thirty-two years later, some of Gadamer's own results and the modern work of Schmid and Karrer[21] and of Schultz and Gmelin[30] have confirmed and amplified the observations of Will and Körner. These later results may be summarized and discussed under three headings.

1. Evidence for the formation of elementary sulphur and of a nitrile during the enzymic hydrolysis of a 'mustard oil gluco-side', or on the decomposition by reagents of the silver compound

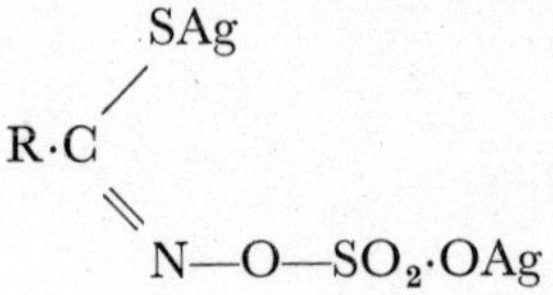

$$R \cdot C \overset{SAg}{\underset{N-O-SO_2 \cdot OAg}{\diagup}}$$ obtained from the glucoside by treatment

with silver nitrate. (Prior to 1956 this was represented by the

structure R·N=C
$\diagup$ SAg
$\diagdown$ O·SO$_2$·OAg
which was derived directly from

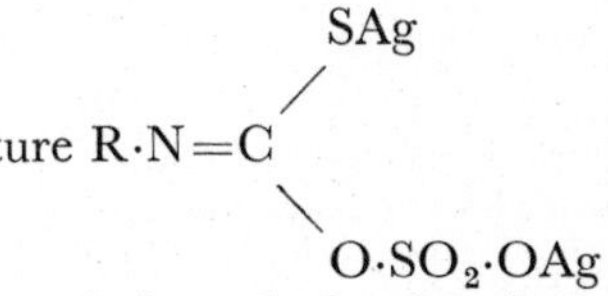

Gadamer's formula for the glucoside.)

2. The diminution in the amount of *iso*thiocyanate and the preponderance of nitrile when the *Cruciferae* are distilled in steam without a preliminary and thorough maceration of the plant with cold water.

3. The presence of carbon disulphide in 'mustard oils'.

1. *Decompositions of the mustard oil glucosides or the derived silver compounds*—(a) *The silver compounds*—The early work of Will and Körner in this connection has been discussed on p. 119. In 1897 Gadamer[31] obtained a crude glucoside from *Nasturtium officinale* (water-cress; German, Brunnen-kresse) which was named gluconasturtiin. With silver nitrate this gave a crude silver derivative which was purified through its addition compound with ammonia. When this addition compound was treated with hydrochloric acid sulphur was liberated and an aromatic odour resembling that of β-phenylpropionitrile was produced. No mention was made of the formation of a pungent *iso*thiocyanate in this experiment.

The addition product formed with ammonia yielded a pure silver compound which was analysed and shown to have the composition $C_6H_5 \cdot CH_2 \cdot CH_2 \cdot CN \cdot Ag_2S_2O_4 \cdot 2H_2O$. Analogy with the corresponding allyl compound suggested the structure (XV)

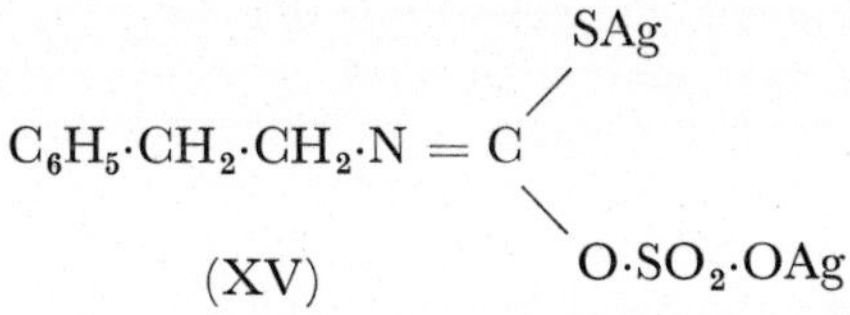

$$C_6H_5 \cdot CH_2 \cdot CH_2 \cdot N = C \begin{array}{l} \diagup \ SAg \\ \diagdown \ O \cdot SO_2 \cdot OAg \end{array}$$

(XV)

which would now in consequence of Ettlinger's work be written

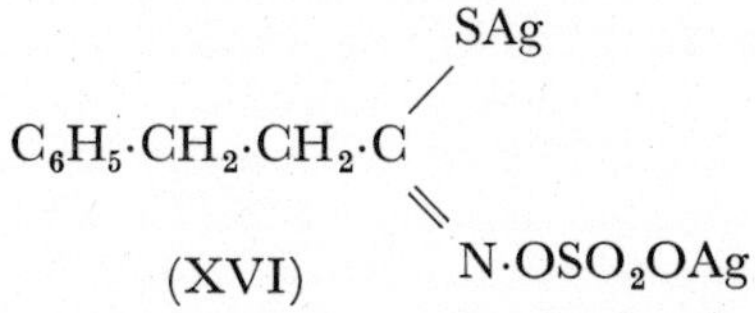

$$C_6H_5 \cdot CH_2 \cdot CH_2 \cdot C \begin{array}{l} \diagup \ SAg \\ \diagdown\!\!\diagdown \ N \cdot OSO_2OAg \end{array}$$

(XVI)

When this silver compound was shaken with aqueous sodium thiosulphate a strong odour of a mustard oil was produced. Extraction with ether yielded an *iso*thiocyanate which was identified as β-phenylethyl *iso*thiocyanate by conversion to the corresponding

127

thiourea $C_6H_5 \cdot CH_2 \cdot CH_2 \cdot NH \cdot CS \cdot NH_2$ by reaction with ammonia.

This decomposition with sodium thiosulphate was also carried out by Gadamer[32] with the silver compounds from other mustard oil glucosides but apparently on a small scale. No mention was made of the formation of the nitrile R·CN but only of the *iso*thiocyanate R·N : C : S. When the corresponding silver compound from sinigrin (silver sinigrinate) was treated with sodium thiosulphate the yield of allyl mustard oil (CH_2 : CH·CH_2·N : C : S) obtained by extraction with ether was 17·4 per cent instead of the calculated figure of 22·15. Here again no mention was made of the formation of allyl cyanide. Gadamer remarks that this thiosulphate reaction appears to be quantitative but gives no amplification of this statement. It is doubtful if the scale of his experiments or his technique would allow of the detection of the nitrile.

The use of sodium thiosulphate by Schmid and Karrer[21] in order to liberate the *iso*thiocyanate sulphoraphene from the silver compound obtained from the crude glucoside of radish seeds has been discussed on p. 120. Here larger quantities of material and adsorption chromatography were employed and the corresponding nitrile was also isolated. Both the *iso*thiocyanate and the nitrile were obtained from a single specimen of the silver compound in the same experiment.

In some early experiments on the decomposition of the silver compounds reference is made only to nitrile formation. The glucoside from the seeds of *Tropaeolum majus* gave a silver compound which with concentrated ammonia formed a crystalline addition product. This with sodium hydroxide liberated benzyl cyanide which was hydrolysed by alkali and the liberated ammonia determined. With hydrochloric acid the same addition compound gave benzyl cyanide and sulphur. The nitrile was hydrolysed to phenylacetic acid, but no analyses were given and it is difficult to be certain whether the conditions were such as to allow of the detection of any *iso*thiocyanate which might have been formed.

Will and Laubenheimer[33] found in 1879 that sinalbin, the glucoside from the seeds of the white mustard, gave with silver nitrate a mixture of silver compounds from which hydrogen sulphide liberated what was later shown to be *p*-hydroxybenzyl cyanide. Sulphur was also formed. No mention is made of the formation of the corresponding *iso*thiocyanate but as it is less volatile than many *iso*thiocyanates it might have escaped notice.

(*b*) *Enzymic decomposition of the mustard oil glucosides*—Gadamer[9] in 1897 confirmed that, as originally stated by Will and Körner[8], sinigrin with myrosinase yields in addition to allyl *iso*thiocyanate, allyl cyanide and sulphur. Carbon disulphide was also recognized and its formation was attributed by Gadamer to the action of water on 'nascent (allyl) mustard oil'. This will be discussed in detail later under section (3).

One of the most satisfactory studies of the enzymic hydrolysis of a mustard oil glucoside is furnished by the work of Schultz and Gmelin[34] at Tübingen in 1954. They separated a glucoside which they named glucoiberin from the seeds of *Iberis amara*.

Glucoiberin with myrosinase gave free sulphur, a nitrile and relatively little *iso*thiocyanate. The presence of the last two classes of compound was proved, however, by infra-red spectrometry. The sulphur separated as crystals, m.p. 113°C from the oil extracted from the myrosinase reaction. Rhombic sulphur melts at 112·8°C. This is the first or almost the first case in which the sulphur, so frequently reported as a product of myrosinase action on *iso*thiocyanate glucosides, or of reagents on the related silver compounds, has been identified by melting point.

The other products of the myrosinase reaction were glucose (detected by paper chromatography using aniline phthalate), potassium and sulphate ions. The potassium was confirmed by precipitation of its insoluble compound potassium tetraphenylboron $\overset{+}{K}\left[\overline{B}(C_6H_5)_4\right]$; this was done with a specimen which had not been eluted from the column with potassium hydroxide.

The *iso*thiocyanate obtained from glucoiberin could not be purified but the authors concluded from the analysis of glucoiberin itself and from its infra-red spectrum that a sulphoxide $(\overset{+}{S}—\overline{O})$ group was present. The difference in R_F between glucoiberin and gluco-cheirolin[35] which has a chain $CH_3 \cdot \overset{++}{\underset{\wedge}{S}} \cdot CH_2 \cdot CH_2 \cdot CH_2 \cdot —$ is similar to

$$O \quad O$$

that between the sulphoxide and sulphone of methionine $CH_3 \cdot S \cdot CH_2 \cdot CH_2 \cdot CH(NH_2) \cdot COOH$. Schultz and Gmelin concluded that the *iso*thiocyanate of glucoiberin is $CH_3 \cdot \overset{+}{\underset{\underset{\overline{O}}{|}}{S}} \cdot CH_2 \cdot CH_2 \cdot CH_2 \cdot N : C : S$.

The glucoside, on the basis of Ettlinger and Lundeen's work, would now be formulated as

$$CH_3 \cdot \overset{+}{\underset{\underset{\overline{O}}{|}}{S}} \cdot CH_2 \cdot CH_2 \cdot CH_2 \cdot \overset{S \cdot C_6H_{11}O_5}{\underset{N \cdot O \cdot SO_2O \cdot K}{\overset{\diagup}{\underset{\diagdown}{C}}}}$$

(XVII)

The isolation of a nitrile and an *iso*thiocyanate from rape seed (*Brassica napus*) has also been achieved, but by two different authors. Schmalfuss[36] in 1936 reported the occurrence of 4-pentenyl cyanide $CH_2 : CH \cdot CH_2 \cdot CH_2 \cdot CH_2 \cdot CN$ in the 'mustard oil' from 50 kg. of rape seed. He also detected what is now known as 3-butenyl*iso*thiocyanate $CH_2 : CH \cdot CH_2 \cdot CH_2 \cdot N : C : S$ and traces of β-phenylethyl *iso*thiocyanate. A quantity of an *iso*thiocyanate of higher boiling point was also obtained which he regarded as $C_5H_9 \cdot N : C : S$. This has now been isolated by Kjaer and Jensen[37] from crushed rape seed, the glucosides being enzymically hydrolysed by addition of milled seeds of white mustard. The *iso*thiocyanate of these seeds is known to be *p*-hydroxybenzyl *iso*thiocyanate and no complication was caused. The compound $C_5H_9 \cdot N : C : S$ was identified as 4-pentenyl *iso*thiocyanate $CH_2 : CH \cdot CH_2 \cdot CH_2 \cdot CH_2 \cdot N : C : S$ by paper chromatography and by infra-red spectroscopy of the corresponding thiourea. It was also synthesized (*see* p. 154).

2. *The effect of experimental conditions on the relative proportions of* iso*thiocyanate and nitrile produced in the enzymic hydrolysis of 'mustard oil glucosides'*—A. W. von Hofmann examined several of the 'mustard oils' obtained from the *Cruciferae*, e.g. the *sec.*-butyl *iso*thiocyanate

$$\begin{matrix} CH_3 \cdot CH_2 \diagdown \\ \diagup CH \cdot N : C : S \\ CH_3 \diagup \end{matrix}$$

which occurs in *Cochlearia officinale* L. or scurvy grass. This plant is mentioned in the municipal accounts of Frankfurt in 1587. The optically inactive *iso*thiocyanate was synthesized by Hofmann[38]. Further references to this compound and to the synthesis of the optical isomers are recorded by Semmler[19].

Hofmann[39] also investigated the so-called crotonyl mustard oil obtained from the seeds of rape, *Brassica napus*[40]. It was therefore with considerable surprise that on steam distillation of *Tropaeolum majus*, *Lepidium sativum* and *Nasturtium officinale*, he obtained no *iso*thiocyanate but only nitriles. The first two plants gave benzyl cyanide and the third β-phenylpropionitrile $C_6H_5 \cdot CH_2 \cdot CH_2 \cdot CN$. In each of these experiments the intact plant was used.

Gadamer[32] repeated this work and used coarsely crushed specimens of *Tropaeolum majus*. The oil resulting from steam distillation was treated with ammonia when benzylthiourea was obtained, $C_6H_5 \cdot CH_2 \cdot NH \cdot CS \cdot NH_2$. That portion of the oil which did not react with ammonia was distilled in steam, separated and hydrolysed with alkali to give phenylacetic acid.

In a similar experiment with the seeds of *L. sativum*[31] the oily steam distillate again gave benzylthiourea with ammonia. Finally using Brunnen-kresse (*N. officinale*) from Erfurt and thoroughly disintegrating the material before distilling in steam an oil was obtained which with ammonia gave β-phenylethylthiourea $C_6H_5 \cdot CH_2 \cdot CH_2 \cdot NH \cdot CS \cdot NH_2$. In the last two cases Gadamer does not appear to have detected the accompanying nitrile. As explained on p. 121 of this chapter the formation of nitrile diminishes as the plant is more carefully disintegrated before distillation. If this is not effectively carried out much of the enzyme is decomposed before it can react with the glucoside which then, to use Gadamer's own words, 'undergoes decomposition only by heat and water giving the nitrile'.

McDowall, Morton and McDowell[52] studied the taint produced in cream and butter through ingestion by cows of the crucifera *Coronopus didymus* (land-cress.) The results resembled those of Hofmann and Gadamer in that varying amounts of benzyl cyanide and benzyl *iso*thiocyanate were detected according to the treatment to which the plant was subjected.

Distillation of the whole plant yielded 0·022 per cent of benzyl cyanide, identified as phenylacetic acid. A smaller fraction contained sulphur and some benzyl *iso*thiocyanate, judging from the refractive index. Steam distillation of the chopped and minced plant after five hours also gave mainly benzyl cyanide in 0·037 per cent yield. There was 'little evidence of the *iso*thiocyanate'. When the uncrushed plant (20 kg.) was steeped in boiling alcohol to destroy enzymes, separated, minced and extracted with hot alcohol a clear solution was obtained. This with silver nitrate gave a solid which on treatment with sodium thiosulphate gave 'almost pure' benzyl *iso*thiocyanate, identified as the thiourea. The yield was 0·029 per cent.

When the minced plant was macerated with water and extracted with ether the product was mainly benzyl cyanide or else a mixture of benzyl cyanide and benzyl *iso*thiocyanate, as indicated by odour and by refractive index. This affords further confirmation of the formation of both nitrile and *iso*thiocyanate by enzymic fission of a 'mustard oil glucoside'. The silver nitrate method was adapted by the authors to the quantitative determination of *iso*thiocyanates. They also examined garden cress (*Lepidium sativum*). Steam distillation of the uncrushed plant gave benzyl cyanide; steam distillation after crushing gave a solid (phenylacetic acid?) and no benzyl *iso*thiocyanate; the silver nitrate method gave an oil (0·030 per cent) with the odour and physical constants of benzyl *iso*thiocyanate; it gave benzylthiourea with ammonia.

In all these experiments with the possible exception of that in which the crushed plant was extracted with ether, appreciable amounts of *iso*thiocyanate were only obtained by the silver nitrate method which does not depend on enzyme action. Whether, as in the experiments of Schmid and Karrer with radish seeds (*see* p. 140), traces of nitrile were also produced is not clear. This absence of *iso*thiocyanate could be explained if the enzyme were almost absent from the plants when the experiments were carried out.

3. Carbon Disulphide in Natural and Synthetic Isothiocyanates

Occurrence, detection and determination—One of the earliest accounts of the presence of carbon disulphide in natural *iso*thiocyanates is due to Hofmann[42] who examined allyl mustard oil from *Sinapis juncea* of Russian origin. Passage of air through the oil into alcoholic sodium hydroxide removed small quantities of carbon disulphide which were thereby converted to sodium xanthate (sodium ethyl

$$\text{dithiocarbonate } C \underset{\diagdown}{\overset{\diagup \text{SNa}}{:}} S \underset{O \cdot CH_2 \cdot CH_3}{}\quad).$$ This was isolated as yellow

cuprous xanthate. A similar method was employed by Macagno[43]. From a statement by Semmler[44] it would appear that carbon disulphide is present in many natural 'mustard oils' and not only in allyl *iso*thiocyanate. Hofmann found that the xanthate method was not quantitative, and removed the carbon disulphide from the oil in carbon dioxide which was passed into an ethereal solution of triethylphosphine mixed with aqueous sodium hydroxide. The red precipi-

$$\text{tate, which has the structure } (CH_3 \cdot CH_2)_3 P \underset{\diagdown}{\overset{\diagup C : S}{\underset{S}{\big|}}}\quad ,$$ was weighed.

By this method the oil from *S. juncea* was found to contain 0·41 and 0·37 per cent of the disulphide; that from *S. nigra* 0·51 and 0·56 per cent. Synthetic allyl *iso*thiocyanate prepared from allyl iodide and ammonium thiocyanate showed 0·32 per cent. This suggests that carbon disulphide arises during manufacture of the oil at some stage which is common to both the natural and synthetic preparations.

Gadamer[45-47] found carbon disulphide as well as sulphur and allyl cyanide in the mustard oil from the action of myrosinase on sinigrin. He also stated that it is formed by the action of hot water on *iso*thiocyanates thus: $2R \cdot N : C : S + 2H_2O = 2R \cdot NH_2 + CO_2 + CS_2$. He also stated that the primary products in this reaction are the dialkylthiourea and carbon oxysulphide produced thus:

$$R \cdot N : C : S + H_2O = RNH_2 + COS$$
$$RNH_2 + RN : C : S = (R \cdot NH)_2 CS$$

The carbon oxysulphide undergoes some hydrolysis to carbon dioxide and hydrogen sulphide, a reaction which proceeds slowly even at ordinary temperature and is accelerated by acid. The hydrogen sulphide probably then reacts with some unchanged *iso*thiocyanate to form a dithiocarbamic acid which then breaks down to the amine and carbon disulphide:

$$R \cdot N : C : S + H_2S = R \cdot NH \cdot CS \cdot SH = RNH_2 + CS_2$$

This decomposition of the dithio-acid was studied by Ponzio[48] and can occur at ordinary temperature.

Sell and Proskauer[49] found as long ago as 1876 that when a stream of hydrogen sulphide is passed through phenyl *iso*thiocyanate, carbon disulphide and diphenylthiourea are slowly formed at ordinary temperature. Allyl *iso*thiocyanate behaved in a similar manner, but less readily. The carbon disulphide was detected by triethylphosphine. Anschütz[50] also showed that at 40°C hydrogen sulphide reacts with ethyl *iso*thiocyanate to form diethylthiourea and carbon disulphide. This was absorbed in ethereal ethylamine and characterized as the ethylamine salt of ethyldithiocarbamic acid

$$\begin{array}{c} NH \cdot CH_2 \cdot CH_3 \\ / \\ CS \\ \backslash \\ SH \cdot NH_2 \cdot CH_2 \cdot CH_3 \end{array}$$

These reactions clearly indicate a close relation between *iso*-thiocyanates, hydrogen sulphide and carbon disulphide. Hofmann stated in 1880 that 'perhaps during the manufacture of the mustard oil under the influence of steam some is converted to allylamine or derivatives such as diallylthiourea on the one hand and to carbon dioxide and hydrogen sulphide on the other. The latter may then (he does not amplify this statement) give rise to formation of small amounts of carbon disulphide'. If carbon disulphide is formed by a hydrolytic reaction during steam distillation of the mustard oil its presence in both natural and synthetic *iso*thiocyanate would be readily explained.

Wheeler and Merriam[51] found that phenyl*iso*thiocyanate and thiobenzoic acid at 100°C give carbon disulphide and benzanilide presumably by way of the benzoyl derivative of a dithiocarbamic acid:

$C_6H_5N : C : S + C_6H_5 \cdot CO \cdot SH = C_6H_5 \cdot NH \cdot CS \cdot S \cdot CO \cdot C_6H_5 = CS_2 + C_6H_5 \cdot NH \cdot CO \cdot C_6H_5$. With thioacetic acid $CH_3 \cdot CO \cdot SH$, acetanilide was isolated. A thioacid $R \cdot CO \cdot SH$ might possibly be formed by hydrolysis of a mustard oil glucoside with loss of glucose,

133

sulphate and hydroxylamine and might then react with an *iso*-thiocyanate (simultaneously present) as shown on p. 133 giving carbon disulphide.

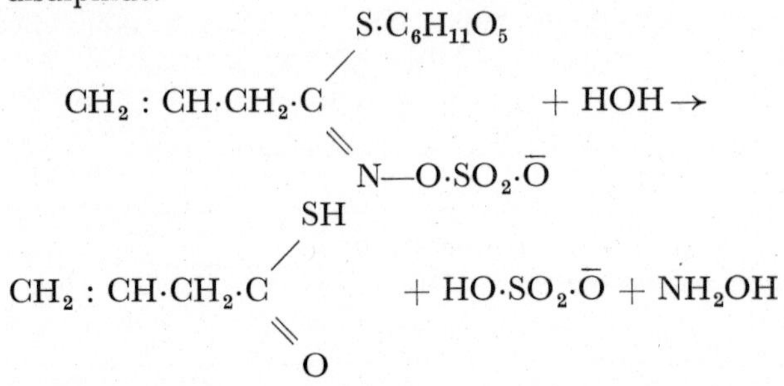

$$CH_2 : CH \cdot CH_2 \cdot C \begin{array}{c} S \cdot C_6H_{11}O_5 \\ \diagup \\ \diagdown \\ N-O \cdot SO_2 \cdot \overline{O} \end{array} \quad + \ HOH \rightarrow$$

$$CH_2 : CH \cdot CH_2 \cdot C \begin{array}{c} SH \\ \diagup \\ \diagdown \\ O \end{array} \quad + \ HO \cdot SO_2 \cdot \overline{O} + NH_2OH$$

The formation of carbon disulphide was thoroughly established in two other reactions, namely those between thiobenzoic acid and allyl *iso*thiocyanate and its 2-chloroderivative $CH_2 : CCl \cdot CH_2 \cdot N : C : S$.

This alternative hypothesis cannot, however, explain the formation of carbon disulphide during the synthesis of allyl *iso*thiocyanate from allyl iodide and appears unlikely.

ENZYMIC AND 'CHEMICAL' FISSION OF MUSTARD OIL GLUCOSIDES

Certain established facts emerge from the foregoing discussion of the decomposition of sinigrin by myrosinase and by purely chemical means:

1. Myrosinase gives allyl *iso*thiocyanate, glucose and potassium hydrogen sulphate as main products and allyl cyanide, sulphur and carbon disulphide (*see* p. 132) as minor products. The formation of both $R \cdot N : C : S$ and $R \cdot C \equiv N$ has also been observed in the enzymic decomposition of another glucoside, glucoiberin, where $R = CH_3 \cdot \overset{+}{S}-CH_2 \cdot CH_2 \cdot CH_2 \cdot$ and there is considerable evidence (*see*

$$\underset{O}{\overset{|}{}}$$

pp. 129, 130, 140) that such a paired occurrence is very frequent.

2. Potassium methoxide eliminates the sulphate anion from sinigrin giving potassium sulphate. The thioglucose residue is probably simultaneously removed because the silver derivative of thioglucose $C_6H_{11}O_5 \cdot S \cdot Ag$ is obtained by addition of ammoniacal silver nitrate to the filtrate after removal of the potassium sulphate.

3. If silver nitrate only be added to sinigrin a compound 'silver sinigrinate' is obtained which almost certainly has the constitution:

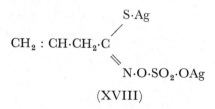

(XVIII)

With hydrogen sulphide this di-silver derivative gives allyl cyanide and sulphur; the nitrile is also obtained with hydrochloric acid (*see* p. 119, 127). Allyl *iso*thiocyanate seems not to be produced, or else was not detected. It should be readily recognized by its pungent odour. On the other hand Gadamer showed that with sodium thiosulphate the di-silver compound gives the *iso*thiocyanate and formation of the nitrile is not mentioned, but the scale of this early experiment of Gadamer's was probably too small.

However, the modern work of Schmid and Karrer[21] has shown that the unpurified glucoside from radish seeds gives a silver compound which with sodium thiosulphate gives mainly the *iso*thio-

cyanate, sulphoraphene, $CH_3 \cdot \overset{+}{S} \cdot CH : CH \cdot CH_2 \cdot CH_2 \cdot N : C : S$ but
$$\underset{\underset{\overline{O}}{|}}{}$$
also the corresponding nitrile which are separable on an alumina column.

Discussion of the enzymic decomposition of the mustard oil glucosides—The simplest explanation of the action of myrosinase would be to suggest that the enzymic decomposition gives only mustard oil and that the nitrile arises by a purely chemical hydrolysis of the glucoside. This was the view put forward by Gadamer to explain his own and Hofmann's results (*see* p. 131). If the enzyme plays no part in nitrile formation it seems strange that so complete a breakdown of the glucoside should occur at ordinary temperature. Possibly, however, the purely chemical hydrolysis may be catalysed by the hydrogen ions of the potassium hydrogen sulphate. The accumulation of this salt during the reaction has been stated to interfere with the action of the enzyme. The formation of vinylacetic acid by acid hydrolysis of sinigrin by Ettlinger and Lundeen (the corresponding nitrile being presumably an intermediate stage in the reaction) supports this view of the effect of potassium hydrogen sulphate.

A second and less simple explanation of the formation of both *iso*thiocyanate and nitrile in the enzymic reaction may be mentioned. According to this view the action of myrosinase gives rise to both the *iso*thiocyanate and the nitrile but one reaction (*a*) which includes a

Lossen transformation and gives the *iso*thiocyanate, predominates over that (*b*) which yields the nitrile and sulphur. Reaction (*a*) would require the preferential attack of the enzyme on the S-glucose link leaving the sulphate anion still attached to nitrogen, thus

$$CH_2 : CH \cdot CH_2 \cdot C \begin{array}{c} \diagup SH \\ \diagdown N \cdot O \cdot SO_2 \cdot \overline{O} \end{array}$$. It is known (*see* p. 125) that the

(*see* p. 125)

Lossen transformation is initiated by the elimination of the anion of the $=N \cdot O\overline{X}$ group. In reaction (*b*) the anion is perhaps preferentially eliminated giving rise to the structure

$$CH_2 : CH \cdot CH_2 \cdot C \begin{array}{c} \diagup N \cdot OH \\ \diagdown S \cdot C_6 H_{11} O_5 \end{array}$$.

Hydrolysis of this compound with loss of glucose yields the thiohydro-

xamic acid $CH_2 : CH \cdot CH_2 \cdot C \begin{array}{c} \diagup NOH \\ \diagdown SH \end{array}$ which then loses water and

gives the nitrile and free sulphur as in the model reactions described on p. 123 and conceivably through the unstable sulphenic acid $H \cdot S \cdot OH$. As the thiohydroxamic acid does not contain an acidic group linked to nitrogen the Lossen rearrangement does not occur.

on p. 123

Discussion of the chemical decomposition of the di-silver compounds from sinigrin and analogous glucosides—The concept of two competing reactions may be applied to explain the behaviour of the di-silver compounds obtained from the mustard oil glucosides. Schmid and Karrer[21] obtained both $RN : C : S$ and $R \cdot CN$ from the silver compound prepared from the crude glucoside of radish seeds. The action of thiosulphate on the silver compound derived from sinigrin (silver sinigrinate) may possibly involve a preferential elimination of the silver of the —SAg group, leaving the sulphate anion still attached

to nitrogen $CH_2 : CH \cdot CH_2 \cdot C \begin{array}{c} \diagup N \cdot O \cdot SO_2 OAg \\ \diagdown SH \end{array}$ and capable of initiat-

ing the Lossen transformation, giving as the main product $R \cdot N : C : S$. If the sulphate anion is also removed the resulting thiohydroxamic

136

acid $CH_2 : CH \cdot CH_2 \cdot C \overset{\text{NOH}}{\underset{SH}{\big\backslash}}$ would then give the nitrile, sulphur and water.

This argument assumes that these di-silver compounds are homogeneous and all have the composition $R \cdot C \overset{N \cdot O \cdot SO_2 OAg}{\underset{S \cdot Ag}{\big\backslash}}$. A modern study of the reaction of silver nitrate with the mustard oil glucosides is, however, desirable.

THE SYNTHESIS OF GLUCOTROPAEOLIN

In a further important preliminary communication by Ettlinger and Lundeen[41] the synthesis of the tetramethylammonium salt of the glucotropaeolate ion (XIX) is described. The product was identical with that obtained when an extract of the seeds of *Tropaeolum majus* (containing the glucoside glucotropaeolin, which is a potassium salt) was adsorbed on an anion 'exchange resin' and eluted with tetramethylammonium hydroxide.

The method of synthesis shows that the structure of glucotropaeolin is analogous to that established for sinigrin. Apparently all the known natural *iso*thiocyanates and thio-oxazolidones (*see* p. 155) arise from precursors of this structural type, though the carbohydrate fragment may vary.

The synthesis may be outlined: Carbon disulphide was treated with magnesium benzyl chloride to give the magnesium salt of phenyldithioacetic acid (XX). With aqueous hydroxylamine hydrochloride at 0°C this was converted to phenyl acetothiohydroxamic acid (XXI). With potassium hydroxide and tetra-acetyl-β-glucosidyl bromide in methanol-acetone this gave S-β-D-1-(tetra-acetylglucopyranosyl)-phenylacetothiohydroxamic acid (XXII). By the action of sulphur trioxide in pyridine solution the hydroxamic acid was converted to the ion of tetra-acetylglucotropaeolic acid (XXIII). This was isolated as the monohydrated potassium salt and identified by its m.p. and by comparison of its infra-red spectrum with that of a sample prepared from natural sources. It was also converted to the tetramethylammonium salt which with methanolic ammonia was de-acetylated to anhydrous tetramethyl-ammonium glucotropaeolate (XXIV).

137

When this synthetic glucotropaeolate was enzymically hydrolysed with a protein preparation obtained from yellow mustard, benzyl *iso*thiocyanate was readily obtained in quantitative yield and isolated and determined as the corresponding thiourea $C_6H_5 \cdot CH_2 \cdot NH \cdot CS \cdot NH_2$.

Ettlinger and Lundeen showed that the hydroxamic acid (**XXI**) was stable below 0°C but decomposed after a few days at 30°C. At 100°C it deflagrated and formed phenylacetonitrile and free

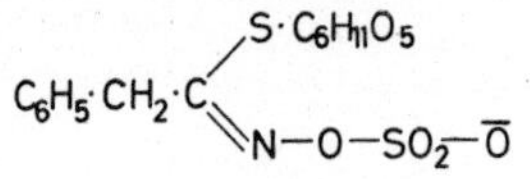

$$C_6H_5 \cdot CH_2 \cdot C \underset{N-O-SO_2-\bar{O}}{\overset{S \cdot C_6H_{11}O_5}{\big<}}$$

(**XIX**)

$$\underset{S}{\overset{S}{\big\|}}C \;+\; Cl \cdot Mg \cdot CH_2 \cdot C_6H_5 \longrightarrow S{:}C\underset{CH_2 \cdot C_6H_5}{\overset{SMg_{1/2}}{\big<}} \qquad \xrightarrow{NH_2OH \cdot HCl}$$

(**XX**)

$$C_6H_5 \cdot CH_2 \cdot \underset{}{\overset{SH}{C}}{=}NOH \longrightarrow C_6H_5 \cdot CH_2 \cdot \underset{NOH}{\overset{}{C}} {\cdot} S \cdot C_6H_7 O(O \cdot COCH_3)_4$$

(**XXI**)   (**XXII**)

Heat ↙   ↓

$$C_6H_5 \cdot CH_2 \cdot CN \quad (C_6H_5 \cdot CH_2 \cdot NH)_2 CS$$
$$+$$
$$S$$

$\underset{in\ Pyridine}{\overset{SO_3}{\searrow}}$

$$C_6H_5 \cdot CH_2 \cdot C\underset{N \cdot O - SO_2 \cdot \bar{O}}{\overset{S \cdot C_6H_7 O \cdot (OCOCH_3)_4}{\big<}}$$

(**XXIII**)

↓ $\begin{array}{c} NH_3 \\ in \\ CH_3OH \end{array}$

$$C_6H_5 \cdot CH_2 \cdot C\overset{}{-}S \cdot C_6H_{11}O_5$$
$$\underset{N \cdot O \cdot SO_2 \cdot \bar{O}}{}$$

(**XXIV**)

$\begin{array}{c} NH_3 \\ in \\ CH_3OH \end{array}$

↓

$$C_6H_5 \cdot CH_2 \cdot \underset{NOH}{\overset{\|}{C}} \cdot S \cdot C_6H_{11}O_5$$

(**XXV**)

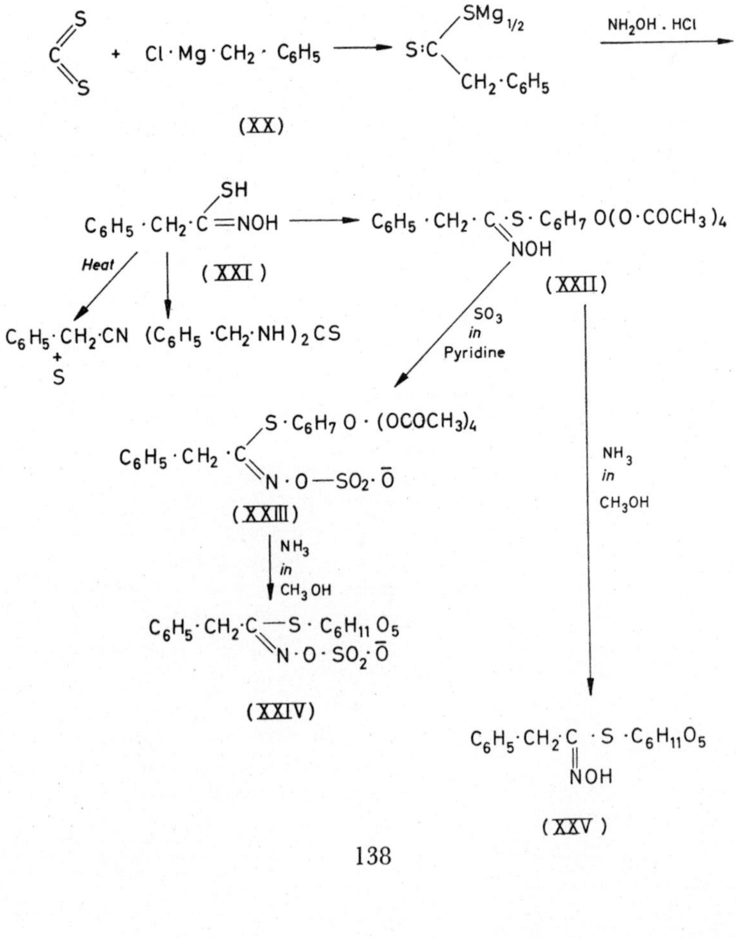

sulphur. Sulphur was quantitatively deposited when a solution in methanol was left for 24 hours at room temperature. Reactions of this type are characteristic of thiohydroxamic acids and are discussed on pp. 122–124. The solid sodium salt of phenylacetylthiohydroxamic acid decomposed during 10 weeks at room temperature giving NN'-dibenzylthiourea, a reaction which involves a Lossen transformation to benzyl*iso*thiocyanate followed by reaction with benzylamine.

With ammonia the thiohydroxamic acid (XXII) lost four acetyl groups giving S-β-D-1-glucopyranosyl phenylacetothiohydroxamic acid. This de-acetylated thiohydroxamic acid (XXV) was barely attacked by myrosinase or at best at 1/50 the rate at which its sulphated derivative underwent cleavage. Benzyl*iso*thiocyanate was not formed. This result is in accordance with the principles governing the Lossen rearrangement as the thiohydroxamic acid (XXV) does not contain an acidic group linked to nitrogen (*see* p. 136).

Ettlinger and Lundeen remark, without further comment, that the probability that the Lossen rearrangement of the glucoside and the removal of the glucose and the sulphate are simultaneous suggests that myrosinase is not to be regarded as a mixture of a thioglucosidase and a sulphatase. Presumably they base this view of the simultaneous removal of the two groups on their observation that very little enzymic reaction occurs when glucose is still present and sulphate absent. The author, on the other hand, has suggested on p. 136 that the enzyme might preferentially remove the glucose residue from the glucosides.

NATURAL METHANESULPHINYL ISOTHIOCYANATES

From the time that Gadamer[9] proposed his structural formulae for sinigrin and sinalbin the chemistry of the mustard oils and their glucosidic precursors has seemed, until recently, to possess little attraction for chemists. Two mustard oils, cheirolin (XXVI) and erysolin (XXVII), occurring as glucosides in the yellow wall-flower (*Cheiranthus cheiri*) and in the orange variety (*Erysimum perowskianum*) were discovered about 45–50 years ago and attracted some attention as they furnished the first examples of the natural occurrence of sulphones.

$$\overset{\bar{O}}{\underset{\underset{\bar{O}}{+}}{\overset{+}{CH_3 \cdot S}}} \cdot CH_2 \cdot CH_2 \cdot CH_2 \cdot N : C : S \qquad \overset{\bar{O}}{\underset{\underset{\bar{O}}{+}}{\overset{+}{CH_3 \cdot S}}} \cdot CH_2 \cdot CH_2 \cdot CH_2 \cdot CH_2 \cdot N : C : S$$

(XXVI) (XXVII)

139

Sulphoraphene and the corresponding nitrile—No further examples of natural mustard oils containing oxidized sulphur were recorded until 1948 when, as mentioned on p. 120 Schmid and Karrer[21] obtained sulphoraphene (**XXVIII**) and the corresponding nitrile (**XXIX**) from the seeds of the radish (*Raphanus sativus*)

$$CH_3 \cdot \overset{+}{S} \cdot CH : CH \cdot CH_2 \cdot CH_2 \cdot N : C : S \text{ and}$$
$$\underset{O}{|} \qquad \text{(XXVIII)}$$

$$CH_3 \cdot \overset{+}{S} \cdot CH : CH \cdot CH_2 \cdot CH_2 \cdot CN$$
$$\underset{O}{|} \qquad \text{(XXIX)}$$

These sulphoxides were optically active owing to the presence of the $R \cdot \overset{+}{S} \cdot R'$ grouping and afforded the first recorded instances of natural
$$\underset{O}{|}$$
products of which the optical activity is solely due to such a linkage. (Other cases have now been reported by Kjaer and his school in Copenhagen, *see* p. 146.) Because both the *iso*thiocyanate and the nitrile were obtained from the same extract of radish seeds it will be necessary to outline the experimental procedure rather carefully to emphasize the improbability that the nitrile is formed from the *iso*thiocyanate during the process of extraction.

Radish seeds were ground and extracted three times with a boiling acetone–water (3 : 1) mixture or repeatedly with cold methanol. The solvents were removed from the extracts at 35°C and the fat then removed from this with petrol. The remaining aqueous liquor was cooled in ice and treated with excess of aqueous silver nitrate solution and the resulting precipitate again treated with silver nitrate solution and finally washed with it. The silver compound which may, for the moment, be presumed to have the structure

$$CH_3 \cdot \overset{+}{S} \cdot CH : CH \cdot CH_2 \cdot CH_2 \cdot C - S \cdot Ag$$
$$\underset{O}{|} \qquad\qquad\qquad \underset{N \cdot O \cdot SO_2 \cdot \underset{+}{O}Ag}{\|}$$

was added to ice-cold aqueous sodium thiosulphate, the mixture filtered and the filtrate extracted with a mixture of ether (peroxide-free) and chloroform. This yielded an optically active oil which was fractionated at 0·01 mm. Eight grams of this were obtained from 4 kilograms of seeds and were passed in ether–chloroform solution through a silica-gel column, and eluted with the same solvent, saturated with water. Fractions of the eluate chosen for their optical rotation were united and fractionated in a high vacuum when pure sulphoraphene $C_6H_9ONS_2$, $[\alpha]_D^{18°} = +108 \pm 2°$ was obtained.

Further elution from the silica-gel column with methanol gave a strongly laevorotatory oil $[\alpha]_D$ approximately $-190°$. This was again passed through silica gel saturated with water and successively eluted with various solvents. The fractions obtained with ether–butanol contained a pure substance C_6H_9ONS, $[\alpha]_D^{13°} = -196 \pm 2°$ which was shown to be the nitrile corresponding to sulphoraphene.

Structure of sulphoraphene and the corresponding nitrile—(a) *Sulphoraphene*—The structures given on p. 140 are supported by considerable evidence. Hot aqueous silver nitrate gives silver sulphide indicating the presence of an —N : C : S group. Cold alcoholic potassium hydroxide and sodium nitroprusside, even in presence of potassium cyanide, give no colour, indicating the absence of thiol and disulphide groups; hot alcoholic potash followed by sodium nitroprusside gives a reddish-violet colour, due to formation of sodium sulphide from R·N : C : S. Only half the sulphur was removed by ammoniacal silver nitrate. The *iso*thiocyanate structure was further indicated by reaction of sulphoraphene with ammonia, aniline and *p*-anisidine when three optically active thioureas were obtained having the structures

R·NH·CS·NH$_2$; R·NH·CS·NHC$_6$H$_5$; R·NH·CS·NH·C$_6$H$_4$·O·CH$_3$

where R = CH$_3$·$\overset{+}{S}\overset{-}{O}$·CH : CH·CH$_2$·CH$_2$—. Aqueous silver oxide reacted with sulphoraphene to give the urea (XXX) which was reduced by hydrogen and Raney nickel (W$_2$) to the corresponding tetrahydro-compound (XXXI). This with hydrogen peroxide gave the corresponding sulphone (XXXII) and with Raney nickel (W$_4$)— a sample poorer in adsorbed hydrogen—and in absence of added hydrogen was desulphurized (*see* Chapter 3), giving a di-*n*-butylurea (XXXIII) identical with a specimen obtained from di-*n*-butyl thiourea and silver oxide.

$$(CH_3 \cdot SO \cdot CH : CH \cdot CH_2 \cdot CH_2 \cdot NH)_2CO$$
$$(XXX)$$

$$(CH_3 \cdot SO \cdot CH_2 \cdot CH_2 \cdot CH_2 \cdot CH_2 \cdot NH)_2CO$$
$$(XXXI)$$

141

$$(CH_3 \cdot SO_2 \cdot CH_2 \cdot CH_2 \cdot CH_2 \cdot CH_2 \cdot NH)_2 CO$$
$$(XXXII)$$

$$(CH_3 \cdot CH_2 \cdot CH_2 \cdot CH_2 \cdot NH)_2 CO$$
$$(XXXIII)$$

Information concerning different preparations of Raney nickel and their varying reactivity will be found in Chapter 3. The two ureas (XXX) and (XXXI) were optically active but the sulphone and the urea (XXXIII) obtained on desulphurization were not. Consequently the optical activity of sulphoraphene and its derivatives is due solely to the $R \cdot \overset{+}{\underset{\underset{O}{|}}{S}} \cdot R'$ grouping. This is also in agreement with the absence of an asymmetric carbon atom in the structure assigned to sulphoraphene.

A $CH_3 \cdot S$— group is indicated by the formation of methanesulphonic acid on oxidation of sulphoraphene with fuming nitric acid. The presence of a double bond follows from the result of the hydrogenation experiment carried out on the urea derivative (XXX). Its position was determined by oxidation of the same unsaturated urea derivative with ozone, and of sulphoraphene itself with aqueous barium permanganate at 0°C. In each case methanesulphonic acid was formed and isolated as the barium salt. The yields were 50 and 71 per cent respectively. Any other position of the double bond would have given methylsulphonylacetic acid $CH_3 \cdot SO_2 \cdot CH_2 \cdot COOH$ or methylsulphonylpropionic acid $CH_3 \cdot SO_2 \cdot CH_2 \cdot CH_2 \cdot COOH$ which are stated to be stable under the conditions of the oxidation. It may be mentioned here that hot alkali decomposes methylsulphonylacetic acid to dimethyl sulphone, which would have volatilized during the evaporation of the permanganate oxidation liquors, but the methylsulphonylpropionic acid should be stable to alkali. However, during the oxidation with barium permanganate the reaction mixture was neutralized with carbon dioxide as soon as the temperature rose to 18°C so alkaline decomposition is very unlikely. Therefore the absence of the two methylsulphonyl-fatty acids may be assumed. Moreover, such complications presumably do not arise in the case of oxidation by ozone.

(b) *The nitrile corresponding to sulphoraphene*—The structure of the nitrile which accompanies sulphoraphene in the oil obtained from *Raphanus sativum* was assigned to it on the following grounds: it gives no silver sulphide with ammoniacal silver nitrate and so contains no *iso*thiocyano– group. Boiling with 2N-sodium hydroxide gives 0·73 mole of ammonia. The Zerewitinoff test with magnesium methyl iodide indicates the absence of active hydrogen atoms. With hydrogen and Raney nickel W_2 six atoms of hydrogen are taken up, of which the first two are absorbed very rapidly indicating the presence of an ethylenic linking. Nitric acid (d. 1·5) gives methane-sulphonic acid and acid of d. 1·41 succinic acid. The ultra-violet absorption spectra of sulphoraphene and the nitrile both show an inflexion at about 225 mμ which is clearly due to the grouping —S$^+$—CH : CH—. The formula

$$\underset{\underline{O}}{\overset{|}{|}} \qquad CH_3\overset{+}{S}\cdot CH : CH\cdot CH_2\cdot CH_2\cdot CN$$

$$\underset{\underline{O}}{\overset{|}{|}} \qquad (XXIX)$$

which is consequently assigned to the nitrile contains no asymmetric carbon atom and, as in sulphoraphene, the optical activity must be due to the $>$ SO group.

RECENT WORK ON NATURAL isoTHIOCYANATE GLUCOSIDES

After the publication of this important study by the Swiss chemists the interest in mustard oils and their glucosides increased somewhat and two parallel investigations by Schulz in Tübingen and by Kjaer in Copenhagen were commenced.

Paper chromatography of iso*thiocyanate glucosides and thioureas*—Both groups of workers used paper chromatography to detect glucosides in suitable (unhydrolysed) extracts of the seeds, or sometimes of the whole plant, and Kjaer has used the same principle for the identification of mustard oils. On the whole, however, the Danish work has consisted mainly in the isolation and, where necessary, the synthesis of the new natural *iso*thiocyanates.

Mustard oil glucosides in alcoholic extracts of the plant or seeds may be recognized by paper chromatography, after development with a mixture of *n*-butanol, acetic acid and water, by spraying with N/50 silver nitrate, drying quickly at 100°C and spraying with N/50 potassium dichromate when the glucosides appear as yellow spots on a red ground. Alternatively the sheet may be sprayed with 4 per cent potassium hydroxide, dried for 20 minutes at 100°C and sprayed with sodium nitroprusside. A blue violet colour which fades in a few minutes is obtained.

Two methods for the paper chromatography of thioureas were used by Kjaer and Rubinstein[53]. The first employs Grote's reagent which is an aqueous solution containing sodium nitroprusside, a hydroxylamine salt and bromine. This gives an intense blue or turquoise colour with a thiourea. In a second method the paper was sprayed with starch solution and then with the iodine-azide reagent of Feigl. Thioureas catalyse the conversion of free iodine and azide ion to free nitrogen and iodide ion;

$$I_2 + 2N_3^- = 3N_2 + 2I^-$$

consequently white spots on a blue ground are formed with the thioureas. Many compounds containing divalent sulphur catalyse this reaction and it may prove of considerable use in their recognition. It has been used by Chargaff[54] and his co-workers for the detection of cystine, cysteine and methionine, though they omit the previous treatment with starch.

THE SCOPE OF THE RECENT DANISH WORK ON NATURAL ISOTHIOCYANATES

The scope of the work of Kjaer and his colleagues can best be envisaged from a consideration of: (1) its botanical aspects; (2) the various types of *iso*thiocyanates which have been isolated; (3) the methods employed in their isolation; (4) the reactions used in the determination of structure and (5) a list of the new *iso*thiocyanates obtained in the course of this work.

1. *Botanical aspects*—Most of Kjaer's work has been concerned with plants belonging to the Natural Order *Cruciferae*, but recently he has examined members of other Natural Orders, e.g. the *Cappardiaceae* and *Tropolaceae*.

2. *Types of natural* iso*thiocyanates*—(a) Simple saturated alkyl *iso*thiocyanates of low molecular weight; (b) simple homologues of allyl *iso*thiocyanate $CH_2 : CH \cdot (CH_2)_n \cdot N : C : S$; (c) methylthio derivatives of alkyl *iso*thiocyanates $CH_3S \cdot (CH_2)_n \cdot N : C : S$; (d) the corresponding sulphoxides [methanesulphinylalkyl*iso*thiocyanates,

$$CH_3\overset{+}{\underset{|}{S}} \cdot (CH_2)_n \cdot N : C : S].$$ It is interesting that two *iso*thiocyanates
$$O$$

of this type containing alkyl chains of nine and ten carbon atoms have recently been isolated by Kjaer; (e) the corresponding sulphones [methanesulphonylalkyl*iso*thiocyanates $CH_3 \cdot SO_2 \cdot (CH_2)_n \cdot N : C : S$]; (f) methanesulphinylalkyl*iso*thiocyanates in which a double bond is adjacent to the sulphur atom, $CH_3\overset{+}{\underset{|}{S}} \cdot CH : CH \cdot CH_2 \cdot$
$$O$$

$CH_2 \cdot N : C : S$. Nitriles of similar chain structure have also been isolated (*see* p. 130); (*g*) this class contains benzyl-, 2-phenylethyl- and *p*-hydroxybenzyl*iso*thiocyanates which have long been known, to which must now be added *p*-methoxybenzyl- and (*h*) 2-hydroxy-3-butenyl *iso*thiocyanate. This last-named compound $CH_2 : CH \cdot CHOH \cdot CH_2 \cdot N : C : S$ occurs combined as a glucoside, progoitrin, in certain *Brassica*. On hydrolysis, however, the liberated *iso*thiocyanate undergoes cyclization giving the 5-vinyloxazolidine-2-thione (*see* p. 158); a similar compound 5 : 5-dimethyloxazolidine-2-thione was obtained from the crucifer *Conringia orientalis* (the hare's ear mustard) several years ago (*see* p. 155). It may also occur as a hydroxylated *iso*thiocyanate $(CH_3)_2 \cdot C \cdot CH_2 \cdot N : C : S$ in glucosidic

$$\underset{OH}{|}$$

combination.

3. *Detection and isolation of* iso*thiocyanates in plants*—The hydrolysis by the natural enzyme accompanying the glucoside or by added myrosinase, followed by noting the resulting odour, is a very simple operation. This should be supplemented by steam distillation and treatment of a few drops of the resulting volatile oil with strong aqueous ammonia or other amine giving a substituted thiourea: $R \cdot N : C : S + R' \cdot NH_2 = R \cdot NH \cdot CS \cdot NH \cdot R'$.

4. *Characterization and identification of* iso*thiocyanates*—The principal methods employed for characterization of natural *iso*thiocyanates consist in conversion to substituted thioureas by reaction with ammonia or amines. The thiourea can be converted to the corresponding urea by reaction with silver oxide as described on p. 141 thus affording further confirmation of identity. The necessary authentic specimens of *iso*thiocyanates are readily prepared by standard methods, e.g. by the action of thiophosgene on an amine

$$CSCl_2 + RNH_2 = R \cdot N : C : S + 2HCl$$

or by the older process in which carbon disulphide reacts with an amine to give $CS(NHR)_2$ which, if R is aromatic, can be decomposed by acid to give the *iso*thiocyanate and the amine hydrochloride, with some triarylguanidine $(R \cdot NH)_2C = N \cdot R$ as a by-product. For aliphatic *iso*thiocyanates the classical Hofmann method in which the amine and carbon disulphide react to give the alkylamine salt of an N-alkyldithiocarbamic acid $R \cdot NH \cdot CS \cdot SH \cdot NH_2R$ which is then decomposed by mercuric chloride to give the amine hydrochloride, mercuric sulphide and the mustard oil, is very rarely employed. The thioureas can be detected and identified by paper chromatography as described on p. 143. Use has also been made of infra-red and ultra-violet spectroscopy for the study of *iso*thiocyanates and thioureas.

5. *Natural* iso*thiocyanates recently identified*—The new *iso*thiocyanates recently isolated from plants or conclusively identified, mainly by Kjaer and his colleagues, may now be listed.

(*a*) *Saturated Alkyl* iso*Thiocyanates of Low Molecular Weight:*

Methyl *iso*thiocyanate $CH_3 \cdot N : C : S$

Ethyl *iso*thiocyanate $CH_3 \cdot CH_2 \cdot N : C : S$

*Iso*propyl *iso*thiocyanate $(CH_3)_2 CH \cdot N : C : S$

(*b*) *Homologues of Allyl* iso*Thiocyanate:*

3-Butenyl *iso*thiocyanate $CH_2 : CH \cdot CH_2 \cdot CH_2 \cdot N : C : S$

4-Pentenyl *iso*thiocyanate $CH_2 : CH \cdot CH_2 \cdot CH_2 \cdot CH_2 \cdot N : C : S$

(*c*) *Methylthio-alkyl* iso*Thiocyanates:*

3-Methylthiopropyl *iso*thiocyanate
$$CH_3 \cdot S \cdot CH_2 \cdot CH_2 \cdot CH_2 \cdot N : C : S$$

4-Methylthiobutyl *iso*thiocyanate
$$CH_3 \cdot S \cdot CH_2 \cdot CH_2 \cdot CH_2 \cdot CH_2 \cdot N : C : S$$

5-Methylthiopentyl *iso*thiocyanate
$$CH_3 \cdot S \cdot CH_2 \cdot CH_2 \cdot CH_2 \cdot CH_2 \cdot CH_2 \cdot N : C : S$$

(*d*) *Methanesulphinylalkyl* iso*Thiocyanates:*

3-Methanesulphinyl-*n*-propyl *iso*thiocyanate
$$CH_3 \overset{+}{S} \cdot CH_2 \cdot CH_2 \cdot CH_2 \cdot N : C : S$$
$$\underset{\underline{O}}{|}$$

4-Methanesulphinyl-*n*-butyl *iso*thiocyanate
$$CH_3 \overset{+}{S} \cdot CH_2 \cdot CH_2 \cdot CH_2 \cdot CH_2 \cdot N : C : S$$
$$\underset{\underline{O}}{|}$$

5-Methanesulphinyl-*n*-pentyl *iso*thiocyanate
$$CH_3 \cdot \overset{+}{S} \cdot CH_2 \cdot CH_2 \cdot CH_2 \cdot CH_2 \cdot CH_2 \cdot N : C : S$$
$$\underset{\underline{O}}{|}$$

9-Methanesulphinyl-*n*-nonyl *iso*thiocyanate
$$CH_3 \cdot \overset{+}{S} \cdot (CH_2)_9 \cdot N : C : S$$
$$\underset{\underline{O}}{|}$$

10-Methanesulphinyl-*n*-decyl *iso*thiocyanate

$$CH_3 \cdot \overset{+}{\underset{\underset{O}{|}}{S}} \cdot (CH_2)_{10} \cdot N : C : S$$

(*e*) *Methanesulphonylalkyl* iso*Thiocyanates*:

3-Methanesulphonyl-*n*-propyl *iso*thiocyanate (cheirolin)

$$CH_3 \cdot \overset{\overset{\overset{O}{|}}{+}}{\underset{\underset{O}{|}}{S}} \cdot CH_2 \cdot CH_2 \cdot CH_2 \cdot N : C : S$$

4-Methanesulphonyl-*n*-butyl *iso*thiocyanate (erysolin)

$$CH_3 \cdot \overset{\overset{\overset{O}{|}}{+}}{\underset{\underset{O}{|}}{S}} \cdot CH_2 \cdot CH_2 \cdot CH_2 \cdot CH_2 \cdot N : C : S$$

(*f*) *Unsaturated Methanesulphinyl* iso*Thiocyanates*:

4-Methanesulphinyl-3-butenyl *iso*thiocyanate (sulphoraphene)

$$CH_3 \cdot \overset{+}{\underset{\underset{O}{|}}{S}} \cdot CH : CH \cdot CH_2 \cdot CH_2 \cdot N : C : S$$

(*g*) iso*Thiocyanates containing Aromatic Nuclei*:

o-Methoxybenzyl *iso*thiocyanate

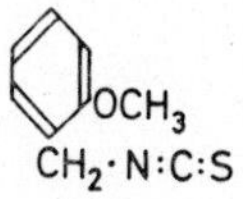

p-Methoxybenzyl *iso*thiocyanate

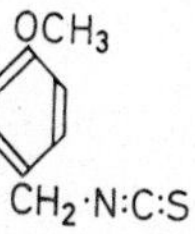

3-benzoyloxypropyl *iso*thiocyanate

$$C_6H_5 \cdot CO \cdot O \cdot CH_2 \cdot CH_2 \cdot CH_2 \cdot N : C : S$$

(h) *2-Hydroxyalkyl (or alkene) iso Thiocyanates :*

2-Hydroxy-3-butenyl *iso*thiocyanate →
5-vinyl-oxazolidine-2-thione

$$CH_2: CH \cdot CHOH \cdot CH_2 \cdot N:C:S \longrightarrow CH_2:CH \cdot \underset{\underset{O}{\big|}}{CH} \overset{CH_2-NH}{\underset{}{\big\backslash \,\, \big/}} C=S$$

2-Hydroxy-2-methylpropyl *iso*thiocyanate →
5 : 5-Dimethyloxazolidine-2-thione

$$\underset{CH_3}{\overset{CH_3}{\big\rangle}}\underset{OH}{\overset{}{C}}-CH_2-N:C:S \longrightarrow (CH_3)_2\, C\overset{CH_2-NH}{\underset{O}{\big\backslash \,\, \big/}} C=S$$

This type of *iso*thiocyanate which, on liberation from its glucoside, undergoes cyclization to an oxazole derivative will be discussed later and an account of the corresponding glucosides will also be given.

EXPERIMENTAL DETAILS OF RECENT WORK ON THE SEPARATION AND IDENTIFICATION OF SOME TYPICAL NATURAL *ISO*THIOCYANATES AND MUSTARD OIL GLUCOSIDES

Methyl iso *Thiocyanate and its Glucoside Glucocapparin*[55,56]—The finely ground seeds of *Cleome spinosa* were freed from fat by extraction with a mixture of ligroin and *iso*propanol. The residue was exhaustively extracted with 70 per cent methanol and then with pure methanol. After filtration, concentration *in vacuo* and renewed filtration, the solution was twice chromatographed, first on neutral, and then on anionic, alumina which quantitatively retained the glucoside. After washing with water the column was eluted with potassium sulphate solution (1 per cent). The eluate was evaporated *in vacuo* and the glucoside extracted with hot methanol and purified by crystallization from 80 per cent ethanol. It had the composition $C_8H_{14}O_9NS_2K$ and its infra-red spectrum was measured. 50 m.g. in 2 c.c. of a phosphate buffer (pH 6·6) was treated with a drop of a myrosinase solution. Next day the mixture was distilled in steam and the volatilized mustard oil converted to the thiourea with ammonia which was identified as N-methylthiourea $H_2N\cdot CS\cdot NH\cdot CH_3$ by paper chromatographic comparison in two solvent systems with an authentic specimen. The ultra-violet spectrum coincided with that of N-methylthiourea. The formation of this thiourea was further confirmed by analysis and by m.p. and mixed m.p. determinations. A solution of glucocapparin was hydrolysed enzymically, evaporated to dryness and the residue extracted with methanol. The insoluble part contained inorganic sulphate and the methanol contained glucose which was detected by paper chromatography.

Glucocapparin was acetylated with acetic anhydride in pyridine, the tetra-acetate analysed and the structure confirmed by ultra-violet and infra-red spectroscopy. Hydrolysis with methanolic ammonia at 0°C regenerated glucocapparin which was satisfactorily identified.

By similar methods the presence of ethyl *iso*thiocyanate[57], combined as a glucoside, has been detected in the seeds of *Lepidium Menziesii* DC. Dragendorff[58] in 1898 referred to the use of various members of the *Capparidaceae* as spices and remedies in folk-medicine, and the presence of volatile constituents has been suspected for some time.

iso*Propyl* iso*Thiocyanate*—The presence of this *iso*thiocyanate in glucosidic combination was recognized[59] in the seeds and fresh plant material of many members of the *Cruciferae*. The chromatographic methods already described on p. 143 were used in a preliminary survey. Thoroughly ground seeds of *Lunaria biennis* Mach. were treated with a hot mixture of light petroleum and ethanol in order to denature the myrosinase. Otherwise it was found that this caused hydrolysis of the glucosides during the necessary exhaustive extraction of fat from the seeds with petroleum ether. It is not stated at what temperature this extraction was carried out.

Enzymic hydrolysis of the residue with a cell-free myrosinase preparation gave an intense odour. The mustard oil was treated with ammonia, and the product was shown to be identical with N-*iso*propylthiourea.

*Iso*propyl *iso*thiocyanate occurs in certain other *Cruciferae* and in the seeds of *Tropaeolum peregrinum* (*canariense*)[59] belonging to the family *Tropaeolaceae*. In two cases it seems to be accompanied by *sec*-butyl *iso*thiocyanate, $CH_3 \cdot CH_2 \cdot CH(CH_3) \cdot N : C : S$.

4-*Methylthiobutyl* iso*Thiocyanate*—Kjaer and Gmelin[60] have established the presence of this *iso*thiocyanate in the seeds of *Eruca sativa* Mill. The compound was obtained by steam distillation of an intimate mixture of the ground seeds and water previously kept at 35°C for 3 hours. The natural enzyme of the seeds effected the hydrolysis of the, as yet, uncharacterized glucoside, gluco-erucin. Treatment of the distillate with ammonia gave a thiourea which was identified as N-(4-methylthiobutyl)-thiourea by m.p. and mixed m.p. and by analysis. Infra-red spectroscopy and paper chromatography applied to the natural and a synthetic specimen gave identical results.

The new *iso*thiocyanate was synthesized from allyl cyanide which, in presence of ultra-violet light and a trace of benzoyl peroxide, reacted with methanethiol to give (contrary to Markownikoff's Rule) γ-methylthiobutyronitrile in 92 per cent yield. Reduction with lithium aluminium hydride in dry ether gave the corresponding δ-methylthio-*n*-butylamine which with thiophosgene in chloroform in presence of sodium hydroxide gave the desired *iso*thiocyanate. This was characterized as the benzylthiourea:

$$CH_2 : CH \cdot CH_2 \cdot CN \xrightarrow[hv]{CH_3 \cdot SH} CH_3 \cdot S \cdot CH_2 \cdot CH_2 \cdot CH_2 \cdot CN \xrightarrow{LiAlH_4}$$

$$CH_3 \cdot S \cdot CH_2 \cdot CH_2 \cdot CH_2 \cdot CH_2 \cdot NH_2 \xrightarrow[NaOH]{CSCl_2} CH_3 \cdot S \cdot CH_2 \cdot CH_2 \cdot CH_2 \cdot$$

$$CH_2 \cdot N : C : S \xrightarrow{C_6H_5 \cdot CH_2 \cdot NH_2} CH_3 \cdot S \cdot CH_2 \cdot CH_2 \cdot CH_2 \cdot CH_2 \cdot NH \cdot$$

$$CS \cdot NH \cdot CH_2 \cdot C_6H_5$$

Kjaer and Conti[61] showed that the addition of methanethiol to allyl cyanide takes place as shown above by oxidizing the δ-methylthio-n-butylamine to the corresponding sulphone $CH_3 \cdot SO_2 \cdot CH_2 \cdot CH_2 \cdot CH_2 \cdot CH_2 \cdot NH_2$, as described by Schneider and Kaufmann[62]. The product was identical with a specimen prepared by these authors by a different and unambiguous route, which may be outlined:

γ-Chloro-n-propyl bromide with potassium cyanide gave the nitrile which with sodium methyl mercaptide yielded the methylthionitrile. This with sodium and alcohol was reduced to the desired amine (XXXIV):

$$Cl \cdot CH_2 \cdot CH_2 \cdot CH_2 \cdot Br \xrightarrow{KCN} Cl \cdot CH_2 \cdot CH_2 \cdot CH_2 \cdot CN \xrightarrow{CH_3 \cdot S \cdot Na}$$

$$CH_3 \cdot S \cdot CH_2 \cdot CH_2 \cdot CH_2 \cdot CN \xrightarrow{Na + C_2H_5OH} CH_3 \cdot S \cdot CH_2 \cdot CH_2 \cdot CH_2 \cdot$$
$$CH_2 \cdot NH_2$$
$$(XXXIV)$$

$$\xrightarrow{KMnO_4} CH_3 \cdot SO_2 \cdot CH_2 \cdot CH_2 \cdot CH_2 \cdot CH_2 \cdot NH_2$$
$$(XXXV)$$

$$CH_3 \cdot SO_2 \cdot CH_2 \cdot CH_2 \cdot CH_2 \cdot CH_2 \cdot N : C : S$$
$$(XXXVI)$$

Schneider and Kaufmann[62] converted the δ-methylsulphonyl butylamine (XXXV) to erysolin (XXXVI) by means of carbon disulphide, iodine and alkali, the product being identical with the natural isothiocyanate which they had isolated from seeds of the crucifer *Erysimum Perowskianum* Fisch et M.

The amino sulphone (XXXV) prepared from allyl cyanide by Kjaer and Gmelin's method was also converted by Kjaer and Conti to erysolin by Dyson's thiophosgene reaction. It was identical with Schneider and Kaufmann's product. This afforded not only a second synthesis of erysolin but further proof that the addition of methanethiol to allyl cyanide in presence of benzoyl peroxide and ultra-violet light proceeds as stated by Kjaer and Conti[61]. No reaction took place between allyl cyanide and methanethiol in presence of sodium methoxide.

(—)-9-*Methanesulphinyl*-n-*nonyl* iso*thiocyanate:* $CH_3 \cdot \overset{+}{S} \cdot (CH_2)_9 N:C:S$
$\underset{O}{\vert}$

—On examination by paper chromatography of extracts prepared from the seeds of the crucifer *Arabis alpina* Schulz and his colleagues Gmelin[63] and Wagner[64] detected two glucosides. One of these, glucoarabin, was then shown by Kjaer and Gmelin[65] to yield a very interesting *iso*thiocyanate. Purified methanolic extracts of the seeds were enzymically hydrolysed at pH 6·5 giving an *iso*thiocyanate (XXXVII) which after extraction with ether was converted to three optically active, homogeneous thioureas by reaction with ammonia, aniline and benzylamine respectively. The infra-red spectrum of the simple thiourea $R \cdot NH \cdot CS \cdot NH_2$ indicated the presence of an $\rangle SO$ linkage. By a series of reactions now to be outlined it was shown that the group R was $CH_3 \cdot \overset{+}{S} \cdot (CH_2)_9$—. The optically active
$\underset{O}{\vert}$

benzylthiourea (XXXVIII) was converted with silver nitrate to the corresponding urea (XXXIX) which was also optically active and still contained sulphur. Reduction of this with zinc and hydrochloric acid gave an optically inactive benzylurea (XL) from which Raney nickel removed sulphur giving a urea derivative (XLI) which was shown to be identical with a specimen of 1-benzyl-3-nonyl urea $CH_3 \cdot (CH_2)_7 \cdot CH_2 \cdot NH \cdot CO \cdot NH \cdot CH_2 \cdot C_6H_5$. This was synthesized from benzyl *iso*thiocyanate and n-nonylamine $CH_3(CH_2)_7 \cdot CH_2 \cdot NH_2$ followed by exchange of the sulphur in the resulting thiourea for oxygen by means of silver nitrate.

$$CH_3 \cdot \overset{+}{\underset{\underset{O}{\vert}}{S}} \cdot (CH_2)_9 \cdot N : C : S \xrightarrow{C_6H_5 \cdot CH_2NH_2}$$
$$(XXXVII)$$

$$CH_3 \cdot \overset{+}{\underset{\underset{O}{\vert}}{S}} \cdot (CH_2)_9 \cdot NH \cdot CS \cdot NH \cdot CH_2 \cdot C_6H_5$$
$$(XXXVIII)$$

$$\xrightarrow{AgNO_3} CH_3 \cdot \overset{+}{\underset{\underset{O}{\vert}}{S}} \cdot (CH_2)_9 \cdot NH \cdot CO \cdot NH \cdot CH_2 \cdot C_6H_5 \xrightarrow{Zn + HCl}$$
$$(XXXIX)$$

151

$$CH_3 \cdot S \cdot (CH_2)_9 \cdot NH \cdot CO \cdot NH \cdot CH_2 \cdot C_6H_5 \xrightarrow{\text{Ni}}$$

(XL)

$$CH_3 \cdot (CH_2)_8 \cdot NH \cdot CO \cdot NH \cdot CH_2 \cdot C_6H_5$$

(XLI) $\uparrow$ AgNO$_3$

$$CH_3 \cdot (CH_2)_8 \cdot NH_2 + C_6H_5 \cdot CH_2 \cdot N : C : S \rightarrow CH_3(CH_2) \cdot {}_8NH \cdot CS \cdot NH \cdot CH_2 \cdot C_6H_5$$

The absence of the $\overset{+}{>}S\overset{-}{—O}$ group in (XL) was confirmed by infra-red spectroscopy.

These results indicate that the *iso*thiocyanate from glucoarabin has a methanesulphinyl group attached somewhere on the *n*-nonyl chain, the exact position not being ascertainable from the procedure adopted. Since so many analogous natural *iso*thiocyanates contain a CH_3S— or $CH_3\overset{+1}{S}\overset{-}{—O}$ group at the end of the alkyl chain it seemed very probable that the new *iso*thiocyanate had the structure $CH_3\overset{+}{S} \cdot (CH_2)_9 \cdot$

$$\overset{|}{\underset{-}{O}}$$

N : C : S a conclusion which (the authors added in a footnote) was later confirmed by synthesis.

In the transformations described above the optically active urea or thiourea derivatives were all strongly laevorotatory and the optical activity must be ascribed solely to the $R \cdot \overset{+}{S} \cdot R'$ grouping, as in

$$\overset{|}{\underset{-}{O}}$$

sulphoraphene (*see* p. 142). Paper chromatography showed that the glycoside glucoarabin contains glucose and sulphate.

(−)-10-*Methanesulphinyl*-n-*decyl* iso*thiocyanate*: $CH_3 \cdot \overset{+}{S} \cdot (CH_2)_9 \cdot CH_2 \cdot$

$$\overset{|}{\underset{-}{O}}$$

N : C : S—This optically active (laevorotatory) *iso*thiocyanate has been isolated[66] by enzymic hydrolysis of a new glucoside, gluco-camelinin, which occurs along with a similar, but as yet unidentified, glycoside in the seeds of the crucifer *Camelina cativa* (L) Crantz. The glucosides were detected by paper chromatography, separately eluted from the paper and subjected to enzymic hydrolysis. A spectrophotometric examination of the liberated *iso*thiocyanates was then made. The *iso*thiocyanates were not of the volatile type.

Quantities sufficient for chemical and physical examination (by reactions entirely analogous with those employed for the 9-methane-sulphinyl derivative—*see* p. 151) were obtained by enzymic hydrolysis of a specimen of the ground seeds which had been treated with aqueous lead acetate to precipitate impurities.

The structure of the new *iso*thiocyanate was confirmed by conversion to the urea

$$CH_3 \cdot S \cdot (CH_2)_{10} \cdot NH \cdot CO \cdot NH \cdot CH_2 \cdot C_6H_5$$

An authentic specimen of this was obtained from the methyl ester of undecenoic acid (XLII) which by an irradiated reaction with methanethiol gave a methylthio ester from which with hydrazine hydrate a hydrazide (XLIII) was obtained. By conversion with nitrous acid to the acid azide (XLIV) and by boiling with alcohol and subsequent hydrolysis the hydrazide was converted through the urethane to 10-methylthiodecylamine (XLV). This gave a thiourea with benzyl *iso*thiocyanate. Desulphurization of this thiourea derivative (XLVI) gave the required 1-benzyl-3-(10-methyl thiodecyl)-urea (XLVII) which was identical with the product obtained from the new *iso*thiocyanate

$$CH_2 : CH \cdot (CH_2)_8 COOCH_3 \xrightarrow[\text{hv}]{CH_3SH}$$
$$\text{(XLII)} \qquad CH_3 \cdot S \cdot CH_2 \cdot CH_2 \cdot (CH_2)_8 \cdot COOCH_3$$

$$\xrightarrow{N_2H_4 \cdot H_2O} CH_3 \cdot S \cdot (CH_2)_{10} CONH \cdot NH_2$$
$$\text{(XLIII)}$$

$$\xrightarrow{HNO_2} CH_3 \cdot S \cdot (CH_2)_{10} CO \cdot N_3$$
$$\text{(XLIV)}$$

$$\longrightarrow CH_3 \cdot S \cdot (CH_2)_{10} \cdot NH_2 \xrightarrow{C_6H_5CH_2 \cdot N : C : S}$$
$$\text{(XLV)}$$

$$CH_3 \cdot S \cdot (CH_2)_{10} \cdot NH \cdot CS \cdot NH \cdot CH_2 \cdot C_6H_5 \xrightarrow{AgNO_3}$$
$$\text{(XLVI)}$$

$$CH_3 \cdot S \cdot (CH_2)_{10} \cdot NH \cdot CO \cdot NH \cdot CH_2 \cdot C_6H_5.$$
$$\text{(XLVII)}$$

153

The addition of methanethiol in the first stage of the synthesis was catalysed by benzoyl peroxide and mercuric acetate in ultra-violet light (see p. 150).

4-Pentenyl iso*thiocyanate:* $CH_2 : CH \cdot CH_2 \cdot CH_2 \cdot CH_2 \cdot N : C : S$—In 1937 Schmalfuss[67] fractionated the mustard oil from 50 kilograms of rape seed and obtained 4-pentenyl cyanide $CH_2 : CH \cdot CH_2 \cdot CH_2 \cdot CH_2 \cdot CN$ and what is now known as 3-butenyl *iso*thiocyanate $CH_2 : CH \cdot CH_2 \cdot CH_2 \cdot N : C : S$ and also a higher boiling product, presumably $C_5H_9N : C : S$ and finally traces of phenylethyl *iso*thiocyanate. This work, which has been confirmed by Kjaer and Jensen, is particularly interesting on account of the isolation of a nitrile having the same chain of carbon atoms in the hydrocarbon residue as the accompanying *iso*thiocyanate.

Kjaer and Jensen[68] mixed ground rape seed cake with water and white mustard seeds as a source of myrosinase. (The seeds themselves gave only traces of volatile *iso*thiocyanates.) Steam distillation followed by fractionation yielded 3-butenyl *iso*thiocyanate and then almost pure $C_5H_9N : C : S$ as found by paper chromatography of the corresponding thiourea which was shown by infra-red spectroscopy to contain a vinyl group.

The α-naphthylthiourea (XLVIII) with silver nitrate gave an α-naphthylurea which with hydrogen and a platinum catalyst gave a dihydroderivative. This was identical with the product obtained from *n*-amylamine and α-naphthyl*iso*cyanate. The chain in the new *iso*thiocyanate was thus shown to be unbranched and the compound itself to be $CH_2 : CH \cdot CH_2 \cdot CH_2 \cdot CH_2 \cdot N : C : S$.

$$C_5H_9N : C : S \xrightarrow{C_{10}H_7 \cdot NH_2} C_5H_9 \cdot NH \cdot CS \cdot NH \cdot C_{10}H_7$$

$$(XLVIII)$$

$$\xrightarrow{AgNO_3} C_5H_9NH \cdot CO \cdot NH \cdot C_{10}H_7 \xrightarrow[H_2]{Pt} C_5H_{11} \cdot NH \cdot CO \cdot NH \cdot C_{10}H_7$$

$$CH_3 \cdot CH_2 \cdot CH_2 \cdot CH_2 \cdot CH_2 \cdot NH_2 + C_{10}H_7 \cdot N : C : O$$

4-pentenyl *iso*thiocyanate was synthesized from tetrahydrofuryl alcohol which was converted to 4-penten-1-ol[69] and this to 4-pentenyl bromide[70]. By Gabriel's phthalimide reaction followed by hydrazinolysis the 4-pentenylamine was formed. With thiophosgene this was converted to the corresponding *iso*thiocyanate (XLIX) and then with α-naphthyl amine to the desired thiourea (XLVIII)

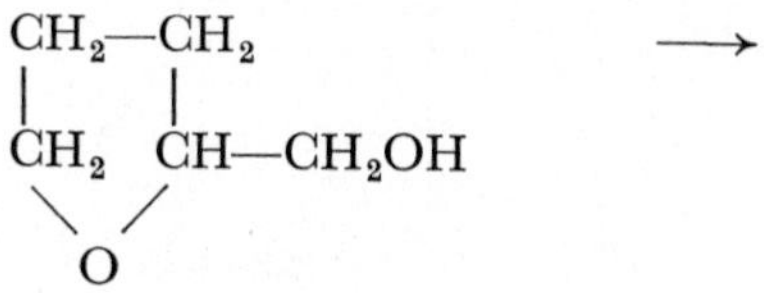

$$CH_2\text{---}CH_2 \qquad \longrightarrow$$
$$CH_2 \quad CH\text{---}CH_2OH$$
$$\diagdown \diagup$$
$$O$$

$$CH_2 : CH\cdot CH_2\cdot CH_2\cdot CH_2\cdot OH \xrightarrow{\ PBr_3\ } CH_2 : CH\cdot CH_2\cdot CH_2\cdot CH_2\cdot Br$$

$$\xrightarrow[NH_2\cdot NH_2]{C_6H_4(CO)_2NK} CH_2 : CH\cdot CH_2\cdot CH_2\cdot CH_2\cdot NH_2 \xrightarrow{\ CSCl_2\ } CH_2 : CH\cdot$$

$$CH_2\cdot CH_2\cdot CH_2\cdot N : C : S$$

(XLIX)

GLUCOCONRINGIN. AN *iso*THIOCYANATE GLUCOSIDE WHICH YIELDS
5 : 5-DIMETHYLOXAZOLIDINE-2-THIONE ON ENZYMIC HYDROLYSIS

Kjaer and his school[71] have isolated a new glucoside from the seeds of the crucifer *Conringia orientalis* which they name glucoconringin. The plant is a common weed in Canada and is known as hare's ear mustard. The glucoside was detected in an acetone extract of the seeds by paper chromatography and shown by the usual methods to yield glucose and sulphate, with myrosinase. It was characterized as the crystalline tetra-acetate which regenerated glucoconringin on treatment with alcoholic ammonia at room temperature. On enzymic hydrolysis the glucoside yielded, in a small scale experiment, a product which was shown by its absorption spectrum and by paper chromatography to be 5 : 5-dimethyloxazolidine-2-thione (L).

Paper chromatography also revealed the presence of glucoconringin in three species of the genus *Cochlearia*. The seeds of *Cochlearia officinalis* are the best source of the glucoside, and were used for the isolation of the dimethyloxazolidinethione in larger amount, by a method similar to that employed by Astwood, Greer and Ettlinger[72] (*see* p. 158) for the isolation of the corresponding vinyl derivative (LI). Kjaer and his colleagues refer to a method for the recognition of compounds of the oxazolidinethione type by paper chromatography.

Synthesis of the cyclic thione—The 5 : 5-dimethyloxazolidine-2-thione was synthesized from acetone cyanohydrin which was reduced by lithium aluminium hydride to 2-aminomethyl-2-propanol (LII). By reaction of this with carbon disulphide and ethyl chloroformate in dioxan in presence of triethylamine, by Kaluza's method[73,74] ring closure to the oxazolidinethione (L) occurred:

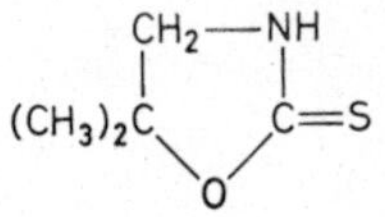

(L) 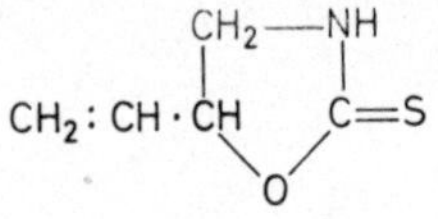   (LI) 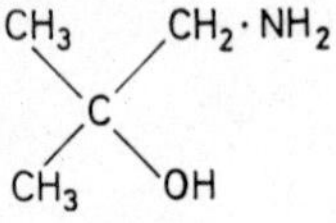   (LII)

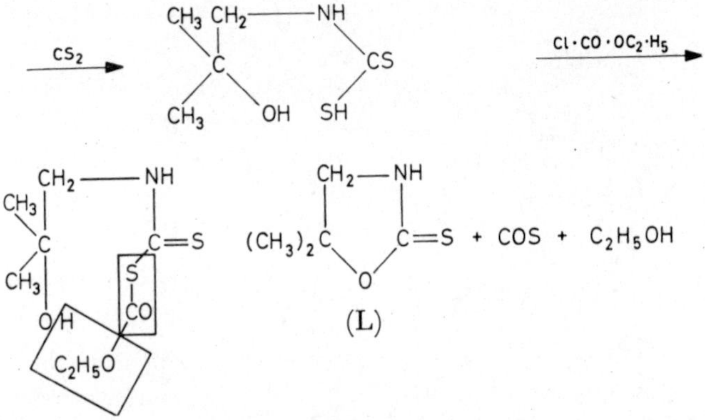

(L)

The synthetic product was identical with that obtained from the glucoside occurring in the seeds of *Cochlearia officinalis* and *Conringia orientalis*.

Hopkins' work on the cyclic thione—The same dimethyloxazolidine-thione had already been isolated in 1938 from the seeds of the hare's ear mustard by Hopkins[75] who employed a very similar method but was unable to purify the parent glucoside.

Hopkins identified his 5 : 5-dimethyloxazolidine-2-thione by comparison with a synthetic specimen prepared by Bruson and Eastes[76] by a method very similar to that employed later (*see* p. 155) by Kjaer *et al.*, namely the action of aqueous ethanolic potassium hydroxide and carbon disulphide on (LII). Both the Danish workers and Hopkins emphasize the unusual observation that a glucoside occurring in a member of the *Cruciferae* should not yield an *iso*thiocyanate on enzymic hydrolysis. Hopkins states 'it is not unlikely, therefore, that the substance 2-mercapto-5 : 5-dimethyl-oxazoline is formed from the *iso*thiocyanate $CH_2=C(CH_3)\cdot CH_2-N : C : S$ by addition of water and ring closure'.

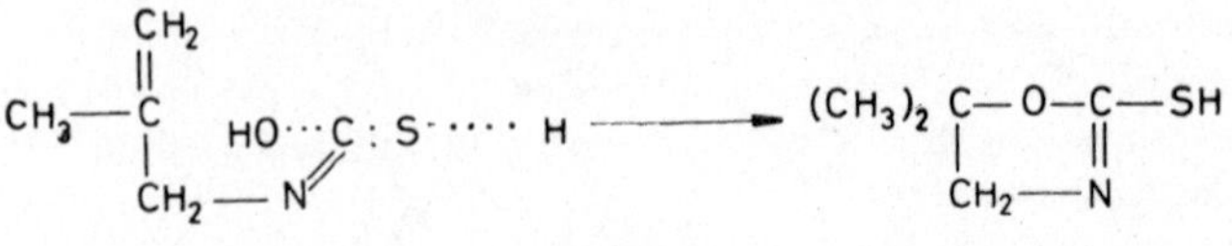

Hopkins preferred the mercapto-structure for this oxazole derivative but gave no reason. Later, Ettlinger[77] showed by infra-red spectroscopy that the thione structure should be assigned to it. Hopkins pointed out that this change has never been observed during the hydrolysis of sinigrin, which yields the unsaturated allyl *iso*thiocyanate $CH_2 : CH \cdot CH_2 \cdot N : C : S$, but that according to Bruson and Eastes the presence of a tertiary carbon atom at the double bond facilitates ring closure of aliphatic *iso*thiocyanates and thioureas.

Kjaer *et al.* have found, however, that synthetic 2-methylallyl *iso*thiocyanate shows no tendency to addition of water and to ring closure. Moreover, the ultra-violet absorption spectrum of an extract of the seeds of *Conringia orientalis* disclosed the presence of only one glucoside which exhibited an absorption spectrum of the usual type, resembling that of sinigrin. This showed that chromophores such as the heterocyclic ring system of the dimethyloxazolidinethione could not be present in glucoconringin. Kjaer, Gmelin and Jensen, therefore, suggest that the formula for the glucoside (represented as its acetyl derivative) is as shown below. Their paper was published prior to Ettlinger and Lundeen's correction of the formula for sinigrin and as Kjaer accepts the new formula for the mustard oil glucosides the author has modified the structure to show the hydroxy-alkyl group linked to carbon instead of nitrogen:

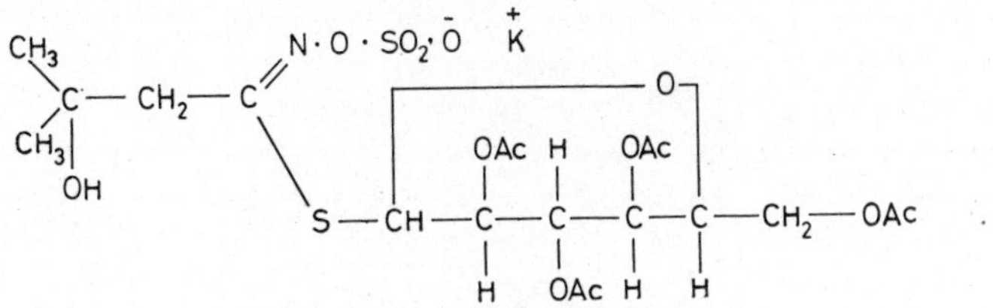

The fact that the hydroxyl group in the alkyl chain is not acetylated by acetic anhydride in pyridine is attributed to its tertiary character. The infra-red spectrum of the tetra-acetate did not, however, show any band attributable to this tertiary hydroxyl group. This Kjaer *et al.* attribute to association. The ready regeneration of glucoconringin from its tetra-acetyl derivative (*see* p. 155) appears to exclude changes of structure during acetylation. They conclude therefore that the 5 : 5-dimethyloxazolidine-2-thione arises by cyclization of the 2-hydroxy-2-methylpropyl *iso*thiocyanate (LIII), initially formed during enzymic hydrolysis. It would be interesting to determine whether a synthetic specimen of (LIII) also undergoes cyclization, so deciding whether the change is enzymic or not. This cyclization can be measured. It was spectroscopically established that a partly purified specimen of glucoconringin, submitted to enzymic hydrolysis, gave only a 40 per cent yield of the cyclic compound in 4 hours at room temperature; 24 hours were required for completion of the isomerization. From analogous cases it appears improbable that the enzymic hydrolysis is the rate-determining factor in this reaction.

(LII)

PROGOITRIN. AN *iso*THIOCYANATE GLUCOSIDE WHICH YIELDS
GOITRIN (L-5-VINYLOXAZOLIDINE-2-THIONE) ON ENZYMIC HYDROLYSIS

Studies on the goitrogenic effects of various foodstuffs on man have shown that the antithyroid effect of rutabaga and turnip and their seeds seems to be due to a compound liberated by enzymic hydrolysis of the crushed seeds from a precursor. Both rutabaga and turnip have an inhibitory effect on the uptake of radio-iodine in man. The effect is not observed if the vegetables are cooked before being fed. Greer[78-80] has isolated this anti-thyroid compound and shown it to be L-5-vinyloxazolidine-2-thione (LIV). It was named goitrin and the glucoside precursor, progoitrin. This compound is closely related to the 5 : 5-dimethyloxazolidine-2-thione (L) isolated from hare's ear mustard.

The concentration of progoitrin is highest in the seeds. Goitrin is not liberated if the seeds are plunged in hot water, but if they are then cooled and filtered and treated with myrosinase, goitrin is liberated. Greer isolated progoitrin from ground seeds of rutabaga by removing fat with dry ether and then treating with boiling water for 30 minutes. The extract was evaporated and protein removed by alcohol. Repeated chromatography of the alcoholic extract on alumina finally gave pure crystals. On treatment with myrosinase stoichiometrical proportions of goitrin, glucose, sulphate ion and sodium were formed. Greer, therefore, proposed the tentative formula (LV) for progoitrin which when modified in the light of Ettlinger and Lundeen's formula for sinigrin becomes (LVI). The 2-hydroxy-3-butenyl *iso*thiocyanate (LVII) which is presumably formed on enzymic hydrolysis undergoes cyclization to the oxazolidinethione derivative (LIV).

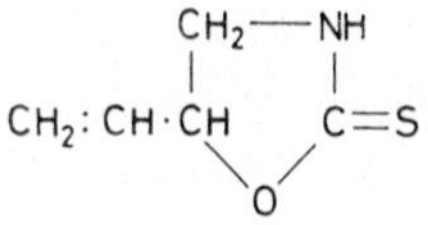

(LIV)

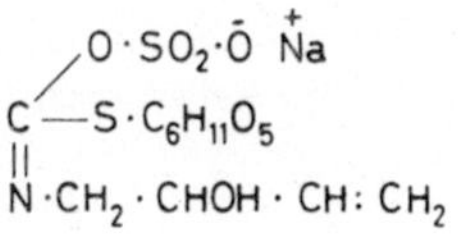

(LV)

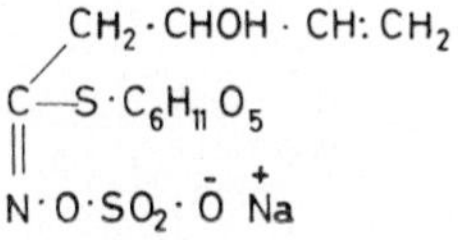

(LVI)

$$CH_2{:}CH{\cdot}CHOH{\cdot}CH_2{\cdot}N{:}C{:}S$$

(LVII)

Progoitrin has a specific absorption at 227 mμ which is very similar to that of sinigrin; the spectral shift to 240 mμ during enzymic hydrolysis indicates cyclization to goitrin.

REFERENCES

[1] Gildemeister, E. and Hofmann, F., *Die Aetherischen Oele*, 1st Ed., J. Springer, Berlin 1899, p. 533

[2] Dumas, J. B. A. and Pelouze, J, *Ann. chim. phys.* **53** II (1833) 181; *Liebig's Ann.* **10** (1834) 324

[3] Boutron, F. and Fremy, E., *Liebig's Ann.* **34** (1840) 230

[4] Bussy, A., *ibid.* **34** (1840) 233

[5] Will, H., *ibid.* **52** (1844) 1

[6] Wertheim, T., *ibid.* **52** (1844) 54

[7] Ludwig, E. and Lange, W, *Zeit. chem. Pharm.* **3** (1860) 430, 577

[8] Will, H. and Körner, W., *Liebig's Ann.* **125** (1863) 257

[9] Gadamer, J., *Ber. dtsch. chem. Ges.* **30** (1897) 2322, 2327, 2328, 2330; *Archiv. der Pharmacie* **235** (1897) 44

[10] Zinin, N., *J. pr. chem.* **64** (1855) 504

[11] Berthelot, M. and de Luca, S, *Compt. rendus* **41** (1855) 21

[12] Oeser, C., *Liebig's Ann.* **134** (1865) 7

[13] Hofmann, A. W. von, *Ber. dtsch. chem. Ges.* **1** (1868) 28

[14] Meyer, V. and Jacobson, P., *Lehrbuch der Organischen Chemie, Erster Band, Zweiter Teil*, von Veit & Co., Leipzig, 1913, pp. 1313–20

[15] Billeter, O., *Ber. dtsch. chem. Ges.*, **8** (1875) 464, 820

[16] Gerlich, G., *ibid.* **8** (1875) 650

[17] Gerlich, G., *Liebig's Ann.* **178** (1875) 89

[18] Schmidt, E., *Ber. dtsch. chem. Ges.* **10** (1877) 187

[19] Semmler, F. W., *Die Aetherischen Öle, Erster Band*, von Veit & Co., Leipzig, 1906, p. 857

20 Robiquet, and Bussy, A., *Journ. de Pharm.* II **26** (1840) 110
21 Schmid, H. and Karrer, P., *Helv. chim. acta.* **31** (1948) 1017, 1087, 1497
22 Kjaer, A. and Gmelin, R., *Acta chem. scand.* **10** (1956) 1100
23 Zwergal, A., *Die Pharmacie* **6** (1951) 245
24 Challenger, F., *Sci. Progr.* **37** (1949) 464
25 Ettlinger, M. G. and Lundeen, A. J., *J. Amer. chem. Soc.* **78** (1956) 4172
26 Voltmer, L., *Ber. dtsch. chem. Ges.* **24** (1891) 378
27 Yamada, T., *Acta. chem. scand.* **9** (1955) 349
28 Sommer, F., Schulz, O. F. and Nassau, M., *Z. anorg. allgem. Chemie* **147** (1925) 142
29 Kharasch, M. S., *Chem. Revs.* **29** (1946) 269
30 Schultz, O. E. and Gmelin, R., *Arch. Pharm.* **287** (1954) 342
31 Gadamer, J., *ibid.* **237** (1899) 507
32 Gadamer, J., *ibid.* **237** (1899) 111
33 Will, H. and Laubenheimer, A., *Annalen* **199** (1879) 150
34 Schultz, O. E. and Gmelin, R., *Arch. Pharm.* **287** (1954) 404
35 Schneider, W. and Schütz, L. A., *Ber. dtsch. chem. Ges.* **46** (1913) 2634
36 Schmalfuss, H., *Forschungsdienst, Sonderheft,* **1** (1936) 37
37 Kjaer, A. and Jensen, R. B., *Acta chem. scand.* **10** (1956) 1365
38 Hofmann, A. W. von, *Ber. dtsch. chem. Ges.* **2** (1869) 102; **7** (1874) 508
39 Hofmann, A. W. von, *ibid.* **7** (1874) 516
40 Sjollema, B., *Rec. Trav. chim. Pays-Bas.* **20** (1901) 237
41 Ettlinger, M. G. and Lundeen, A. J., *J. Amer. chem. Soc.* **79** (1957) 1764
42 Hofmann, A. W. von, *Ber. dtsch. chem. Ges.* **13** (1880) 1732
43 Macagno, I., *Z. analyt. Chem.* **21** (1882) 133
44 Semmler, F. W., *Die Aetherischen Oele*, Vol. 1, p. 856
45 Gadamer, J., *Ber. dtsch. chem. Ges.* **30** (1897) 2322
46 Gadamer, J., *Arch. Pharm.* **237** (1899) 103
47 Gadamer, J., *Z. physiol. Chem.* **23** (1897) 123
48 Ponzio, G., *Gazzetta* **26** (1) (1896) 326
49 Sell, E. and Proskauer, B., *Ber. dtsch. chem. Ges.* **9** (1876) 1266
50 Anschütz, R., *Liebig's Ann.* **371** (1910) 216
51 Wheeler, H. L. and Merriam, H. F., *J. Amer. chem. Soc.* **23** (1901) 284
52 McDowall, F. H., Morton, I. D. and McDowell, A. K. R., *N. Zealand J. Sci. Tech.* **28,** A, (1947) 305
53 Kjaer, A. and Rubinstein, K., *Acta chem. scand.* **7** (1953) 528
54 Chargaff, E., Levine, C. and Green, C., *J. biol. Chem.* **175** (1948) 67
55 Kjaer, A. and Gmelin, R., *Acta chem. scand.* **10** (1956) 335
56 Kjaer, A., Gmelin, R. and Larsen, I., *ibid.* **9** (1955) 857
57 Kjaer, A. and Larsen, I., *ibid.* **8** (1954) 699
58 Dragendorff, G., *Die Heilpflanzen der verschiedenen Völker und Zeiten.* F. Enke, Stuttgart, 1898, p. 260
59 Kjaer, A. and Conti, J., *Acta chem. scand.* **7** (1953) 1011
60 Kjaer, A. and Gmelin, R., *ibid.* **9** (1955) 542
61 Kjaer, A. and Conti, J., *ibid.* **8** (1954) 295
62 Schneider, W. and Kaufmann, H., *Liebig's Ann.* **392** (1912) 1
63 Schulz, O. E. and Gmelin, R., *Z. Naturf.* **8b** (1953) 157

[64] Schulz, O. E. and Wagner, W., *Z. Naturf.* **11b** (1956) 73, 417

[65] Kjaer, A. and Gmelin, R., *Acta chem. scand.* **10** (1956) 1358

[66] Kjaer, A., Gmelin, R. and Jensen, R. B., *ibid.* **10** (1956) 1614

[67] Schmalfuss, H., *Forschungsdienst, Sonderheft*, **1** (1936) 37

[68] Kjaer, A. and Jensen, R. B., *Acta chem. scand.* **10** (1956) 1365

[69] La Forge, F. B., Green, N. and Gersdorff, W. A., *J. Amer. chem. Soc.* **70** (1948) 3707

[70] Juvala, A., *Ber. dtsch. chem. Ges.* **63** (1930) 1989

[71] Kjaer, A., Gmelin, R. and Jensen, R. B., *Acta chem. scand.* **10** (1956) 482

[72] Astwood, E. B., Greer, M. A. and Ettlinger, M. G., *J. biol. Chem.* **181** (1949) 121

[73] Kaluza, L., *Monatsh.* **30** (1909) 701, 717; **33** (1912) 363

[74] von Braun, J. and Deutsch, H., *Ber. dtsch. chem. Ges.* **45** (1912) 2198

[75] Hopkins, C. Y., *Can. J. Res.* **16** (1938) 341

[76] Bruson, H. A. and Eastes, J. W., *J. Amer. chem. Soc.* **59** (1937) 2011

[77] Ettlinger, M. G., *ibid.* **72** (1950) 4699

[78] Greer, M. A., *J. clin. Endocrin.* **9** (1949) 1069

[79] Greer, M. A., *J. biol. Chem.* **181** (1949) 121

[80] Greer, M. A., *J. Amer. chem. Soc.* **78** (1956) 1260

5

BIOLOGICAL METHYLATION WITH PARTICULAR REFERENCE TO COMPOUNDS OF SULPHUR

INTRODUCTION

IN the strictest sense the term 'biological methylation' implies either, (1) the transfer under biological conditions of an intact methyl group from a compound (A) to a second compound (B), or (2) the fission under biological conditions of some compound (C), not necessarily containing a methyl group, so as to eliminate a molecule such as formaldehyde or formic acid, a 'one carbon fragment'. This is finally captured by a compound (D) and afterwards the resulting group, e.g. $-CH_2OH$ or $H-\overset{|}{C}=O$ is reduced to $-CH_3$.

In (1) compound (A) is known as a methyl donor and the process is a true transmethylation; in (2) compound (C) is called a methyl source and the term transmethylation is, perhaps, better not employed to designate the process. This chapter presents a discussion of such reactions, as observed in animals, higher and lower plants and in micro-organisms with particular reference to compounds of sulphur. Much work has been carried out on the mechanism of these processes and, although a great deal remains to be learned about the intermediate stages, the use of isotopic indicators has thrown considerable light on the main lines along which biological methylation proceeds. The author has reviewed the progress of research in this field[1-5] and du Vigneaud has published a valuable account of the historical development of the study of methylation processes in animals[6].

Simple organic compounds of sulphur such as methanethiol CH_3SH[7] and dimethyl sulphide[8] $CH_3 \cdot S \cdot CH_3$ or more complex derivatives, e.g. methionine $CH_3S \cdot CH_2 \cdot CH_2 \cdot CH(NH_2) \cdot COOH$, or a dimethyl-$\beta$-propiothetin salt[9-11] $(CH_3)_2\overset{+}{S}(\overline{X}) \cdot CH_2 \cdot CH_2 \cdot COOH$ are very closely involved with the phenomena of biological methylation. It will therefore be necessary to present a preliminary account of the development of the study of methylation processes in general before describing the recent important advances in which methionine and related compounds have played so dominant a part.

The importance of the methyl group in organic and biochemistry is apparent from a consideration of some of the commonest natural products. Trimethylamine occurs in the blossom of the hawthorn, *Crataegus oxyacantha*, the goosefoot, *Chenopodium vulvarea*, and in herring-brine where it probably arises by bacterial reduction of trimethylamine oxide $(CH_3)_3\overset{+}{N}{-}\overset{-}{O}$, which is an ingredient in the tissues of many fish and of the muscle of crabs and lobsters. The corresponding quaternary ammonium base, tetramethylammonium hydroxide $(CH_3)_4 N \cdot OH$, and also methylpyridinium hydroxide are elaborated by the sea-anemone, *Actinia equina*[12]. The presence of choline $(CH_3)_3\overset{+}{N}(\overset{-}{OH}) \cdot CH_2 \cdot CH_2OH$ in plant and animal tissues is well known. The closely related compound betaine $(CH_3)_3\overset{+}{N} \cdot CH_2 \cdot CO\overset{-}{O}$ occurs not only in sugar beet but also in many marine animals.

Creatine $NH_2 \cdot C(:NH) \cdot N(CH_3) \cdot CH_2 \cdot COOH$ found in the muscle of animals, has received much attention from biochemists especially in its relation to methionine $CH_3 \cdot S \cdot CH_2 \cdot CH_2 \cdot CH(NH_2)COOH$. This amino acid, isolated from protein by Mueller[13] and synthesized by Barger and Coyne[14] has now acquired immense importance in biochemistry. It is converted in the body to cystine $COOH \cdot CH$ $(NH_2) \cdot CH_2 \cdot S \cdot S \cdot CH_2 \cdot CH(NH_2) \cdot COOH$ by a remarkable reaction in which serine $HOCH_2 \cdot CH(NH_2) \cdot COOH$ is involved. Methionine is doubtless the precursor of the methyl sulphone *iso*thiocyanate cheirolin $CH_3 \cdot SO_2 \cdot CH_2 \cdot CH_2 \cdot CH_2 \cdot N : C : S$ which occurs in the wallflower[15].

The occurrence of $-NCH_3$ and $-OCH_3$ groups in alkaloids is so well known as to need no illustration by examples. In addition to these compounds, numerous natural products such as vanillin (I) eugenol (II) and anethole (III) contain methoxy groups. Allied to these are piperine (IV) and safrole (V) containing the $CH_2 : O_2$ grouping which has the same biological origin as $-OCH_3$ (see p.195).

(I)   (II)   (III)

(IV)   (V)

THE DEVELOPMENT OF THE CONCEPTION OF BIOLOGICAL METHYLATION

It is now necessary to trace, in chronological order, the development of our knowledge of biological methylation and of its mechanism. His[16] in 1887 showed that pyridine acetate given to dogs is excreted as methylpyridinium acetate. The same reaction occurs in turtles and an analogous methylation of quinoline in dogs. As early as 1824, however, Gmelin[17] mentioned the exhalation of a strong garlic odour on administration of potassium tellurite to animals. In 1853 Hansen described the same effect in man and stated that the odour resembled that of diethyl telluride $Te(C_2H_5)_2$.

In 1894 Hofmeister[18], aware of the work of His, regarded the tellurium gas' as dimethyl telluride, though without proof. In this article we note the first, rather vague conception of the possibility of methyl transfer. He considered that 'the methyl group is already present in the tissues which possess the capacity for methylation. In presence of pyridine and tellurium these are methylated, whereas under normal conditions methyl derivatives such as choline and creatine are produced'. Hofmeister did not mention any particular compound as the source of the methyl group. A distinct advance was made in 1913 by Riesser[19] who concluded that the methyl groups of the (assumed) dimethyl telluride synthesized by the animal body from potassium tellurite, and the methyl group of creatine were probably furnished by choline or betaine.

In 1912 Ackermann[20] showed that in dogs, nicotinic acid (VI) is converted to trigonelline (VII), and to nicotinuric acid (VIII). A similar process occurs in other animals but in most cases, N'-methylnicotinamide (IX) and not trigonelline is produced.

(VI)   (VII)   (VIII)   (IX)

Glycine is obviously concerned in the formation of the nicotinuric acid. Similar 'detoxications' are summarized by Williams[21]. The author[22] suggested in 1935 that glycine might also be responsible for the methylation of the heterocyclic nitrogen atom of nicotinic acid, possibly after oxidative deamination to formaldehyde and, in another connection, that glycine might in a similar manner methylate itself to betaine (see p. 178). Fifteen years later the work on

164

one-carbon fragments (*see* p. 177) indicated that this suggestion may be somewhere near the truth.

Until 1932 the study of biological methylation had been confined to animals but in that year Challenger, Miss C. Higginbottom and Ellis[23] showed that the volatile arsenic compound, Gosio-gas (*see* p. 166) evolved from cultures of the mould *Scopulariopsis brevicaulis* containing arsenious oxide was not diethylarsine $(C_2H_5)_2AsH$, as had previously been believed, but trimethylarsine, $(CH_3)_3As$. The recognition that mycological methylation was involved directed this almost *ad hoc* study of Gosio-gas into a very much broader field, and led to similar work on compounds of selenium and tellurium, methylation in mould cultures again being observed. On the other hand, methylation of sulphur was detected only with a few compounds and this led to a study of the stability of the —S—S— and the C—S—C links in mould cultures and finally to an investigation of the natural formation of dimethyl sulphide and the occurrence of dimethylsulphonium derivatives $X\text{-}\left\{(CH_3)_2\overset{+}{S}\cdot R\right.$ in plants.

METHYLATION OF ARSENIC COMPOUNDS BY MOULDS

The work on Gosio-gas (*see* p. 166), arose from observations made in 1839 or earlier and some account of the background of this research and its development in the last 20 years may now be given. It will be found to fit into the larger picture of biological methylation as a whole.

Over 100 years ago cases of arsenical poisoning occurred in Germany due to the use of domestic wall-papers, the pigments on which contained copper hydrogen arsenite. Gmelin[24] in 1839 noticed a garlic odour in 'arsenical' rooms. He ascribed the poisoning to a volatile arsenic compound liberated from the damp and mouldy wall-paper. Selmi[25] suggested in 1874 that the moulds might play a definite part in the volatilization of the arsenic, producing hydrogen from the paper and paste which then gave rise to arsine, AsH_3.

The work of Gosio and Biginelli—In 1893 Gosio[26,26a] exposed a potato-mash containing arsenious oxide to air; it became infected with moulds and bacteria and evolved a garlic odour. Some organisms were isolated in pure culture and their effect on media containing arsenious oxide studied. The bacteria produced no volatile arsenic compounds but some moulds were intensely active especially *Penicillium brevicaule (Scopulariopsis brevicaulis)*.

Biginelli[27] aspirated the gas from the arsenical mould cultures through mercuric chloride in dilute hydrochloric acid. The resulting precipitate was assigned the composition $(C_2H_5)_2AsH \cdot 2HgCl_2$. He therefore stated that the gas was diethylarsine. Meanwhile, Cevey[28] had observed a garlic odour when the inorganic arsenic of the cultures is replaced by sodium cacodylate, $(CH_3)_2As : O \cdot ONa$.

The work of the Leeds School—Further work was commenced by Challenger *et al.*[1-5] in 1931. Sterile bread crumbs were inoculated with *S. brevicaulis,* and incubated and sterilized aqueous solutions of various arsenic compounds added to the cultures arranged in series. Sterile air was then passed through, volatile arsenic compounds being absorbed in Biginelli's solution. Using arsenious oxide (0·2–0·25 per cent in the bread) two different deposits were obtained according to the concentration of the mercuric chloride, consisting of the dimercurichloride and monomercurichloride of trimethylarsine $(CH_3)_3As \cdot 2HgCl_2$ and $(CH_3)_3As \cdot HgCl_2$. Gosio-gas is therefore trimethylarsine, $(CH_3)_3As$. Arsine, AsH_3 and diethylarsine $(C_2H_5)_2AsH$ are not formed by the mould. This conclusion was confirmed by absorption in nitric acid and in benzyl chloride, when trimethylhydroxyarsonium nitrate and benzyltrimethylarsonium chloride (characterized as picrates) were obtained respectively. With sodium methylarsonate $CH_3AsO(ONa)_2$ (1–1·3 per cent in the bread) or sodium cacodylate (0·1–0·3 per cent) (both free from inorganic arsenic), the evolved gas gave the same mercurichloride.

Alkylarsonic acids and S. brevicaulis—It seemed possible that with sodium methylarsonate and cacodylate, the mould might have hydrolysed the As—C link, giving inorganic arsenic. With sodium ethylarsonate in bread cultures dimethylethylarsine $(CH_3)_2AsC_2H_5$ was evolved and identified as the mercurichloride, ethyldimethylbenzylarsonium chloride, and as ethyldimethylhydroxyarsonium nitrate (both characterized as picrates) thus eliminating this possibility. Addition of other alkylarsonic acids to the mould in concentrations varying from 0·2 to 0·5 per cent gave mixed methylated arsines. The relations: $R \cdot AsO_3H_2 \rightarrow R \cdot As \cdot (CH_3)_2$ and $R \cdot R' \cdot AsO \cdot OH \rightarrow R \cdot R' \cdot As \cdot CH_3$ summarize these results.

METHYLATION OF INORGANIC COMPOUNDS OF SELENIUM AND TELLURIUM

Rosenheim showed that when *S. brevicaulis* was grown upon sterile bread containing inorganic compounds of selenium and tellurium, unpleasant odours were evolved. The substances responsible were not identified.

The gas evolved from the selenium cultures was identified by Challenger and North[29]. The volatile products from cultures of *S. brevicaulis* on bread containing sodium selenate or selenite were characterized as dimethyl selenide mercurichloride and mercuri-bromide $(CH_3)_2Se \cdot HgX_2$, dimethylhydroxyselenonium nitrate $\overline{NO}_3 \big\{ (CH_3)_2 \overset{+}{Se} \cdot OH$, dimethyl selenide α-platinochloride, and dimethylbenzylselenonium chloride $\overline{Cl} \big\{ (CH_3)_2 \cdot \overset{+}{Se} \cdot CH_2Ph$ isolated as the picrate. *Aspergillus niger* also converted sodium selenate to dimethyl selenide[30] (*see* p. 189). Bird and Challenger[31] aspirated the gases evolved from cultures of *S. brevicaulis* on bread containing potassium tellurite through various reagents. Dimethyl telluride mercurichloride was obtained and converted to the dibromide. Absorption in alcoholic iodine gave the di-iodide. The mould gas is therefore dimethyl telluride, $(CH_3)_2Te$.

No proof exists that the odour exhaled by men and animals in receipt of tellurite is actually dimethyl telluride; bearing in mind, however, the well-established instances of biological methylation by animals no reasonable doubt can remain that both animals and moulds methylate tellurium and selenium.

The Biological Methylation of Compounds of Sulphur

Attempts were made at Leeds to obtain dimethyl sulphide by the addition of sulphur or its compounds to cultures of two different strains of *S. brevicaulis*. Negative results were obtained with sulphur, sodium sulphite, sodium thiosulphate, sodium tetrathionate, thiourea, thiodiglycollic acid, sodium formaldehydesulphoxylate ('rongalite') and also with sodium ethanesulphonate and ethanesulphinate.

This was surprising, because Pohl[32] noticed a leek-like odour in the breath of animals receiving injections of thiourea. The odorous product was non-reactive to sodium hydroxide or mercuric cyanide, and was therefore not an alkanethiol. It was, however, absorbed by sulphuric acid and gave a precipitate with mercuric chloride. Pohl therefore concluded that the product was an alkyl sulphide. A similar odour is exhaled by patients suffering from hyperthyroidism (thyrotoxicosis) and receiving thiourea, but not when this drug is replaced by thiouracil or 4-methylthiouracil. Neither of these uracil derivatives gives a volatile sulphur compound in cultures of *S. brevicaulis*[33].

The occurrence in nature of compounds such as methionine, $CH_3S \cdot CH_2 \cdot CH_2 \cdot CH(NH_2) \cdot CO_2H$, cheirolin[15], $CH_3 \cdot SO_2 \cdot CH_2 \cdot CH_2 \cdot CH_2 \cdot N : C : S$, and sulphoraphene[34], $CH_3 \cdot SO \cdot CH : CH \cdot CH_2 \cdot CH_2 \cdot N : C : S$ and the relation of methionine to cysteine and to cystine suggested that compounds containing the —SH or —S—S— links might be more amenable to the methylating action of the mould.

S. Brevicaulis *and Dialkyl Disulphides. Fission of the Disulphide Link and Methylation of the —S Alkyl group*

The behaviour of disulphides to mercuric chloride having been established (*see* Chapter 1, p. 15) dialkyl disulphides (methyl to *n*-pentyl) were added in dilute aqueous suspension to the bread cultures and volatile products aspirated first through mercuric cyanide and then through mercuric chloride. The products consisted of the alkanethiol RSH [absorbed in mercuric cyanide giving $(RS)_2Hg$], the unchanged disulphide R—S—S—R and the methyl alkyl sulphide, $RSCH_3$. The precipitates obtained with mercuric chloride were mixtures of the mercuric chloride addition product of the methyl alkyl sulphide with varying amounts of $RSHgCl \cdot HgCl_2$ or of $R \cdot S \cdot HgCl$ only, arising from fission of $RS \cdot SR$ (*see* p. 18). On treatment of these mixtures with sodium hydroxide pure methyl alkyl sulphide was evolved and converted to the mercurichloride, the benzylmethylalkylsulphonium picrate, or the double compound with platinous chloride. The fission and methylation of the disulphide link by *S. brevicaulis* appears therefore to be a general reaction of the simple aliphatic disulphides[35,36].

Methylation of Inorganic Sulphur

Birkinshaw, Findlay and Webb[37] showed that the wood-destroying fungus *Schizophyllum commune*, Fr., when grown on an aqueous medium containing glucose, inorganic salts, and a trace of 'Marmite' converts inorganic sulphate to methyl mercaptan CH_3SH. This was characterized as mercury di-thiomethoxide $(CH_3S)_2Hg$. Dimethyl disulphide and traces of hydrogen sulphide and dimethyl sulphide are also formed[38]. This is the only recorded instance of the biological methylation of inorganic sulphur.

THE MECHANISM OF BIOLOGICAL METHYLATION

The Formaldehyde Hypothesis

When the methylation of arsenious acid and ethylarsonic acid, $CH_3 \cdot CH_2 \cdot AsO(OH)_2$ by *S. brevicaulis* was reported by Challenger and Miss Higginbottom they suggested[23] that formaldehyde, possibly arising from carbohydrate or protein, might be the source of the methyl group. Production of trimethylarsine $(CH_3)_3As$, might occur by condensation of formaldehyde with arsenious acid to give, as the first product, hydroxymethylarsonic acid $HO \cdot CH_2 \cdot AsO(OH)_2$. This hypothesis was discussed in greater detail[39] in 1935 and in several later publications. The same authors concluded from a survey of the evidence that glycine was the most likely source of formaldehyde—or of the closely related glyoxylic acid HOOC·CHO. Robinson[40,41] had already drawn attention to formaldehyde, arising from glycine as a probable source of the methyl groups of many alkaloids.

Challenger and Higginbottom[39] proposed the following sequence of reactions to explain the mycological formation of trimethylarsine:

$$CH_2O + H\cdot AsO(OH)_2 \rightarrow HO\cdot CH_2\cdot AsO(OH)_2 \xrightarrow{\text{Reduction}}$$

$$CH_3\cdot AsO(OH)_2 \xrightarrow{\text{Reduction}} CH_3\cdot As(OH)_2 \rightarrow CH_3\cdot AsH(O)OH$$
Methylarsonic acid

$$\xrightarrow{CH_2O} HO\cdot CH_2\cdot As(CH_3)\cdot O\cdot OH \rightarrow (CH_3)_2AsO\cdot OH \xrightarrow{\text{Repetition}}$$
Cacodylic acid

$$(CH_3)_3AsO \xrightarrow{\text{Reduction}} (CH_3)_3As$$
Trimethylarsine
oxide

It was not possible to detect methylarsonic or cacodylic acids in cultures of *S. brevicaulis* containing arsenious oxide, but both these acids and also trimethylarsine oxide readily yield trimethylarsine in bread cultures of the mould. Hydroxymethylarsonic acid could not be synthesized and its homologue $HO\cdot CH_2\cdot CH_2\cdot AsO(OH)_2$ in bread cultures gave no volatile product. Had reduction of the $-CH_2\cdot CH_2OH$ group to $-CH_2\cdot CH_3$ occurred, the formation of ethyldimethylarsine would have been expected.

If selenious and tellurous acids can react as $HSeO_2\cdot OH$ and $HTeO_2\cdot OH$ the formaldehyde hypothesis could explain their methylation in mould cultures.

As applied to the fission of disulphides and methylation of the resulting thiol the hypothesis demands the formation of $R\cdot S\cdot CH_2OH$ as suggested by Challenger and Rawlings[35]. The compound $C_2H_5\cdot S\cdot CH_2OH$ could not be freed from traces of ethanethiol and so its capability of reduction to $C_2H_5\cdot S\cdot CH_3$ in mould cultures could not be examined. This reaction of thiols and formaldehyde has recently been invoked by Berg[42] and by Greenberg[43] to explain the conversion of homocysteine to methionine in animal enzyme systems.

An enzyme (glycine oxidase) which converts glycine to glyoxylic acid and ammonia[44] occurs in the liver and kidneys of many animals. Moreover, formate and formaldehyde are produced from the 3-carbon atom of serine and the 2-carbon atom of glycine in liver slices (*see* p. 177). Paretsky and Werkman[45] also obtained formic

169

acid and formaldehyde (isolated as the dimedone derivative) by the oxidation of glycine by a species of *Achromobacter*. The formaldehyde hypothesis, merged in the slightly wider conception of the one-carbon fragment, now affords a very satisfactory explanation of some, though not all, aspects of biological methylation. Thus, if sodium formate labelled with ^{14}C is added to certain mould cultures containing arsenious oxide or sodium selenate the resulting tri-methylarsine and dimethyl selenide are radioactive (*see* p. 188).

The Transfer of a Methyl Group

Shortly after the formaldehyde hypothesis was advanced to explain the processes of methylation by moulds, Challenger and Higginbottom suggested an alternative mechanism[39] and stated in 1935: 'It is not impossible that some ingredient of the cell sub-stance containing a methylated nitrogen atom may, under the special conditions obtaining in the cell, lose a methyl group *which if it be eliminated with a positive charge could be easily co-ordinated by the unshared electrons of tervalent arsenic or quadrivalent selenium and tellurium*'. The italics indicate the degree to which this suggestion extends those of Hofmeister and Riesser.

This conception was developed in detail in 1942[1]. It was pointed out that almost all the compounds which undergo methylation by moulds or animals can furnish negative ions and contain unshared electrons, so that co-ordination of a positive methyl group by the ion would yield a neutral molecule which could then undergo *reduction and ionisation* followed by further co-ordination of positive methyl. This positive methyl 'may be assumed to be derived from betaine, choline, or methionine'. By 1942 the classical work of du Vigneaud and his school (*see* p. 173) on transmethylation in animals had rendered these speculations particularly attractive.

The suggested process was illustrated for arsenic and selenium as shown below[1-5]:

Arsenic

$$: As(OH)_3 \rightarrow H^+ + (HO)_2 \ddot{A}s : O \xrightarrow{ CH_3^+ } CH_3 \cdot AsO(OH)_2 \rightarrow H^+ +$$

Methylarsonic acid

$$CH_3 \cdot AsO(OH)\bar{O} \xrightarrow{\text{Reduction}} CH_3 \cdot \ddot{A}s(OH)\bar{O} \xrightarrow{CH_3^+} (CH_3)_2 AsO \cdot OH \xrightarrow[\text{and Reduction}]{\text{Ionization}}$$

Cacodylic acid

$$(CH_3)_2 \ddot{A}s \cdot \bar{O} \xrightarrow{CH_3^+} (CH_3)_3 As : O \xrightarrow{\text{Reduction}} (CH_3)_3 As :$$

Trimethylarsine oxide   Trimethylarsine

The suggested intermediate compounds were not detected in mould cultures but all yielded trimethylarsine in bread cultures of *S. brevicaulis*.

Selenium

$$H_2SeO_3 \rightarrow H^+ + \text{ : } SeO(OH)\cdot\bar{O} \xrightarrow{CH_3^+} CH_3\cdot SeO_2\cdot OH \xrightarrow[\text{and Reduction}]{\text{Ionization}}$$

Selenious acid — Methaneselenonic acid

$$CH_3\cdot Se(O)\bar{O} \xrightarrow{CH_3^+} (CH_3)_2SeO_2 \xrightarrow{\text{Reduction}} (CH_3)_2SeO \xrightarrow{\text{Reduction}} (CH_3)_2Se$$

Ion of Methane-seleninic acid — Dimethyl Selenone — Dimethyl Selenoxide

The postulated intermediate selenium compounds have not been detected in the media but Bird and Challenger[46] showed that *S. brevicaulis* and certain *Penicillia* convert methane-, ethane-, and propane-1-seleninic acids, $RSeO_2H$, to dimethyl, methyl ethyl, and methyl *n*-propyl selenides, $RSeCH_3$, as required by the suggested mechanism, thus:

$$R\cdot Se\bar{O}_2 + \overset{+}{C}H_3 \longrightarrow R\cdot SeO_2CH_3 \xrightarrow{\text{reduction}} R\cdot Se\cdot CH_3$$

Dimethyl selenone is unknown but the selenoxide $(CH_3)_2SO$ could be formed in its reduction to $(CH_3)_2Se$. Its nitrate,

$$N\bar{O}_3 \left\{ \overset{+}{S}e(CH_3)_2\cdot OH \right.$$

readily gives dimethyl selenide in bread cultures of *S. brevicaulis*.

Potassium methane-, ethane-, and propane-1-selenonates, $RSeO_2OK$, in cultures of the same moulds gave only dimethyl selenide, due to hydrolysis of the selenonate to selenite. This does not necessarily invalidate the suggested mechanism since methaneselenonic acid might be sufficiently stable, within the cell, to reach the next stage without hydrolysis. The reactions set out above could equally well be represented as the addition of a $^+CH_3$ ion to a neutral molecule, followed by expulsion of a proton:

$$\overset{+}{C}H_3 + As(OH)_3 \rightarrow \overset{+}{C}H_3\cdot As(OH)_3 \rightarrow CH_3\cdot AsO(OH)_2 + H^+$$

An alternative mechanism to methylation by elimination of a free positive methyl ion was also mentioned by the author in 1942 as it seemed possible that the $^+CH_3$ ion might be expected to give some methyl alcohol in aqueous media. This could not be detected in arsenical cultures of *S. brevicaulis* by Dr Higginbottom at Leeds in 1935 nor by F. Kieffer (unpublished observation) in 1945.

The alternative to methylation by elimination of a positive

methyl ion (reaction of S_N1 type) is a bimolecular reaction of the S_N2 type thus:

$$[R'R''R''' \overset{+}{N} \!-\! CH_3]\overline{X} \longrightarrow NR'R''R''' + CH_3X$$

The positive charge on the nitrogen of the quaternary ammonium ion attracts the electrons of the bond which links it to methyl. This group therefore becomes sufficiently positive to co-ordinate the unshared electrons of the ion X which may be arsenite, selenite, tellurite or possibly the $R\overline{S}$ ion of an alkanethiol arising from a disulphide as in Rawlings' experiments[35]. Conceivably also attachment of CH_3 to the sulphur of a disulphide could occur prior to fission of the S—S link.

This differs from the S_N1 reaction only in its kinetics and not in its products. If, as seems probable this bimolecular mechanism is preferable, then the representation of the co-ordination of $^+CH_3$ by the arsenite or other negative ion should be replaced by a scheme in which the transfer of methyl takes place without actual separation as an ion. Since, however, this also ultimately involves the attachment of methyl to the unshared electrons of the metalloid the formulations on p. 170 may be retained for convenience in representing the suggested intermediate stages in the methylation process.

The above representation assumed that the methyl donor is a quaternary ammonium compound. Further work on mould methylation using tracers containing $^{14}CH_3$ (see p. 188) points strongly to methionine rather than choline or betaine as the methyl donor. Moreover, in du Vigneaud's animal experiments (see p. 173), it is only with methionine that a true transmethylation involving intact methyl has yet been rigidly established.

In the last few years much attention has again been directed to methionine, as Cantoni[47] has shown (see p. 181) that in liver or kidney enzyme systems which can effect methylation, added methionine is converted to a sulphonium compound, the S-adenosinylmethionine ion or 'active methionine'. This has the formula $C_5H_4N_5 \cdot C_4H_6O_3 \cdot$

$$\overset{+}{CH_2} \!\cdot\! S \!\cdot\! (CH_3) \!\cdot\! CH_2 \!\cdot\! CH_2CH(NH_2) \!\cdot\! CO_2H \text{ (see p. 182).}$$

If it be formulated as $R \!\cdot\! \overset{+}{S} \!\cdot\! (CH_3) \!\cdot\! R'$ the bimolecular S_N2 reaction with, for example, arsenite could be represented thus, assuming that methionine is similarly 'activated' in moulds:

$$R\,R'\,\overset{+}{S} \!\cdot\! CH_3 + : As(OH)_3 \longrightarrow \left[RR'S \longleftarrow \overset{+}{C}H_3 : As(OH)_3\right]$$
$$R \!\cdot\! S \!\cdot\! R' + \left[CH_3 \!\cdot\! \overset{+}{As}(OH)_3\right] \longrightarrow CH_3 \!\cdot\! AsO(OH)_2 + H^+$$

The attraction of the positive sulphur pole for the electrons of the

—S—CH_3 link might allow nucleophilic attack on the methyl group by the arsenic atom with its unshared electrons. The resulting transition state would lead to methylarsonic acid, to a neutral sulphide $R \cdot S \cdot R'$ (S-adenosinylhomocysteine $C_5H_4N_5 \cdot C_4H_6O_3 \cdot CH_2 \cdot S \cdot CH_2 \cdot CH_2CH(NH_2)COOH$ which has recently been detected in the enzymic methylation of guanidinoacetic acid to creatine, *see* p. 187) and a proton, without formation of a free positive methyl ion at any stage.

TRANSMETHYLATION. DU VIGNEAUD'S EXPERIMENTS USING ISOTOPIC INDICATORS

Transmethylation from methionine and choline—The conclusion that biological methylation might be effected by methyl groups detached from choline or betaine was established for animals by du Vigneaud[48] who showed that homocystine $(CO \cdot OH \cdot CH(NH_2) \cdot CH_2 \cdot CH_2 \cdot S \cdot)_2$ can replace methionine $CO \cdot OH \cdot CH(NH_2)CH_2 \cdot CH_2 \cdot S \cdot CH_3$ in the diet of the white rat only in presence of choline or betaine. It was suggested that a methyl group is transferred from the nitrogen of choline or betaine to the sulphur of homocysteine $CO \cdot OH \cdot CH(NH_2) \cdot CH_2 \cdot CH_2 \cdot SH$, by transmethylation (*see* pp. 162 and 174) to give methionine and that the reaction might be reversible, methionine acting as a methyl donor to a choline precursor. This hypothesis was tested by feeding deuteriomethionine $CO \cdot OH \cdot CH(NH_2)CH_2 \cdot CH_2 \cdot SCD_3$ containing (*a*) 83·6 and (*b*) 87·5 atom per cent of deuterium in the methyl group, to rats on a methionine–choline-free diet. The deuterium content of urinary creatinine (X) closely follows that of the creatine (XI) and choline $H\bar{O}\left\{ \overset{+}{N}(CH_3)_3 \cdot CH_2 \cdot CH_2 \cdot OH \right.$ of the tissues.

$$
\begin{array}{cc}
\begin{array}{c}
\text{NH——CO} \\
\text{HN:C} \quad \text{CH}_2 \\
\text{N·CH}_3
\end{array}
&
\begin{array}{c}
\text{H}_2\text{N} \\
\text{HN}=\text{C} \\
\text{CH}_3\text{·N·CH}_2\text{·COOH}
\end{array}
\end{array}
$$

(X)   (XI)

The experiment with specimen (*a*) was, therefore, continued for 94 days until the methyl group of the creatinine contained 72·4 atom per cent. The animal was then killed and the choline isolated from the tissues as the chloroplatinate. The atom percentage of deuterium in the methyl groups of this choline was 74·2, and in the tissue creatine 73. These figures represent in each case approximately 83 per cent of the theoretically possible amount of deuterium, assuming that all the methyl groups had come from deuteriomethionine. This figure is the 'deuterium ratio', i.e. 100 times atom per cent deuterium in the methyl group of the isolated compound divided by atom per cent deuterium in the methyl group of the deuteriomethionine administered. On oxidation of the choline to trimethylamine all the deuterium was found in the methyl groups.

These reactions are true transmethylations (the methyl group being transferred as a whole) and do not involve the elimination of dideuterioformaldehyde CD_2O. This, if produced, would react with the amino-group of the choline precursor, presumably ethanolamine $HOCH_2 \cdot CH_2 \cdot NH_2$, to give $-NH \cdot CD_2OH$ which on reduction in the organism would give $-NH \cdot CD_2H$ and not $-NH \cdot CD_3$. Consequently the deuterium content of each methyl group of the choline could not exceed two-thirds of that in the methyl group of the methionine administered, i.e. the 'deuterium ratio' would have a maximum of 66·6 per cent. Similar arguments hold for the deuteriocreatine. This conclusion was completely established when deuteriomethionine and methionine containing ^{14}C in the methyl group were fed to a rat. The ratio of D to ^{14}C in the isolated choline and creatine was the same as in the original mixture. For a further discussion of this type of experiment and its limitations *see* p. 179.

du Vigneaud[48] then administered trideuteriocholine chloride $\overline{Cl}\left\{(CD_3)_3 \cdot \overset{+}{N}CH_2 \cdot CH_2OH\right.$ to rats, on a methionine–choline-free diet containing homocystine, for 23 and 56 days respectively. The deuterium content of the creatine was 24 and 29 per cent of the theoretical maximum and the deuteriomethyl group was also detected in tissue methionine. The methyl groups of choline can therefore take part in methylation but this experiment does not prove that they are transferred intact. It appears that homocysteine is formed from methionine by the animal, and that methionine is continuously re-formed through the methyl group or a one-carbon fragment (*see* pp. 177–179) supplied by choline. On feeding deuteriomethionine and an adequate supply of ordinary choline, formation of deuteriocholine still occurred.

Methionine can also provide a methyl group in the rabbit[49] and in man[50]. The work of du Vigneaud and his colleagues which has been discussed in this section is frequently, and correctly, designated by the adjective 'classical.'

BIOLOGICAL IMPORTANCE OF THE THETINS

We may now consider a rather remarkable instance of the convergence of two apparently dissimilar lines of work. When du Vigneaud discovered the biological mobility of the methyl group in choline, methionine, and betaine, he tested many other methyl derivatives but of these only the sulphonium compound dimethyl-acetothetin chloride, $\overline{Cl}\{(CH_3)_2\overset{+}{S}\cdot CH_2\cdot COOH$ (which has not as yet been detected in nature), exhibited methyl mobility[51]. Toennies, and Toennies and Kolb[52] had already suggested that sulphonium derivatives of methionine might play a part in biological phenomena. (du Vigneaud, commenting upon this suggestion, remarked that methionine is rather resistant to purely chemical demethylating reagents but that formation of a sulphonium compound might loosen the methyl group.)

After the isolation of dimethyl–β–carboxyethylsulphonium chloride (dimethyl–β–propiothetin chloride), $\overline{Cl}\{(CH_3)_2\overset{+}{S}\cdot CH_2\cdot CH_2\cdot COOH$, from seaweed (Chapter 2, p. 34), du Vigneaud and his colleagues confirmed that dimethylacetothetin chloride can replace methionine in the diet of the white rat, the resulting growth being comparable with that obtained with choline or betaine plus homocystine. Maw and du Vigneaud[53] also showed that the thetin chloride from seaweed has a mobile methyl group and will support the growth of rats on a basal methionine-free diet containing homocystine. Maw and du Vigneaud also showed that, whereas the chloride of methylethylacetothetin, $CH_3\cdot CH_2\cdot(CH_3)\overset{+}{S}CH_2\cdot CO\overline{O}$, is a moderately active growth factor under similar conditions, diethylacetothetin chloride is quite inactive. A similar replacement of the methyl groups in choline and methionine by ethyl groups leads to decreased growth-promoting activity and increased toxicity (*see* p. 200).

S-Methylthioacetic acid, $CH_3\cdot S\cdot CH_2\cdot COOH$, is unable to support growth. Its inability to act as an efficient methyl source for homocystine was confirmed by labelling the S-methyl group with deuterium, when only slight traces of deuterium were found in the methyl groups of tissue choline and creatine after 11 days. This acid would therefore appear not to undergo appreciable methylation to thetin in the rat under the conditions employed by these authors.

Onium-compounds as methyl sources—Maw and du Vigneaud point out that the chlorides of choline, 2-hydroxyethyldimethylethyl-ammonium hydroxide ('monoethyl-choline'), betaine, dimethyl-acetothetin, methylethylacetothetin, and dimethyl-β-propiothetin —all of which can supply, directly or indirectly, a methyl group to homocystine *in vivo*—contain a methyl group or groups directly linked to an onium pole.

In a review written in 1950 the author stated[4]:

'The only other well-established biological methyl donor is methionine. Here the methyl group is not linked to a positive pole. The exception may, however, be only apparent as it was suggested several years ago that methionine may undergo conversion to a quaternary compound prior to release of the methyl group.'

Since 1950 the happy intuition of Toennies and Kolb[52] (see p. 175) has been amply confirmed by Cantoni's work on 'active methionine' which is discussed on pp. 181–188.

Thetin and betaine transmethylases—Dubnoff and Borsook[54] showed that the two thetin chlorides can methylate homocysteine to methionine in rat liver or kidney. The enzyme 'dimethylthetin transmethylase' was partially purified by fractional precipitation with ethanol, and separated from the accompanying 'betaine transmethylase' (see p. 190), as the latter is destroyed at pH 4·5. The transmethylation is independent of oxygen and is not inhibited by oxidative poisons such as azide, cyanide, arsenate, or arsenite. Only one methyl group is transferred from dimethylthetin when homocysteine is in excess; in agreement with this finding methylthioacetic acid, CH_3SCH_2COOH, is inactive thus confirming the results of Maw and du Vigneaud. Ericson and his colleagues[55] have recently described the results of a further study of betaine transmethylase. In Dubnoff and Borsook's experiments the methionine from the thetins was estimated colorimetrically. Maw[56] has pointed out that consideration of the reactions involved shows that in each case methylation of homocysteine is accompanied by liberation of a proton. He has carried out the enzymic reaction with dimethylacetothetin as the methyl donor in a bicarbonate buffer and followed the formation of methionine by determining the rate of carbon dioxide formation[57]. With rat liver suspensions at pH 7·4 the volume of carbon dioxide is equivalent to the amount of methionine synthesized.

The reactions may be represented thus:

$$(CH_3)_2\overset{+}{S}\cdot CH_2\cdot CO\overline{O} + H\cdot S\cdot CH_2\cdot CH_2\cdot CH(\overset{+}{N}H_3)\cdot CO\overline{O}$$

$$CH_3\cdot S\cdot CH_2\cdot CH_2\cdot CH(\overset{+}{N}H_3)\cdot CO\overline{O} + CH_3\cdot S\cdot CH_2CO\overline{O} + H^+$$

With betaine $(CH_3)_3\overset{+}{N}\cdot CH_2\cdot CO\overline{O}$ as the methyl donor, methionine synthesis is accompanied by the formation of equivalent amounts of dimethylglycine, i.e. of an additional basic group; no evolution of carbon dioxide was observed.

Maw suggests that as active methionine (S-adenosinylmethionine $C_5H_4N_5\cdot C_4H_6O_3\cdot CH_2\cdot S^+(CH_3)\cdot CH_2\cdot CH_2\cdot CH(NH_2)\cdot CO_2H$, abbreviated to $R\cdot R'\overset{+}{S} CH_3$) is a thetin, it should be possible to employ this method in following the methylation of guanidinoacetic acid to creatine and of dimethylethanolamine $(CH_3)_2N \cdot CH_2 \cdot CH_2OH$ to choline, by 'active methionine'. On the other hand it appears improbable that the methylation of nicotinamide by 'active methionine' could be followed in this manner, since a proton is not eliminated.

Maw[58] has shown that thetins which are methyl sources yield much urinary sulphate in rats. Diethylacetothetin and trimethyl-sulphonium chlorides do not. Experiments with liver and kidney slices led to the same conclusion. S-methylthioacetic acid, the product of demethylation of dimethylacetothetin is readily oxidized to sulphate. Loss of methyl appears to precede oxidation.

SYNTHESIS OF LABILE METHYL IN THE BODY

Until 1947 it was believed that the animal organism is incapable of synthesizing methyl groups and that sources such as methionine and choline must be present in the diet.

du Vigneaud[6] occasionally found animals capable of showing some growth on a homocystine diet without added choline, and Bennett[59] also observed the growth of rats on a methyl-free diet. du Vigneaud, Simmonds, Chandler and Cohn[60] raised the concentration of deuterium in the body water of two rats to about 3 atom per cent by intraperitoneal injection of 99·5 per cent D_2O and maintained this by giving drinking water containing 4 atom per cent of D_2O for 3 weeks. The deuterium content of the choline chloroplatinate then isolated from the tissues indicated that 7·7 and 8·5 per cent respectively of the choline methyl was derived from the body water. At that time the synthesis of methyl groups by intestinal bacteria seemed the most probable interpretation of their results. Later, however, du Vigneaud, Ressler and Rachele[61] showed that germ-free rats maintained under completely sterile conditions with D_2O in their drinking water synthesized choline containing deuterium in the methyl groups to the extent of 3·3 and 6·4 per cent of that in the body water after 10 and 23 days respectively. This synthesis must therefore have been achieved by the tissues of the rats.

Reactions Involving One-carbon Fragments

In some fundamental work of Sakami[62] carried out in 1947, rats received glycine containing ^{13}C in the carboxyl group and formate containing [14]C. The serine from the liver contained ^{13}C, almost exclusively in the —COOH group, and ^{14}C, mainly in the 3-position. The reaction may be represented thus:

$$H^{14}CO_2H + H_2NCH_2{}^{13}CO_2H \rightarrow {}^{14}CH_2OH \cdot CHNH_2 \cdot {}^{13}CO_2H$$

Whether the formate reacts as such with the —CH$_2$— of glycine, giving $H^{14}CO \cdot CH(NH)_2 \cdot {}^{13}CO_2H$ as an intermediate stage or undergoes reduction to formaldehyde giving $CH_2OH \cdot CHNH_2 \cdot CO_2H$ was not decided. Formation of $HO_2{}^{14}C \cdot CH(NH_2){}^{13}CO_2H$ by fixation of $^{14}CO_2$ arising from $H^{14}CO_2H$, or by dehydrogenation of a molecule of formate and one of glycine, appears to be excluded since such a compound would be expected to yield serine containing at least 50 per cent of $HO^{13}CH_2 \cdot CH(NH_2){}^{14}CO_2H$ on reduction.

Sakami also showed that on feeding glycine, $H_2N^{14}CH_2CO_2H$, to rats, the liver serine contains ^{14}C in both the 2 and 3 carbon atoms to an almost equal extent. Glycine is, under these conditions, a major source of formate or formaldehyde which then reacts with unchanged glycine.

Siekevitz, Winnick, and Greenberg[63] observed the reverse change with serine. Formate and formaldehyde are produced in liver slices from carbon atom 3 of serine and carbon atom 2 of glycine. Furthermore Ratner[44] had already described an oxidase, present in the liver and kidneys of all animals examined, which converted glycine to glyoxylic acid and ammonia. The biological formation of formaldehyde or glyoxylic acid from glycine had frequently been postulated.

This work explains some results of Sakami[62], who found that when choline labelled with ^{14}C in the methyl group was administered to rats the tracer element was found in the 3-position in serine. This suggests that formate or some closely related compound is an intermediate in the oxidation of the methyl groups of choline. It seemed possible, therefore, that this reaction might be reversible and that the methyl groups of choline might arise, under some circumstances and to some extent, from compounds such as methanol or sodium formate. If so, light might be thrown on those cases reported by du Vigneaud in which rats appeared to be capable of synthesizing methyl groups on a methyl-free diet (see also p. 177, and Arnstein and Neuberger[65]). Arnstein[64], therefore, fed isotopically labelled (^{14}C) formate, methyl alcohol, and various potential sources of these compounds such as DL-3^{14}C-serine, L-3-^{14}C-serine, 2-^{14}C-glycine, 1-^{14}C-glycine (NH$_2 \cdot$CH$_2 \cdot {}^{14}$COOH), and also D-3-^{14}C-serine to rats maintained on a normal diet. After 1–5 days the rats were killed and the choline isolated as the reineckate, converted to chloroplatinate and thence to trimethylamine chloroplatinate. The first five compounds gave rise to choline containing ^{14}C in the methyl groups.

Carbon dioxide is known to arise by *in vivo* oxidation of D-3-^{14}C-serine and 1-^{14}C-glycine. These compounds were not converted to choline containing ^{14}C in the methyl groups, from which it follows that the intact rat is unable to reduce carbon dioxide to methyl to any appreciable extent. This agrees with the results of du Vigneaud, Verly and Wilson[66] who found that when sodium bicarbonate NaH^{14}CO$_3$ is fed to rats the choline of the tissues is free from the ^{14}C isotope.

Arnstein pointed out that the identity of the methyl precursor was unknown and that although serine and glycine both yield formaldehyde and formate as degradation products these compounds may be involved in the form of derivatives (*see* Chapter 2, p. 61).

The work summarized in this section establishes three important points: (1) that the attachment of a methyl group to a choline or creatine precursor can take place by some process which in its early stages, at any rate, is not identical with the 'transfer of methyl as a whole,' which we associate with the 'transmethylation' as established by du Vigneaud; (2) carbon dioxide is not the source of the methyl group—this is important in view of the significance of carbon dioxide fixation in other fields of biochemistry; and (3) that the body is not entirely dependent on exogenous methyl groups. Verly and du Vigneaud[67] injected dilute aqueous ^{14}C-methyl alcohol subcutaneously into a rat on a diet containing DL-methionine. A total radioactivity of about half that injected appeared in the expired carbon dioxide. The creatine and choline were isolated from the tissues and the choline converted to trimethylamine. All three compounds were radioactive. No exchange of methyl occurred between choline and the labelled methyl alcohol during several days. By the use of methyl alcohol labelled with both deuterium and ^{14}C Verly[68] showed that in rats the methyl group is not transferred direct but that oxidation to a one-carbon fragment (or fragments) occurs (*see* p. 177).

Isotopic selection—the isotopic effect in chemical reactions—depends on the different reactivities of isotopes of the same element, e.g. protium, deuterium and tritium. The heaviest isotope is the least reactive, as is shown in oxidation reactions[69,70]. Failure to allow for this may lead to incorrect conclusions from experiments with isotopic tracers in biochemistry. In 1951 Thorn[71] found that succinic acid is more readily dehydrogenated by succinodehydrogenase than its isomer containing deuterium in the methylene groups. du Vigneaud and his school[72,73] find that in rats a definite fractionation of the three isotopes of hydrogen is observable on oxidation of labelled methyl alcohol. Thus, when a mixture of $CH_2D \cdot OH$, $CH_2T \cdot OH$ and $^{14}CH_3 \cdot OH$ furnishes the methyl groups of choline and creatine, a 'fractionation value' of about $1 \cdot 3$ was observed for T : D. The urine yielded formate which showed a value of about $1 \cdot 7$.

A similar effect was observed in rats during the oxidation of the methyl group of methionine to carbon dioxide[68,73]. On injection the rat oxidizes the $-S-^{14}CD_3$ group to $^{14}CO_2$ to only 60–80 per cent of the value found for the $-S-^{14}CH_3$ linkage.

In true transmethylation where, for instance, a $-CD_3$ group is transferred intact, as in du Vigneaud's classical experiments[48,49], isotopic selection is not involved. However, biological oxidation of a methyl group containing different hydrogen isotopes might occur followed by final reduction to labelled methyl, thus:

$$^{14}CH_2T \cdot OH \ + \ O \ = \ {}^{14}CHT{:}O \ + \ H_2O$$
$$^{14}CHT{:}O \ \ + \ R \cdot H \ = \ R \cdot {}^{14}CHT \cdot OH$$
$$R \cdot {}^{14}CHT \cdot OH + \ 2H \ = \ R \cdot {}^{14}CH_2T \ + \ HOH$$

Here the ratio $T/^{14}C$ in the re-formed methyl group is unchanged and it could be wrongly inferred that true transmethylation had occurred. Consequently Verly[68] fed rats with a *mixture* of ordinary L-methionine, L-14C-methionine and mono-tritio-L-methionine $(-S \cdot CH_2T)$. The $T/^{14}C$ ratio in the choline of the tissues was the same as in the original mixture. It was concluded that a true transmethylation had occurred because earlier experiments in which labelled methyl alcohol $^{14}CH_2T \cdot OH$ was injected into rats had shown that in the resulting labelled choline of the tissues the ratio $T/^{14}C$ was less than in the methyl alcohol administered. Most of the oxidation had been exerted on the protium but some tritium had also been removed. Had this happened in Verly's experiments with labelled methionine a fall in the $T/^{14}C$ ratio would have been expected*. If this interpretation be correct the earlier conclusions of du Vigneaud and his school are confirmed. They had shown that when a mixture of ^{14}C-methionine and trideuteriomethionine was fed to rats the $D/^{14}C$ ratio in the choline of the tissues was the same as that in the methionine mixture administered[70,74,75], indicating a true transmethylation. Nevertheless, oxidation of the methyl group of methionine can occur in animals and has been studied exhaustively[76,77].

* Until recently this 'mixture device' has always been employed to simulate a 'doubly labelled' compound. It is hoped shortly to prepare compounds containing, e.g., deuterium and ^{14}C or tritium and ^{14}C in the same molecule.

Influence of Conditions on Methylation in Enzyme Systems

Borsook and Dubnoff[78] in 1947 distinguished between two types of methylation reactions in preparations of rat or guinea-pig liver. One is dependent on oxygen and is inhibited by oxidation inhibitors. Catalytic activity is lost by homogenization of the tissue and is not restored by simple addition of methionine although in intact slices of rat liver methionine accelerates the reaction. The activity is restored to the homogenate however when adenosine triphosphate (XII) is present in addition to methionine. In Category I is the methylation by methionine of guanidinoacetic acid to creatine and of nicotinamide to N'-methyl-nicotinamide. Characteristic of Category II is independence of oxygen, non-susceptibility to oxidation inhibitors and persistence of catalytic activity after cell structure is destroyed. Examples are the methylation of homocystine or homocysteine to methionine by choline (*see* pp. 184 and 193), betaine, dimethylacetothetin and dimethyl-β-propiothetin.

In Category I adenosine triphosphate is ineffective without methionine. Borsook and Dubnoff considered that the chief function of oxidation in methylation by methionine in liver slices or in homogenates is the continuous production of the necessary adenosine triphosphate. Biochemical oxidation is frequently associated with vigorous phosphorylation. Borsook and Dubnoff did not elucidate the significance of adenosine triphosphate in methylation by methionine.

FORMATION OF 'ACTIVE METHIONINE' IN ENZYME SYSTEMS

Light was thrown on these observations by Cantoni[79,80], who showed that the effect of adenosine triphosphate did not depend on the formation of a phosphorylated derivative of methionine. By addition of methionine, adenosine triphosphate, magnesium ions and glutathione to an enzyme preparation obtained from rat, pig, ox or rabbit liver, and suitable separation of the resulting complex mixture, he obtained a product which he named 'active methionine' and also showed that orthophosphoric acid was liberated.

In presence of an enzyme from pig liver which he called nicotinamide methylpherase (a transmethylation enzyme) this 'active methionine' was able to methylate nicotinamide to N'-methylnicotinamide in absence of adenosine triphosphate or any other source of high-energy phosphate links (*see* p. 182). Similarly the quite different enzyme guanidinoacetic acid methylpherase (obtained from rabbit liver) in presence of 'active methionine' and absence of adenosine triphosphate converted guanidinoacetic acid to creatine.

181

Not only was adenosine triphosphate unnecessary for these methylations (after its initial participation in the conversion of methionine to the 'active methionine'), but treatment of an impure preparation of this substance with alcoholic barium acetate precipitated phosphate. The filtrate was free from phosphate and contained the 'active methionine' which could then be readily separated. It was shown to contain no phosphorus and by analysis and a study of its breakdown products to be S-(5'-deoxyadenosine)-5'-methionine with the structure (XIII).

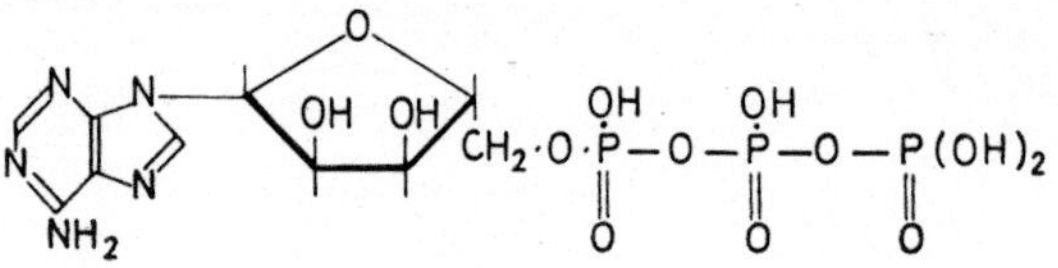

(XII)

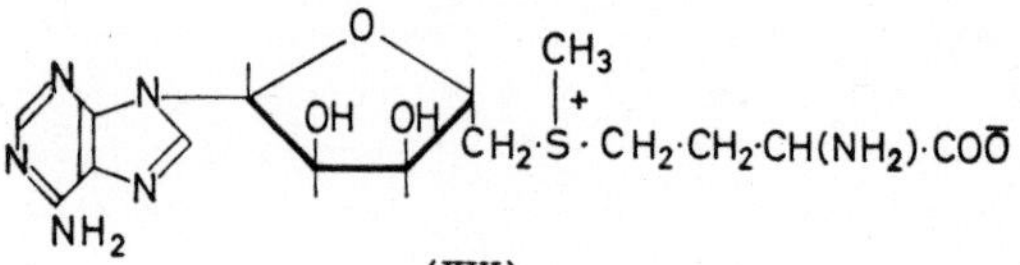

(XIII)

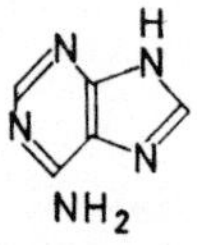

(XIV) 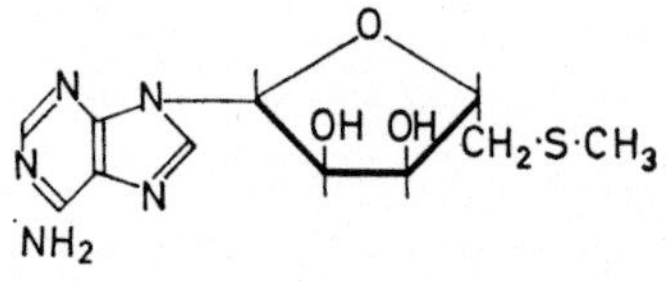　　　　　　(XV)

Properties of Active Methionine

Acid hydrolysis at 100°C gave adenine (XIV), homoserine, $HO\cdot(CH_2)_2\cdot CH(NH_2)\cdot COOH$ and a sulphur compound believed to be a thioribose or a methylthioribose. More gentle hydrolysis at 100°C in an acetate buffer at pH 7 gave some adenine, but mainly a crystalline compound which was conclusively shown to be identical with the adenine methylthiopentoside isolated many years earlier from yeast and shown by synthesis to be 5'-deoxy-5'-methyl-thioadenosine (XV). No adenosine or S-(5'-deoxyadenosine-5'-homocysteine (*see* p. 186) were, however, observed. The unusual structure of this methylthiopentoside had always interested a few chemists but its biological origin was not clear and no natural compounds of analogous structure were known. Its formation by

182

micro-organisms (*see* p. 200) requires an ample supply of methionine in the culture media. It seems probable that it may arise from 'active methionine'. If 'active methionine' is present in yeasts it seems rather surprising that the few species which have been tested should not be able to methylate inorganic arsenic[81]. A detailed study of the capacity of bacteria and yeasts as compared with moulds to effect methylation should be made[82]. The behaviour of 'active methionine' on paper chromatography is consistent with formula (XIII). It moves very slowly in mixtures consisting mainly of organic solvents and rapidly in salt solutions. It gives a positive ninhydrin reaction. Oxidation with periodate on paper and spraying with Schiff's reagent gives a purple colour due to formation of an aldehyde. This shows that the two hydroxyl groups on carbon atoms 2' and 3' of the ribose residue are unsubstituted. In accordance with the presence of a positively charged sulphonium grouping in the molecule 'active methionine' moves rapidly towards the cathode on paper electrophoresis.

It appears that methionine must be converted to a sulphonium compound before it can transfer its methyl group and in view of the results of du Vigneaud and of the Canadian school (*see* pp. 173 and 193) it may be assumed that the methyl group of 'active methionine' is transferred intact. Probably methionine can also furnish a one-carbon fragment which can finally appear as a methyl group. The ready oxidation of methionine methyl in animals is in keeping with such an alternative mode of methylation.

It was suggested by Toennies[83] in 1940 that methionine might undergo conversion to a sulphonium compound prior to release of its methyl group. At that time no sulphonium compound had been detected in nature with the exception of the recognition by Neuberg and Grosser that dogs' urine probably contained some compound of this type. The actual reaction suggested by Toennies was unsupported by experiment but the essential idea was most stimulating and was borne in mind by many chemists. The onium structure of the methyl sources choline, betaine and dimethylacetothetin was soon emphasized. Then followed the isolation of dimethyl-β-propiothetin from seaweed and its recognition as a methyl source and possibly a methyl donor.

The following facts may now be summarized:

1. Methionine can transfer its methyl group intact.

2. Methylation by methionine in enzyme systems *in vitro* requires *either* air and an intact tissue slice *or* adenosine triphosphate in which case the tissue can be homogenized.

3. Methionine and adenosine triphosphate with the appropriate

enzyme system give the sulphonium compound S-(5′-deoxy-adenosine-5′)-methionine.

4. Methylation *in vitro* by the use of -onium compounds such as betaine, choline (which is first converted to betaine[4]) and the two thetins does not require oxygen nor adenosine triphosphate and is not inhibited by homogenizing the tissue. This is presumably because these compounds are already of -onium type. The conclusion follows, but has not been experimentally established*, that betaine and the thetins may also be able to transfer their methyl groups intact, though methylation by an oxidized one-carbon fragment may also be possible. It is desirable that this suggestion, which is not new but receives support from Cantoni's work, should be tested, e.g., by the use of a compound containing a $^{14}CD_3$ group (*see* p. 179).

5. Betaine, dimethylaceto- and dimethyl-β-propiothetins, 'active methionine' and methylmethioninesulphonium iodide (which are also thetins) are all either methyl donors or sources in intact animals or in tissue slices. These all contain a twin ion structure, e.g.,

$$\overset{+}{M}\cdot(CH_2)_n\cdot\bar{C}O_2, \text{ or } \overset{+}{M}\cdot(CH_2)_2\cdot CH(NH_2)\cdot\bar{C}O_2.$$

INVESTIGATIONS LEADING TO THE SYNTHESES OF 'ACTIVE METHIONINE'

(I) SYNTHESIS OF ADENINE METHYLTHIOPENTOSIDE

Baddiley[84] has synthesized adenine methylthiopentoside (adenine 5′-deoxy-5′-methylthiopentoside) (*see* p. 182) and has also provided an independent proof of its structure. The sulphur atom is attached to the carbohydrate portion of the molecule since adenine and a sugar containing sulphur were obtained on acid hydrolysis. For some time it was uncertain whether the sugar contained a methylthio group or a thiol group and a methoxy group. Later, on evidence summarized by Baddiley, it appeared probable that the constitution was 5-deoxy-5-methylthioribose. Its osazone was shown by Weygand, Trauth and Lowenfeld[85] to be identical with that of synthetic 5-deoxy-5-methylthio-D-arabinose. The two thio-sugars were not identical and as arabinose and ribose differ only in the configuration of carbon atom 2 it was clear that the natural sugar from the adenine methylthiopentoside was 5-deoxy-5-methylthio-D-ribose. Gulland[86], had already concluded that the pentose residue was attached to N(9) of the adenine ring.

* The Canadian work makes it probable, *see* p. 193.

It seemed probable that adenine methylthiopentoside, like other natural nucleosides was a β-glycoside and experiments on its synthesis from adenosine which is known to have the β-configuration were therefore commenced. Conversion of adenosine to its 2' : 3' *iso*propylidene derivative by condensation with acetone was followed by formation of the 5'-toluene-*p*-sulphonyl compound (XVI) and reaction in dimethylformamide solution with the potassium derivative of methanethiol. Separation of the product and removal of the acetone residue by dilute sulphuric acid yielded 5'-deoxy-5'-methylthioadenosine (XVII) identical with the natural product.

Similar operations carried out on inosine which differs from adenosine in that C_6 carries a hydroxyl group instead of the amino group, yielded a 5'-deoxy-5'-methylthioinosine. This was shown by Weygand *et al.*[85,87] to be identical with the product obtained by deamination of natural adenine methylthiopentoside by nitrous acid, thus affording a further proof of the structure of the natural product. Simultaneously with Baddiley's investigations, Weygand and Trauth synthesized the methylthiopentoside by a very similar method[87]. The two nucleosides and the thio-sugars and purines liberated on hydrolysis were indistinguishable by paper chromatography tests. Reduction of the thio-sugar from the synthetic compound with sodium amalgam gave 5-methylthio-D-ribitol identical with a specimen prepared from authentic adenine methylthiopentoside. Finally Satoh and Makino[88] synthesized 2' : 3'-*iso*propylidene-5'-deoxy-5'-methylthioadenosine and showed that its picrate was identical with the picrate of the *iso*propylidene derivative of the natural nucleoside. These results clearly established the structure of adenine methylthiopentoside as 9-(5'-deoxy-5'-methylthio-β-D-ribofuranosyl) adenine.

(II) SYNTHESIS OF 'ACTIVE METHIONINE'. S-(5'-DEOXYADENOSINE-5')-METHIONINE

Active methionine has been synthesized by Baddiley and Jamieson[89]. The hydrobromide of DL-α-amino-γ-bromobutyric acid (XVIII) was obtained from DL-α-amino-γ-butyrolactone (XIX) and hydrogen bromide in glacial acetic acid at 100°C. This hydrobromide was added to 5'-deoxy-5'-methylthioadenosine (adenine methylthiopentoside) in a mixture of formic acid and acetic acids. Removal of solvents left a residue which was separated by paper chromatography giving a product which after elution with water was indistinguishable from the natural 'active methionine' (XX) in its behaviour on paper chromatography and electrophoresis, when

185

it moved to the cathode. Water at 120°C regenerated the adenine methylthiopentoside. Enzyme tests showed that this synthetic DL-material had 40–50 per cent of the activity of the natural substance in the methylation of nicotinamide and guanidinoacetic acid.

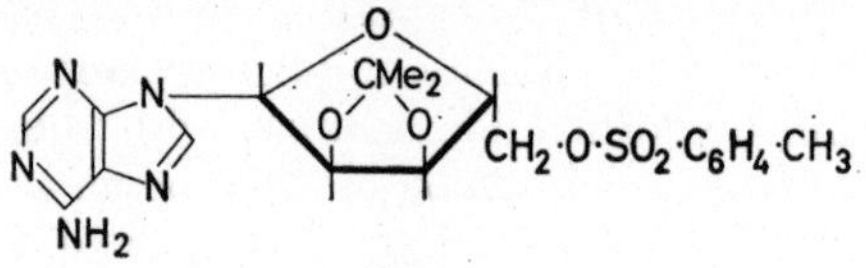

(XVI)

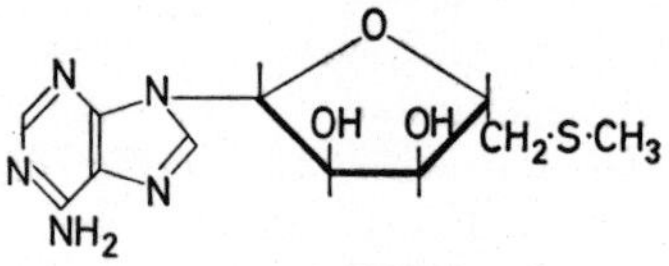

(XVII)

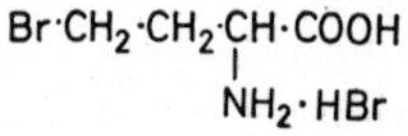

Br·CH₂·CH₂·CH·COOH
        |
        NH₂·HBr

(XVIII)

CH₂·CH₂·CH(NH₂)
 | |
 O————CO

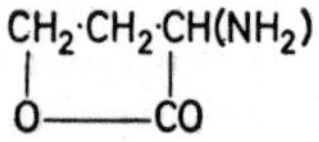

(XIX)

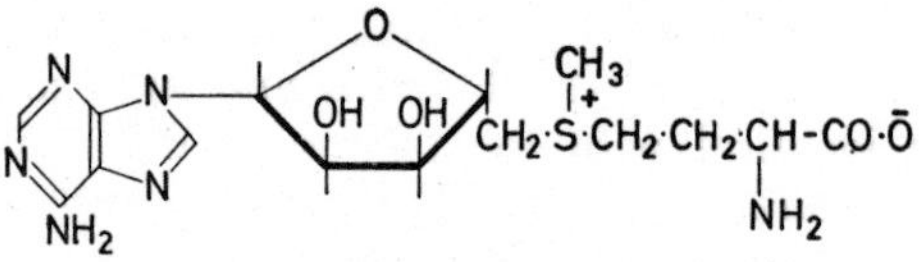

(XX)

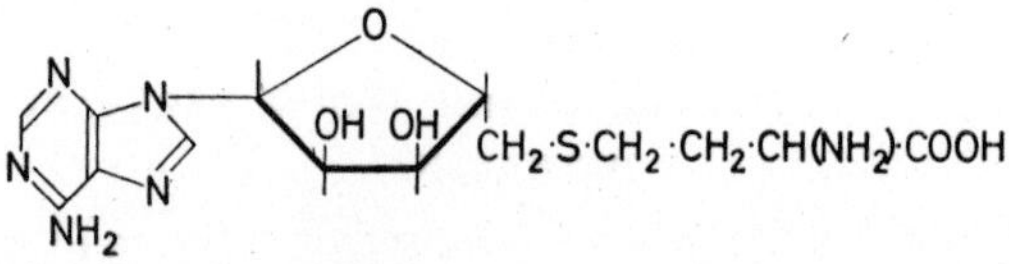

(XXI)

(III) ISOLATION AND SYNTHESIS OF S-(5'-DEOXYADENOSINE-5')-HOMOCYSTEINE LEADING TO A FURTHER SYNTHESIS OF ACTIVE METHIONINE

When methionine takes part in transmethylation the by-product to be expected is homocysteine $HS·CH_2·CH_2·CH(NH_2)·COOH$. This amino acid has, however, never been isolated from any natural product nor detected in an enzymic process. The recognition of

S-(5'-deoxyadenosine-5')-methionine as the methyl donor in transmethylations involving methionine suggested that the primary product resulting from this process should be S-(5'-deoxyadenosine-5')-homocysteine, thus

$$\overset{\displaystyle CH_3}{\underset{\displaystyle |}{}}$$

$$C_5H_4N_5{\cdot}C_4H_6O_3{\cdot}CH_2{\cdot}\overset{+}{S}{\cdot}CH_2{\cdot}CH_2{\cdot}CH(NH_2){\cdot}COOH + RH \longrightarrow$$
$$R{\cdot}CH_3 + C_5H_4N_5{\cdot}C_4H_6O_3{\cdot}CH_2{\cdot}S{\cdot}CH_2{\cdot}CH_2{\cdot}CH(NH_2){\cdot}COOH$$
$$+ H^+$$

This probability was pointed out by Woolley[90], Baddiley, Cantoni and Jamieson[91] and Challenger[92]. The expectation was confirmed by isolation of this substituted homocysteine from the enzymic reaction in which creatine is produced from guanidinoacetic acid[93] (Cantoni and Scarano). It was identical with an authentic specimen synthesized by Baddiley and Jamieson[94] from homocysteine. The disodium derivative of this was allowed to react with 2' : 3'-O-*iso*propylidene-5'-O-toluene-*p*-sulphonyladenosine (XVI) either in liquid ammonia or in dimethylformamide at 100°C. Removal of sodium and toluene-*p*-sulphonate ions from the product in aqueous solution with Amberlite 1R-120 (ammonium form) and Amberlite 1R-4B (hydroxyl form) respectively gave S-(5'-deoxy-2'- : 3'-O-*iso*propylideneadenosine-5')-homocysteine. Removal of the *iso*propylidene group by dilute sulphuric acid yielded crystalline S-(5'-deoxyadenosine-5')-homocysteine (XXI). This was indistinguishable from the natural product of Cantoni and Scarano in R_F and in chemical reactions on paper.

Second Synthesis of 'Active Methionine'

Confirmation of the structure of this homocysteine derivative was obtained[94] by reaction with methyl iodide in acetic acid, when active methionine was formed and purified through its reineckate which, with silver sulphate, yielded the corresponding sulphate. Its identity was confirmed by paper chromatography and by conversion with water at 90°C to 5'-deoxy-5'-methylthioadenosine. This second synthesis of active methionine forms a very convenient route for its preparation in quantity.

THE ENZYMIC TRANSFER OF METHYL FROM THETINS

An essentially homogeneous preparation of the enzyme thetin homocysteine methylpherase has been obtained from horse liver[95] as indicated by electrophoretic and ultra-centrifugal analysis. Its specific activity is one hundred times that of the crude liver extracts.

When isolated it appears to be a polymer and to dissociate to its monomeric units on treatment with mercaptans. This suggests polymerization through disulphide links. The enzyme produces methionine from homocysteine in a reaction which appears to be irreversible and independent of metal cations or of other co-factors. The only methyl acceptor so far recognized for the enzyme is homocysteine, but betaine and several thetins are effective as methyl donors. L-homocysteine is methylated 50 times faster than the D-enantiomorph, but with the racemic form only L-homocysteine reacts. The thermodynamic relations in the transfer of methyl from dimethylacetothetin by this enzyme have also been studied[96].

THE SELENIUM ANALOGUES OF METHIONINE AND OF 'ACTIVE METHIONINE'

The selenium analogue of methionine has been synthesized by Schrift[97]. There is evidence that it is also formed biologically from inorganic compounds of selenium. Mudd and Cantoni[98] have recently shown that in presence of adenosinetriphosphate, excess pyrophosphatase and Cantoni's methionine-activating enzyme[99] prepared from rabbit liver or from yeast, selenomethionine $CH_3 \cdot Se \cdot CH_2 \cdot CH_2 \cdot CH(NH_2) \cdot COOH$ is converted to 'active seleno-methionine' (Se-adenosinylmethionine) at a rate which is similar to that at which 'active methionine' is formed under identical conditions. The reaction can be followed by the rate of elimination of orthophosphoric acid. The new selenonium compound is then precipitated as the trireineckate and converted to the sulphate. When this tertiary sulphate is incubated with guanidinoacetic acid and the enzyme creatine methylpherase (from pigs' liver) creatine is formed in excellent yield by transmethylation. This demonstration that selenium can replace sulphur in biologically important compounds without serious alteration in their functions is an extension of the early work of Horn and Jones[100] on the seleniferous amino acid of cereals grown on soils containing selenium. Recent further work on this subject is reported by Cowie and Cohen[101].

THE USE OF RADIOACTIVE CARBON ^{14}C IN THE INVESTIGATION OF MYCOLOGICAL METHYLATION. THE IMPORTANCE OF METHIONINE

The Leeds school[102,103] has made a study of the effect of various potential sources of the methyl group, labelled with ^{14}C, on the methylation of compounds of arsenic, selenium and sulphur in mould cultures. The sources were choline chloride, betaine, sodium formate, and DL-methionine. Only one methyl group in choline and betaine was labelled. The methylated products were collected as the mercurichlorides and their radioactivity measured. The 'methylation percentage' was calculated from the ratio

$$\frac{100}{nf} \times \frac{\text{Radioactivity of methylated product per mole}}{\text{Radioactivity of methyl source per mole}}$$

where n is the number of methyl groups produced by methylation per molecule of the product and f is the fraction of the total of labelled methyl groups or carbon atoms per molecule which are theoretically labile.

Thus $n = 1$ when the product is $CH_3 \cdot S \cdot C_2H_5 \cdot 2HgCl_2$; $n = 2$ for $(CH_3)_2S \cdot HgCl_2$. The value f is of importance since in choline, betaine, dimethylacetothetin $(CH_3)_2S^+ \cdot CH_2 \cdot CO\bar{O}$, and dimethyl-$\beta$-propiothetin $(CH_3)_2S^+ \cdot CH_2 \cdot CH_2 \cdot CO\bar{O}$ only one methyl group is labile in animals or in tissue preparations.

The methylation percentage was very considerable in all experiments with methionine, ranging from 25 to 95, but small with choline chloride, betaine, and sodium formate. In bread cultures of *A. niger* containing selenate and methionine the methylation percentage was only 45 whereas on a synthetic medium containing sucrose, glycine and inorganic salts the figure rose to over 90. The protein of the bread is probably an excellent source of natural methionine which considerably dilutes the radioactive amino acid. Apparently, the $^{14}CH_3$ of methionine is transferred intact to arsenic and selenium so that in mycological methylation the part played by this amino acid is as dominating as in the analogous animal processes.

This was suggested by the observation that the methylation percentage for the systems ^{14}C-betaine-selenate and ^{14}C-formate-selenate in bread cultures of *A. niger* under comparable conditions was 2–5 times greater in presence of homocystine than in its absence. Borsook[104] showed that homocystine or homocysteine is necessary before the methyl-carbon atom of choline can be transferred to guanidinoacetic acid, yielding creatine.

The methylation of sulphur in bread cultures of *S. brevicaulis* containing diethyl disulphide or S-ethylcysteine was studied in presence of [Me-^{14}C] choline and [^{14}C] formate. Fission of the S—S and the S—C linkages produced inactive ethanethiol and radioactive ethyl methyl sulphide in each case. The methylation percentages were on an average about 3–4, with a maximum of 8.

Methylsulphonium compounds as methyl sources—The work of Maw and du Vigneaud[53] and of Borsook and Dubnoff has shown that dimethylacetothetin and dimethyl-β-propiothetin salts are methyl sources (see p. 175). Handler and Bernheim[105] found that this is also true of another thetin, methylmethioninesulphonium iodide $I^-\left\{Me_2S^+ \cdot CH_2 \cdot CH_2 \cdot CH(NH_2) \cdot CO_2H\right.$ which can replace methionine in promoting the growth of young white rats. The question arose whether these three compounds are methyl donors and comparable with methionine in mycological methylations or only methyl sources and comparable with choline or betaine.

This was tested by competition experiments[102] in which the non-radioactive thetins were added to A. niger cultures on a sucrose–glycine-salts medium containing [Me-^{14}C] methionine and selenate. With the first two thetins and also with betaine the usual high values for the methylation percentage (80–100) were obtained, indicating that no appreciable dilution of the radioactive methyl groups had occurred and that, consequently, these compounds are not direct methyl donors.

It remained to be seen whether the thetins are methyl sources in mould cultures. When these compounds labelled with ^{14}C in one methyl group were added to bread cultures of S. brevicaulis containing selenate the methylation percentage was only 1–1·6 whereas betaine hydrochloride under similar conditions gave a value of 4·0. The thetins are therefore very poor methyl sources.

Since dimethylacetothetin and dimethyl-β-propiothetin salts cannot be utilized as methyl sources even to the same extent as betaine, choline or formate it seems that the 'thetin transmethylase' reported to occur in rat liver preparations by Borsook and Dubnoff[104] and by Dubnoff[106] is not present in A. niger or S. brevicaulis under the experimental conditions.

The position of methylmethioninesulphonium iodide is more complex. When unlabelled and in competition with labelled methionine, in liquid cultures of A. niger containing selenate, the methylation percentage fell to 60; when labelled and used in similar cultures a value of 35 was obtained. There was evidence of the formation of methionine in this second experiment; possibly the sulphonium iodide is not itself a methyl donor or source but the effective agent is the methionine. As only one methyl group in the sulphonium iodide was labelled, 50 per cent of the methionine produced would presumably be non-radioactive which would explain the low methylation percentage. In all these mould experiments with radioactive methyl compounds the evolved carbon dioxide is radioactive which is in agreement with the results of du Vigneaud, Mackenzie[76,77] and others on the oxidation of methyl-^{14}C methionine in animals.

Availability of the optical isomers of methionine as methyl donors— Cantoni[107] found that L-methionine was twice as active as the DL-isomer in the methylation of nicotinamide to N′-methylnicotinamide by the enzyme nicotinamide methyl kinase in presence of adenosine triphosphate and phosphoglycerate. This system involves the formation of S-adenosinylmethionine[79,80,93]. It was concluded that D-methionine is inactive in this system. Betaine and dimethylacetothetin when used alone were also ineffective as methyl donors, but in presence of DL-homocysteine, methylation of nicotinamide occurred readily, presumably due to formation of methionine. Cantoni's result with dimethylacetothetin alone agrees with those obtained in mould cultures at Leeds, but the behaviour of the thetins in presence of added homocysteine has not been studied.

Handler and Bernheim[105] found that L-methionine was twice as effective as the D-isomer in the methylation of guanidinoacetic acid to creatine by rat liver slices. The α-keto-acid however, $CH_3 \cdot S \cdot CH_2 \cdot CH_2 \cdot CO \cdot COOH$ which would arise by enzymic deamination of D- or L-methionine by the appropriate oxidase was as effective as L-methionine itself. Possibly therefore D-methionine is first converted to the keto acid and this is then re-aminated asymmetrically to the L-amino acid prior to methylation. This agrees with the observation that transmethylation from D-methionine did not take place in the presence of benzoic acid, which inhibits D-amino-acid oxidase.

It was therefore decided to study the relative utilization of D- and L-methionines in the methylation of sodium selenate by *A. niger* giving dimethyl selenide. The results showed that D-, L- or DL methionine are equally effective[103]. It was clear, however, that the amount of competing natural methionine synthesized by the mould from sulphate in the synthetic aqueous medium would be small compared with that of the radioactive methionine added. Consequently although D-methionine was clearly being utilized, the effect may have been magnified by the lack of the natural isomer and so a true comparison with L-methionine would not be provided by Experiments 1–4 (*see* p. 192).

Experiments (p. 192) were therefore set up in which D-[Me-^{14}C]-methionine and an equal amount of non-radioactive L-methionine was added to the cultures containing selenate. Since absolute values for the methylation percentage were not known due to uncertainties such as the magnitude of the 'back scatter' correction for mercurichloride precipitates, an experiment (Table 1, Expts. 5–7) employing radioactive L- and non-radioactive D-methionine was carried out at the same time and under the same conditions. The results clearly showed that the L- and D- enantiomorphs of methionine are utilized with equal facility in mycological methylations.

TABLE 1

Expt. no.	Methionine used and its concn. (m. mole per flask)	(1) Aspiration time (days)	(2) Methylation (%)
1	DL-[Me-14C], 2·0	10	95·2
		26	86·6
		41	13·3
		50	3·2
2	L-[Me-14C], 2·0	19	95
		31	99
3	D-[Me-14C], 2·0	18	88
		30	100
4	D-[Me-14C], 2·0	11	74
		24	93
		35	15
		50	3
5	D-[Me-14C], 1·0	10	61
	L-, 1·0	22	48
6	D-[Me-14C], 1·0	13	53
	L-, 1·0		
7	L-[Me-14C], 1·0	10	63
	D-, 1·0	22	37

This means either (a) that the methyl group of D-methionine *as such* is labile in mould cultures, or (b) that if D-methionine cannot be utilized as such, its conversion to the L-form must take place in the mould cell as rapidly as the competing L-methionine can be utilized, or (c) that both processes (a) and (b) occur simultaneously.

Utilization of D-methionine in other systems—Horowitz[108] has summarized experiments on the D-amino-acid oxidases from various sources and the significance of the α-keto acids in the formation of

L-amino acids. As already stated, however (*see* p. 191), Cantoni regards D-methionine as inactive in the methylation of nicotinamide by the enzymes of liver tissue and as probably incapable of forming an S-adenosinyl derivative under these conditions. It should be emphasized moreover that it has not yet been demonstrated that Cantoni's 'active methionine'[109] is concerned in plant methylation, but it has been detected in Chlorella. Moreover, the isolation of 5'-deoxy-5'-methylthioadenosine (adenine methylthiopentoside $C_5H_4N_5 \cdot C_4H_6O_3 \cdot CH_2 \cdot S \cdot Me$, which is a hydrolysis product of Cantoni's S-adenosinylmethionine) from yeast (*see* p. 200) suggests that the significance of S-adenosinylmethionine is not confined to animal biochemistry.

RECENT WORK ON METHYLATION IN HIGHER PLANTS
THE IMPORTANCE OF METHIONINE

Before 1950 very few studies on methylation in higher plants had been made. In 1942 however Barrenscheen and Vályi-Nagy[110] reported that, in extracts of wheat seedlings, the methylation of guanidinoacetic acid to creatine was greatly stimulated by methionine and by betaine. Eight years later work of the first importance was carried out in Canada and the United States which threw light not only on the origin of the $-NCH_3$ group but also of the $-OCH_3$ and methylenedioxy-groups in plant products.

Origins of the methyl groups of hordenine—Hordenine, N-dimethyl-tyramine, $HO^4 \cdot C_6H_4 \cdot CH_2 \cdot CH_2 \cdot N(CH_3)_2$ was isolated from barley by Léger[111] in 1906. Kirkwood and Marion[112] showed that certain strains of the plant produce the N-monomethyl derivative instead. Moreover, the plant *Trichocereus candicans* contains not only hordenine but its betaine candicine so that all stages of the methylation of tyramine are found in nature.

When ^{14}C-sodium formate is fed to sprouting barley the activity is found almost entirely in the $-NCH_3$ groups of hordenine and choline, as was shown by degradation of the choline to trimethylamine. A similar result was observed with L-[Me-^{14}C]-methionine, but [Me-^{14}C]-choline contributed no labelled methyl to hordenine. Possibly choline oxidase (*see* p. 184) is absent from the plant. As choline produces much labelled carbon dioxide under these conditions it appears that this one-carbon fragment is not a source of the methyl group.

Origin of the methyl group of nicotine—Brown and Byerrum[113] and Byerrum and Wing[114] find that the methyl carbon of both methionine

and choline and the carbon of formate serve as precursors of the
—NCH_3 group of nicotine in *Nicotiana rustica*. Formate is probably
the precursor of methionine. The nicotine was isolated as the
dipicrate, demethylated and the resulting methyl iodide absorbed in
triethylamine and the quaternary iodide assayed.

By a similar procedure it has been shown that the —OCH_3 and
—NCH_3 groups of some opium alkaloids can be derived from
methionine[115].

Origin of the —NCH₃ and —OCH₃ groups of ricinine—This was investigated by Dubeck and Kirkwood[116] by feeding the germinating
seeds of *Ricinus communis* (the castor oil plant) with [Me-¹⁴C]-
methionine and choline and ¹⁴C-formate. Only with methionine
was the ricinine (**XXII**) appreciably labelled. The methyl of the
—OCH_3 group was removed from the ricinine as methyl iodide by
hydriodic acid and that of the —NCH_3 group by more vigorous
treatment of the residue. The methyl iodide was absorbed in
trimethylamine and assayed as tetramethylammonium reineckate
(**XXIII**).

(**XXII**)   (**XXIII**)   (**XXIV**)

Radioactivity was found only in the —NCH_3 and —OCH_3
groups, which had almost the same activity. It would be interesting
to carry out a similar study on damascenin, which in addition to
—NCH_3, and —OCH_3 also contains the group —$COOCH_3$.

Origin of the —OCH₃ groups of lignin—This work along with that of
Byerrum, Dewey and Ball[117] affords the first proof of the origin of
the methoxy-groups which are so common in plant products. By
the use of ¹⁴C as before it was found that the methyl group of methionine furnishes the methoxy groups of the lignin of barley and
tobacco. The lignin was separated from the seedlings, demethylated
with hydriodic acid and the methyl iodide assayed as methyltriethylammonium iodide. By employing the device introduced by
du Vigneaud and using a mixture of 10 per cent of [Me-¹⁴C]-
methionine and 90 per cent deuteriomethionine it was shown that
the methyl group of methionine is transferred intact. The D : ¹⁴C
ratios in the methyltriethylammonium iodide were 94 and 95 per

cent of that in the $^{14}CD_3$ group of the methionine fed to barley and tobacco respectively. Formate was also shown to be a precursor of the lignin methoxyl but when administered to barley plants along with an equimolecular quantity of methionine about 26 methoxy groups were formed from the amino acid for each one arising from formate. This suggests that methionine is very close to the final stage in the methylation process.

The methylenedioxy group—An interesting result of the Canadian work was the announcement that the carbon atoms of the —NCH₃ and $CH_2 : O_2$ groups of the alkaloid protopine are derived from methionine. This second group appears to be peculiar to plants and has not been detected in animal products.

Sribney and Kirkwood[118] grew *Dicentra* hybrids in media containing L-[Me-^{14}C]-methionine, methyl-^{14}C-choline and ^{14}C-sodium formate. On demethylation of the resulting radioactive protopine (XXIV) the —NCH₃ group yielded methyl iodide which was converted to tetramethylammonium iodide and reineckate. The methylenedioxy groups were assayed by hydrolysis of the alkaloid with 20 per cent sulphuric acid, followed by the isolation and radioactive assay of the liberated formaldehyde as it dimedone derivative. With methionine, the activity of the —NCH₃ and $CH_2 : O_2$ groups was very similar. Formate also contributed ^{14}C to the molecule but to a much smaller degree.

In concluding the discussion of the phenomenon of biological methylation we may consider some work carried out by Snow[119] at Blackley, Manchester, on the changes undergone by ethanethiol in mice and guinea pigs. This arose from a study of the anti-tubercular effect of ethanethiol and of compounds which can yield it by breakdown in the animal body. It was important to determine the fate of the ethanethiol, and the results have shown that the animal body deals with this substance in a manner which is very similar to the methylation exerted by the mould *S. brevicaulis* on ethanethiol and diethyl disulphide (*see* p. 168). Snow's results emphasize the close relationship existing between the processes of methylation in moulds and in animals stressed in the early part of this chapter.

The Anti-tubercular Effect of S-ethyl Compounds

Much research has been in progress since 1953 on the anti-tubercular effect of derivatives of ethanethiol. In that year Pianto[120] reported that sodium ethylthiosulphate $CH_3 \cdot CH_2 \cdot S \cdot SO_2 \cdot ONa$ does not inhibit the development of *Mycobacterium tuberculosis, in vitro*. On oral administration with the diet the survival time of the infected mice is increased by 15–51 days as compared with 20 days observed with comparable doses of *p*-aminosalicyclic acid.

It is well known that sodium alkylthiosulphates yield dialkyl disulphides on boiling with alkali and that the disulphide link readily undergoes fission under biological conditions. It seemed therefore, very probable that the beneficial effect of the sodium ethylthio-sulphate depended on the production of diethyl disulphide or ethanethiol. Davies *et al.*[121] showed that a large number of sodium alkyl- and arylthiosulphates including the methyl derivative were devoid of anti-tubercular action.

Owing to the volatility and unpleasant odour of ethanethiol, various derivatives were tested for anti-tubercular effect in the hope that they would yield the thiol in the animal body. Diethyl disul-phide, ethylthiobenzoate $C_6H_5 \cdot CO \cdot S \cdot CH_2 \cdot CH_3$ and diethyl dithio-*iso*phthalate $C_6H_4(CO \cdot S \cdot CH_2 \cdot CH_3)_2$ were found to be strong anti-tubercular agents in guinea-pigs and mice. Brown *et al.*[122] studied a series of S-alkyl-β-mercaptopropionic acids $C_nH_{2n+1}S \cdot CH_2 \cdot CH_2 \cdot COOH$ and found that definite protection was afforded to mice infected with *Mycobacterium tuberculosis* (human type; strain H_{37} Rb) when S-ethyl-β-thiopropionic acid $CH_3 \cdot CH_2 \cdot S \cdot CH_2 \cdot CH_2 \cdot COOH$ (0·2 per cent) was administered in an unrestricted diet. Substitu-tion of the ethyl group by other alkyl groups from methyl to octadecyl produced inactive compounds. Moreover variation of the dis-tance between the sulphur atom and the carboxyl group, using terminal ethylthio-derivatives of the acids acetic to *n*-valeric, e.g. $CH_3 \cdot CH_2 \cdot S \cdot CH_2 \cdot COOH$ to $CH_3 \cdot CH_2 \cdot S \cdot CH_2 \cdot CH_2 \cdot CH_2 \cdot CH_2 \cdot COOH$ showed that the β-relation between carboxyl and sulphur is necessary. This would suggest that the elimination of $CH_3 \cdot CH_2 \cdot SH$ from $CH_3 \cdot CH_2 \cdot S \cdot CH_2 \cdot CH_2 \cdot COOH$ is a β-elimination depending on the extraction of the positive hydrogen on the α-carbon atom, probably giving acrylic acid $CH_2{=}CH \cdot COOH$ as the other product.

Some observations recorded by Challenger and Liu[123] may be relevant in this connection. S-methylthioacetic acid and S-ethyl-thioacetic acid give no thiol ($CH_3 \cdot SH$ or $CH_3 \cdot CH_2 \cdot SH$) in bread cultures of *S. brevicaulis*, but S-methyl-2-thiopropionic acid in cultures of this mould on bread or on inorganic salts–glucose medium yields methanethiol. β-Elimination is impossible in the case of the two acetic acid derivatives, but can occur with S-methyl-2-thiopropionic acid. Replacement of —COOH by —CHO, —COOR or —CH₂OH in Brown's experiments was achieved with retention of activity. S-ethyl-L-cysteine, $CH_3 \cdot CH_2 \cdot S \cdot CH_2 \cdot CH \cdot (NH_2) \cdot COOH$ appeared promising. The authors concluded that structural modifications which decrease the tendency to fission of the $CH_3CH_2 \cdot S$—C bond decrease the activity against *M. tuberculosis*.

The metabolism of S-ethyl derivatives in animals—Snow[119] points out that the ethanethiol is inactive towards the tuberculosis bacillus *in vitro* but may be converted *in vivo* to some active derivative to which the observed effect is due. He has studied the metabolism in mice, rats and guinea-pigs of various precursors of ethanethiol, labelled with ^{35}S diethyl disulphide, S-ethylthiobenzoate and SS'-diethyl dithio*iso*phthalate being chosen. In a preliminary experiment the last-named compound *unlabelled* was injected subcutaneously (200 mg. per kilo of body weight) as a 50 per cent (v/v) solution in arachis oil. The collected urine was extracted with chloroform, the solvent removed and the residue stirred with water and ether. The aqueous layer on extraction with chloroform yielded an oil which, on distillation at 0·05 mm., gave three fractions. That with the lowest b.p. solidified and on crystallization from ether was identified by analysis and mixed m.p. as methyl ethyl sulphone $CH_3 \cdot SO_2 \cdot CH_2 \cdot CH_3$. A similar result was obtained with unlabelled diethyl disulphide in guinea pigs. The process was then investigated by administration of the S-ethyl compounds labelled with [35]S. Radioactive sulphone was compared with radioactive concentrates of urine by paper chromatography and countercurrent distribution. The materials in three different solvent systems gave spots almost identical in position. The countercurrent method confirmed this result.

No protecting effect against tubercular infection in mice was observed either with methyl ethyl sulphone or with an unknown metabolite obtained in small amount from the urine and their formation is probably unconnected with the curative effect of the $-S \cdot CH_2 \cdot CH_3$ group. The methylation of the ethanethiol and the fission of diethyl disulphide accompanied by methylation, in the animal body presents a close analogy with the behaviour of these compounds and of the dialkyl disulphides $R \cdot S \cdot S \cdot R$ ($R = CH_3$, n-C_3H_7, n-C_4H_9 and n-C_5H_{11}) in cultures of *Scopulariopsis brevicaulis*[35,36], when the thiol $R \cdot SH$ and the alkyl methyl sulphide $R \cdot S \cdot CH_3$ are produced. It is regrettable that Challenger and his co-workers did not examine the cultures for the corresponding sulphones $R \cdot SO_2 \cdot CH_3$. Their formation seems very probable and as sulphones are not attacked by *S. brevicaulis* they may have accumulated in quantity. The occurrence of sulphones in plants and animals is discussed in Chapter 4.

197

THE METHYLATION AND OXIDATION OF ^{14}C-ETHANETHIOL
IN ANIMALS

In a private communication in April 1957, Dr Snow kindly informed the author that Dr J. S. Lowe has carried out further work on derivatives of ethanethiol labelled with ^{14}C. The results confirmed those obtained by the use of material labelled with ^{35}S. The main radioactive product in the urine behaved as methyl ethyl sulphone. Fifty per cent of the ^{14}C radioactivity administered was found in the breath as ^{14}CO$_2$. This is analogous to the complete oxidation of much of the ethanethiol to sulphuric acid observed in the experiments with ^{35}S. A second radioactive urinary component is urea (20 per cent) derived from the labelled carbon dioxide pool. Considerable amounts of sulphur compounds which react with mercuric chloride (presumably mercaptan or disulphide) appeared in the breath, representing 3–7 per cent of the radioactive dose administered.

SPECULATIONS ON THE MECHANISM OF THE ANTI-TUBERCULAR
EFFECT OF ETHANETHIOL

Snow has considered the possibility that the remarkable effect of ethanethiol, or of compounds which yield it, on the tubercle bacillus *in vivo* may possibly involve competition and consequent inhibition of some essential metabolic process of the bacillus which is connected with the metabolism of methyl or of methylthio-compounds. He finds that the higher homologues of ethanethiol have no such action. A large number were tested, e.g. *n*-propane-, *n*-butane-, *iso*butane-, *n*-heptane-, β-aminoethane- and β-dimethylaminoethanethiols and many containing pyrimidine, triazine and other heterocyclic systems. Certain dithiols including 2 : 3-dimercaptopropanol (British Anti-Lewisite) were also examined. It appeared possible that some oxidation product of ethanethiol or of methyl ethyl sulphide or diethyl sulphide such as the sulphoxide or sulphone or ethanesulphinic or sulphonic acids or their derivatives; hydroxy ethyl sulphides and their sulphoxides or sulphones; thioacetic acid and amide and the S-methyl derivative CH$_3$·S·CH$_2$·COOH might show an anti-tubercular effect. The results with these and several analogous compounds were, however, entirely negative.

One important result of the work at Blackley is the finding that the anti-tubercular effect of ethanethiol and of compounds which yield it[123a] is nullified if an analogous compound capable of yielding methanethiol is also administered concurrently. Experiments were carried out with several pairs of compounds—the results are shown in Table 2 and are due to Davies *et al*[121].

TABLE 2

	Source of Ethanethiol	Antagonist	Therapeutic effect in days	
			Without antagonist	With antagonist
1	$C_2H_5 \cdot S \cdot SO_2 \cdot ONa$	$CH_3 \cdot S \cdot SO_2 \cdot ONa$	5·6	−0·6
2	$C_6H_5 \cdot CO \cdot S \cdot CH_2 \cdot CH_3$	$C_6H_5 \cdot CO \cdot S \cdot CH_3$	26·1	0·3
3	$CH_3 \cdot CH_2 \cdot S \cdot S \cdot CH_2 \cdot CH_3$	$C_6H_5 \cdot CO \cdot S \cdot CH_3$	20·0	5·1
4	$m\text{-}C_6H_4 \begin{cases} CO \cdot S \cdot CH_2 \cdot CH_3 \\ CO \cdot S \cdot CH_2 \cdot CH_3 \end{cases}$	$C_6H_5 \cdot CO \cdot S \cdot CH_3$	33·2	10·2
5	$CH_3 \cdot CH_2 \cdot S \cdot S \cdot CH_2 \cdot CH_3$	$CH_3 \cdot S \cdot S \cdot CH_3$	28·2	23·9
6	$C_6H_5 \cdot CO \cdot S \cdot CH_2 \cdot CH_3$	$CH_3 \cdot S \cdot S \cdot CH_3$	25·0	26·0
7	$CH_3 \cdot CH_2 \cdot S \cdot S \cdot CH_2 \cdot CH_3$	$n\text{-}C_3H_7 \cdot S \cdot S \cdot C_3H_7$	28·2	16·2
8	$CH_3 \cdot CH_2 \cdot S \cdot S \cdot CH_2 \cdot CH_3$	$iso\text{-}C_3H_7 \cdot S \cdot S \cdot C_3H_7$	28·2	32·0

The results are clear in the case of the first four pairs of compounds. It is surprising, however, that dimethyl disulphide exerts no very strong effect when administered along with its ethyl analogue and none at all in competition with ethylthiobenzoate. In Experiment 7 the di-*n*-propyl disulphide considerably reduces the curative effect of the corresponding ethyl derivative whereas in Experiment 8 the di-*iso*-propyl compound is without action. Study of these phenomena is necessary. This conclusion is emphasized by the fact that ethyl benzoate is strongly antagonistic to ethylthiobenzoate and to diethyl dithio*iso*phthalate. It should be emphasized that dimethyl disulphide and methanethiol or compounds yielding it in the animal body are devoid of anti-tubercular action.

Oginsky[124] has studied the enzymic production of ethanethiol from various compounds *in vitro* and finds that homogenates of mouse liver and lung produce ethanethiol from various thiol esters and reduce diethyl disulphide. Thiol esters were also hydrolysed by *E. coli* and *S. faecalis* from mouse gut. *S. faecalis* readily released ethanethiol from S-ethylcysteine and β-ethylthiopropionic acid $CH_3 \cdot CH_2 \cdot S \cdot CH_2 \cdot CH_2 \cdot COOH$. These results recall those of Binkley[125] with the S-alkylcysteines and a thionase and of the Leeds school with *Scopulariopsis brevicaulis*[35,36].

The Antagonism between Methionine and Ethionine

The literature contains many references to the inhibiting effect of ethionine $CH_3 \cdot CH_2 \cdot S \cdot CH_2 \cdot CH_2 \cdot CH(NH_2) \cdot COOH$ on reactions involving methionine. Thus DL-ethionine was fed to adult male rats at a level of 0·3 per cent in a synthetic diet containing 0·7 per cent of deuterio-DL-methionine[126]. The deuteriomethyl content of the choline and creatine of the tissues was compared with that of choline and creatine obtained from 'pair-fed' control animals receiving the labelled methionine, but no ethionine. In the animals receiving ethionine transmethylation from methionine to choline was reduced by about 20 per cent. No effect, however, was observed in the case of the creatine. Cohn and Harris[127] showed that ethionine is an antimetabolite of methionine in cultures of *E. coli*. This work is cited by Woolley in *A Study of Antimetabolites*[128], where a few other examples of the antagonism between ethionine and methionine are recorded. Thus, ethionine is toxic to rats receiving a diet deficient in methionine but when the deficiency is removed the ethionine ceases to be toxic. Ethionine also prevents the incorporation of radioactive methionine into the proteins of rats or mice and again additional methionine restores a normal uptake of this amino acid. Clearly ethionine has an influence on the methylation process. We now know, through Cantoni's work, that methylation in animals involves the formation of the tertiary S-adenosinylmethionine ion—'active methionine' (XXV).

Some work of Schlenk and his colleagues[129-131] on the formation of (XXVI) S-methylthioadenosine ('methylthiopentoside') which is a 'fragment' of the S-adenosinylmethionine molecule is relevant in this connection. They found that formation of this nucleoside in yeast cultures requires the presence of methionine.

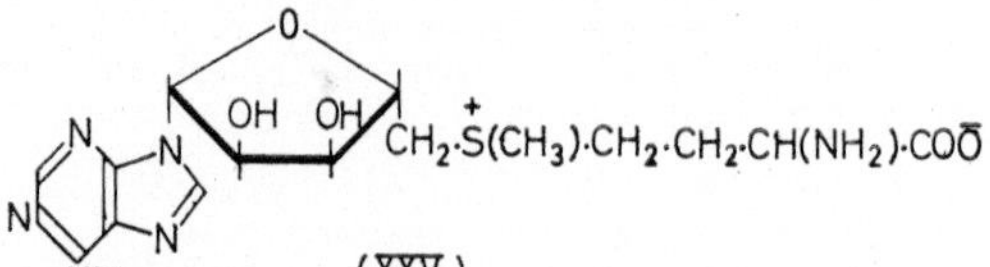

(XXV)

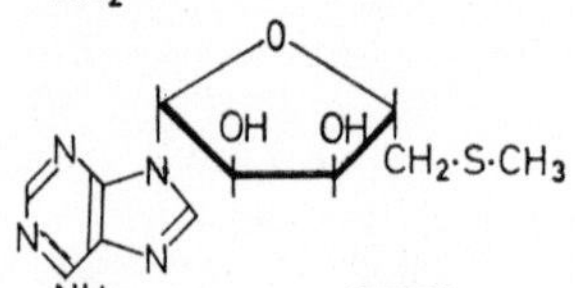

(XXVI)

Biological synthesis of S-ethylthioadenosine—In later experiments Schlenk and Tillotson[132,133] found that the yeasts *Torulopsis utilis* and

Saccharomyces cerevisiae when grown in a medium containing DL-ethionine produce a new nucleoside containing sulphur which appears to be S-ethylthioadenosine. This biosynthesis resembles the metabolic relation between methionine and S-methylthioadenosine mentioned above. The identity of the new S-ethyl derivative has not yet been confirmed by synthesis but the following considerations appear to leave little doubt as to its structure: (1) analysis; (2) absorption spectrum and (3) the loss of adenine on hydrolysis. It gives the same orcinol reaction for pentoses that is given by S-methylthioadenosine. The authors state, 'It may be that some of the inhibitory actions attributed to ethionine actually occur after its conversion to S-adenosinylethionine' (i.e. the ethyl analogue of Cantoni's 'active methionine') 'or to S-ethylthioadenosine'. Cantoni has informed the author that ethionine is utilized somewhat less effectively than methionine by the enzyme which converts methionine to S-adenosinylmethionine. He has also prepared S-adenosinyl-ethionine, presumably by an enzyme method.

Schlenk and Tillotson find that yeast supplied with both methionine (3mM) and ethionine (3mM) yields $3 \cdot 1 \mu M$ of S-methylthioadenosine and $1 \cdot 6 \mu M$ of the corresponding S-ethyl derivative. The S-*n*-propyl and S-*n*-butylhomocysteines form practically none of the *n*-propyl or *n*-butyl analogues. This observation may have a bearing on the well-established fact that homologues of ethanethiol exert no anti-tubercular action *in vivo*, as has been mentioned already. S-ethylthioadenosine has been tested with a mutant of *Aerobacter aerogenes* which requires methionine or S-methylthioadenosine for growth, but no response was obtained.

A possible mechanism of the anti-tubercular effect of ethanethiol—In the light of the foregoing discussion it is possible to formulate a tentative hypothesis based on the results of Stekol and Weiss[134,135] who showed in 1950 that when ethionine, labelled with ^{14}C in the ethyl group, was fed to rats the radioactivity was found in the choline of the tissues and the creatinine of the urine, presumably as the corresponding ethyl analogues (**XXVII**) and (**XXVIII**):

$$(CH_3 \cdot CH_2)_3 \overset{+}{N} \cdot CH_2 \cdot CH_2 \cdot OH$$
$$\overline{OH}$$

(XXVII)

(XXVIII)

'Triethylcholine' (**XXVII**) was then found to inhibit the growth of rats in the same manner as does ethionine and the effect was

201

counteracted by choline or methionine. 'Triethylcholine' may be the inhibitor or antimetabolite and ethionine may be converted to this by way of the quaternary salt S-adenosinylethionine. Some earlier experiments of du Vigneaud[136] showed that 'triethylcholine' was unable to support the growth of rats on a diet free from choline and methionine.

While much more work remains to be done before the mechanism of the anti-tubercular action of ethanethiol can be explained, it would appear that a useful hypothesis is that it interferes with the normal methyl metabolism of the tubercule bacillus through the formation of S-adenosinylethionine or of some other ethyl compound closely related to Cantoni's S-adenosinylmethionine. This would presumably be present in much greater amount than the normal Cantoni compound and therefore ethyl transfer rather than methyl transfer might be expected to predominate and 'triethylcholine' to be produced.

Snow is not prepared, from the results of his experiments up to the present, to formulate any mechanism to explain the curative action of ethanethiol in animals infected with the tubercle bacillus and informs the author that he is doubtful whether the ethyl group of ethanethiol is likely to be incorporated into ethionine.

REFERENCES

1 Challenger, F., *Chem. & Ind.* **61** (1942) 399, 413, 456
2 Challenger, F., *Chem. Rev.* **36** (1945) 315
3 Challenger, F., *Ann. Reports* **43** (1946) 262
4 Challenger, F., *Advances in Enzymology* **12** (1951) 429
5 Challenger, F., *Quart. Rev. chem. Soc.* **9** (1955) 255
6 du Vigneaud, V., *A Trail of Research*, Cornell University Press, Ithaca, New York, 1952
7 Challenger, F. and Walshe, J. M., *Biochem. J.* **59** (1955) 372
8 Haas, P., *ibid.* **29** (1935) 298
9 Challenger, F. and Simpson, Miss M. I., *J. chem. Soc.* (1948) 1591
10 Bywood, R., Challenger, F., Leaver, D. and Whitaker, Mrs. M. I., *Biochem. J.* **48** (1951) XXX
11 Bywood, R. and Challenger, F., *ibid.* **53** (1953) XXVI
12 Ackermann, D., Holtz, F. and Reinwein, H., *Z. Biol.* **79** (1923) 113; **81** (1924) 61
13 Mueller, J. H., *J. biol. Chem.* **56** (1923) 1157
14 Barger, G. and Coyne, F. P., *Biochem. J.* **22** (1928) 1417
15 Armstrong, E. F. and Armstrong, K. F., *The Glycosides*, Longmans, Green (1931) p. 66
16 His, W., *Arch. exp. Path. Pharmak.* **22** (1887) 253

[17] Gmelin, C., *Wirkungen . . . auf den tierischen Organismus*, Tübingen (1824) p. 43

[18] Hofmeister, W., *Arch. exp. Path. Pharmak.* **33** (1894) 198

[19] Riesser, O., *Z. physiol. Chem.* **86** (1913) 440

[20] Ackermann, D., *Z. Biol.* **59** (1912) 17

[21] Williams, R. T., *Detoxication Mechanisms*, Chapman and Hall, London, 1947

[22] Challenger, F., *Chem. & Ind.* (1936) 900

[23] Challenger, F., Higginbottom, Miss C. and Ellis L., *J. chem. Soc.* (1933) 96

[24] Gmelin, C. *Karlsruher Zeitung*, November 1839

[25] Selmi, F., *Ber. dtsch. chem. Ges.* **7** (1874) 1642

[26] Gosio, B., *Arch. ital. Biol.* **18** (1893) 253, 298; **35** (1901) 201

[26a] Gosio, B., *Ber. dtsch. chem. Ges.* **30** (1897) 1024

[27] Biginelli, P., *Gazz. chem. Ital.* **31** (1) (1901) 58

[28] Cevey, F., Dissertation, Lausanne (1902) 40

[29] Challenger, F. and North, H. E., *J. chem. Soc.* (1934) 68

[30] Bird, Miss M. L., Challenger, F., Charlton, P. T. and Smith, J. O., *Biochem. J.* **43** (1948) 78

[31] Bird, Miss M. L. and Challenger, F., *J. chem. Soc.* (1939) 163

[32] Pohl, F., *Arch. exp. Path. Pharmak.* **51** (1904) 341

[33] Challenger, F. and Liu, Y. C., *Rec. Trav. chim. Pays-Bas* **69** (1950) 334

[34] Schmid, H. and Karrer P., *Helv. chim. acta.* **31** (1948) 1017, 1087, 1497

[35] Challenger, F. and Rawlings, A. A., *J. chem. Soc.* (1937) 868

[36] Blackburn, S. and Challenger, F., *ibid.* (1938) 1872

[37] Birkinshaw, J. H., Findlay, W. P. K. and Webb, R. A., *Biochem. J.* **36** (1942) 526

[38] Challenger, F. and Charlton, P. T., *J. chem. Soc.* (1947) 424

[39] Challenger, F. and Higginbottom, Miss C., *Biochem. J.* **29** (1935) 1757

[40] Robinson, R., *J. chem. Soc.* **111** (1917) 877; **113** (1918) 868

[41] Robinson, R., *J. roy. Soc. Arts* **96** (1948) 796

[42] Berg, P., *J. biol. Chem.* **205** (1953) 145

[43] Greenberg, D. M., *ibid.* **190** (1951) 611; *Fed. Proc.* **13** (1954) 221

[44] Ratner, S., Nocito, V. and Green, D. E., *J. biol. Chem.* **152** (1944) 119

[45] Paretsky, D. and Werkman, C. H., *Arch. Biochem.* **25** (1950) 295

[46] Bird, Miss M. L. and Challenger, F., *J. chem. Soc.* (1942) 574

[47] Cantoni, G. L., *J. Amer. chem. Soc.* **74** (1952) 2942

[48] du Vigneaud, V., Cohn, M., Chandler, J. P., Schenck, J. R. and Simmonds, S., *J. biol. Chem.* **140** (1941) 626; Simmonds, S., Cohn, M., Chandler, J. P. and du Vigneaud, V., *ibid.* **149** (1943) 519

[49] Schenck, J. R., Simmonds, S., Cohn, M., Stevens, C. M. and du Vigneaud, V., *ibid.* **149** (1943) 355

[50] Simmonds, S. and du Vigneaud, V., *ibid.* **146** (1942) 685

[51] du Vigneaud, V., *Harvey Lectures* **38** (1942–3) 39

[52] Toennies, G., *J. biol. Chem.* **132** (1940) 455; Toennies, G. and Kolb, J., *J. Amer. chem. Soc.* **67** (1945) 849

[53] Maw, G. A. and du Vigneaud, V., *J. biol. Chem.* **174** (1948) 381; **176** (1948) 1029, 1037

54 Dubnoff, J. W. and Borsook, H., *J. biol. Chem.* **176** (1948) 789; Borsook, H. and Dubnoff, J. W., *ibid.* **169** (1947) 247

55 Ericson, L. E., Williams, J. N. and Elvehjem, C. A., *ibid.* **212** (1955) 537

56 Maw, G. A., *Biochem. J.* **63** (1956) 116; **70** (1958) 168

57 Smythe, C. V., *J. biol Chem.* **114** (1936) 607

58 Maw, G. A., *Biochem. J.* **58** (1954) 665

59 Bennett, M. A., Medes, G. and Toennies, G., *Growth* **8** (1944) 59

60 du Vigneaud, V., Simmonds, S., Chandler, J. P. and Cohn, M., *J. biol. Chem.* **159** (1945) 755

61 du Vigneaud, V., Ressler, C. and Rachele, J. R., *Science* **112** (1950) 267

62 Sakami, W., *J. biol. Chem.* **176** (1948) 995; **179** (1949) 495; *Fed. Proc.* **9** (1950) 222

63 Siekevitz, P., Winnick, T. and Greenberg, D. M., *J. biol. Chem.* **180** (1949) 845

64 Arnstein, H. V. R., *Biochem. J.* **48** (1951) 27

65 Arnstein, H. V. R. and Neuberger, A. *ibid.* **55** (1953) 259

66 du Vigneaud, V., Verly, W. G. and Wilson, J. E., *J. Amer. chem. Soc.* **72** (1950) 2819

67 du Vigneaud, V. and Verly, W. G., *ibid.* **72** (1950) 1049

68 Verly, W. G., *Arch. internat. Physiol. Biochim.* **64** (1956) 309

69 Verly, W. G., Rachele, J. R., du Vigneaud, V., Eidinoff, M. L. and Knoll, J. E., *J. Amer. chem. Soc.* **74** (1942) 5491

70 du Vigneaud, V., Verly, W. G., Wilson, J. E., Rachele, J. R., Ressler, C. and Kinney, J. M., *ibid.* **73** (1951) 2782

71 Thorn, M. B., *Biochem. J.* **49** (1951) 602

72 Rachele, J. R., Kuchinskas, E. J., Knoll, J. E. and Eidinoff, M. L., *J. Amer. chem. Soc.* **76** (1954) 4342

73 Rachele, J. R., Kuchinskas, E. J., Kratzler, F. H. and du Vigneaud, V., *J. biol. Chem.* **215** (1955) 593

74 Keller, E. B., Rachele, J. R. and du Vigneaud, V., *ibid.* **177** (1949) 733

75 Thompson, R. C. and Ballou, J. E., *ibid.* **206** (1954) 101

76 Mackenzie, C. G. and du Vigneaud, V., *ibid.* **172** (1948) 353

77 Mackenzie, C. G., Chandler, J. P., Keller, E. B., Rachele, J. R., Cross, N. and du Vigneaud, V., *ibid.* **180** (1949) 99

78 Borsook, H. and Dubnoff, J. W., *ibid.* **169** (1947) 247

79 Cantoni, G. L., *J. Amer. chem. Soc.* **74** (1952) 2942

80 Cantoni, G. L., *J. biol. Chem.* **189** (1951) 208, 211; (1953) 403

81 Challenger, F. and Higginbottom, Miss C., *Biochem. J.* **29** (1935) 1757

82 Challenger, F., *Conférences et Rapports, 3éme Congrès International de Biochimie*, Bruxelles 1955, p. 238

83 Toennies, G., *J. Biol. Chem.* **132** (1940) 455; Toennies, G. and Kolb, J., *J. Amer. chem. Soc.* **67** (1945) 849

84 Baddiley, J., *J. chem. Soc.* (1951) 1348

85 Weygand, F., Trauth, O. and Lowenfeld, R., *Chem. Ber.* **83** (1950) 563

86 Falconer, R. and Gulland, J. M., *J. chem. Soc.* (1937) 1912

87 Baddiley, J., Trauth, O. and Weygand, F., *Nature, Lond.* **167** (1951) 359

88 Satoh, K. and Makino, K., *ibid.* **167** (1951) 238

[89] Baddiley, J. and Jamieson, G. A., *J. chem. Soc.* (1954) 4280; (1953) 2662

[90] Woolley, D. W., *Nature, Lond.* **171** (1953) 323

[91] Baddiley, J., Cantoni, G. L. and Jamieson, G. A., *J. chem. Soc.* (1953) 2662

[92] Challenger, F., *Endeavour* **12** (1953) 173

[93] Cantoni, G. L. and Scarano, E., *J. Amer. chem. Soc.* **76** (1954) 4744

[94] Baddiley, J. and Jamieson, G. A., *J. chem. Soc.* (1955) 1085

[95] Dowell, J., Anderson, D. G. and Cantoni, G. L., *Biochim. Biophys. acta* **26** (1957) 270

[96] Durell, J. and Sturtevant, J. M., *ibid.* **26** (1957) 282

[97] Schrift, A., *Amer. J. Bot.* **41** (1954) 345

[98] Mudd, S. H. and Cantoni, G. L., *Nature, Lond.* **180** (1957) 1052

[99] Cantoni, G. L. and Durell, J., *J. biol. Chem.* **225** (1957) 1033

[100] Horn, M. J. and Jones, D. B., *ibid.* **139** (1941) 649

[101] Cowie, D. B. and Cohen, G. N., *Biochim. Biophys. acta* **26** (1957) 252

[102] Challenger, F., Lisle, D. B. and Dransfield, P. B., *J. chem. Soc.* (1954) 1760

[103] Challenger, F. and Dransfield, P. B. *ibid.* (1955) 1153

[104] Borsook, H. and Dubnoff, J. W., *J. biol. Chem.* **176** (1948) 789

[105] Handler, P. H. and Bernheim, M. L. C., *ibid.* **150** (1943) 335

[106] Dubnoff, J. W., *Arch. Biochem.* **22** (1949) 474; **24** (1949) 251

[107] Cantoni, G. L., *J. biol. Chem.* **189** (1951) 208, 211

[108] Horowitz, N. H., *ibid.* **154** (1954) 141

[109] Mudd, S. H. and Cantoni, G. L., *ibid.* **231** (1958) 481

[110] Barrenscheen, K. H. and Vályi-Nagy, T., *Z. physiol. Chem.* **277** (1942) 97

[111] Léger, E., *Compt. rend.* **142** (1906) 108

[112] Kirkwood, S. and Marion, L., *J. Amer. chem. Soc.* **72** (1950) 2522

[113] Brown, S. A. and Byerrum, R. U., *ibid.* **74** (1952) 1523

[114] Byerrum, R. U. and Wing, R. E., *J. biol. Chem.* **205** (1953) 637

[115] Battersby, A. R. and Harper, B. J. T., *Chem. & Ind.* (1958) 365

[116] Dubeck, M. and Kirkwood, S., *J. biol. Chem.* **199** (1952) 307

[117] Byerrum, R. U., Dewey, L. J. and Ball, C. D., *J. Amer. chem. Soc.* **76** (1954) 3997

[118] Sribney, M. and Kirkwood, S., *Nature, Lond.* **171** (1953) 931

[119] Snow, G. A., *Biochem. J.* **65** (1957) 77

[120] Pianto, E. del., *Ricerca Sci.* **23** (1953) 1785

[121] Davies, G. E., Driver, G. W., Hoggarth, E., Martin, A. R., Paige, M. F. C., Rose, F. L. and Wilson, B. R., *Brit. J. Pharmacol. Chemotherapy* **11** (1956) 351

[122] Brown, H. D., Matsuk, A. R., Becker, H. J., Conbere, J. P., Constantin, J. M., Solotorovsky, M., Winsten, S., Ironson, E. and Quastel, J. H. *J. Amer. chem. Soc.* **76** (1954) 3860

[123] Challenger, F. and Liu, Y. C., *Rec. Trav. chim. Pays-Bas* **69** (1950) 334

[123a] Kushner, S., Dalalian, H., Bach, F. L., Centola, D., Sanjurjo, J. L. and Williams, J. H., *J. Amer. chem. Soc.* **77** (1955) 1152

[124] Oginsky, E. L., Solotorovsky, M. and Brown, H. D., *Amer. Rev. Tuberculosis* **74** (1956) 78

[125] Binkley, F. and Watson, J., *Fed. Proc.* **9** (1950) 151

126 Simmonds, S., Keller, E. B., Chandler, J. P. and du Vigneaud, V., *J. Amer. chem. Soc.* **183** (1950) 191
127 Harris, J. S. and Cohn, H. L., *J. Pharm. Exptl. Therapy* **73** (1941) 383
128 Woolley, D. W., *A Study of Antimetabolites*, Wiley and Sons, New York; Chapman and Hall, London (1952), pp. 54 and 98
129 Smith, R. L. and Schlenk, F., *Arch. Biochem. Biophys.* **38** (1952) 167
130 Schlenk, F. and Smith, R. L., *J. biol. Chem.* **204** (1953) 27
131 Schlenk, F. and de Palma, R. E., *Arch. Biochem.* **57** (1955) 266
132 Schlenk, F. and Tillotson, J. A., *Fed. Proc.* **13** (1954) 290
133 Schlenk, F., *J. biol. Chem.* **206** (1954) 687
134 Stekol, J. A., Weiss, K. and Weiss, S., *J. Amer. chem. Soc.* **72** (1950) 2309
135 Stekol, J. A. and Weiss, K., *J. biol Chem.* **185** (1950) 577, 585
136 du Vigneaud, V., *Biol. Symposia,* Jaques Cattell Press, Lancaster, Pennsylvania, U.S.A. **5** (1941) 234; *See* also Challenger, F., *Adv. Enzymol.* **12** (1951) 459

6

CO-ENZYME A, ITS S-ACETYL DERIVATIVE AND RELATED COMPOUNDS

CO-ENZYME A

IN 1948 Kaplan and Lipmann[1] described the results obtained by the study of concentrated and highly active, though crude, preparations of a substance which was present in liver and in many bacteria. Later it was found to be extremely widespread in living organisms including plants. An excellent account of its occurrence is given by Lipmann[3-5]. As it was shown to take part in a number of biological acetylation processes it was named Co-enzyme A. In a letter to the Editor of the *Journal of Biological Chemistry*, which may be recommended as a source of useful information on the early work dealing with Co-enzyme A, Lipmann[2] stated 'the action of a novel co-enzyme of general occurrence was first observed with acetylation of aromatic amines in liver preparations'. This substance is concerned not only in the metabolism of acetic acid, but also in that of aceto-acetic acid, in the synthesis and breakdown of fatty acids and in the synthesis of proteins, porphyrins, glycogen and steroids. Since 1947 very much work has been carried out both on the chemical and biochemical relations of Co-enzyme A but in this short account of its discovery and extraction and of its significance in biochemistry, emphasis will mainly lie on the work which has led to the determination of its structure. It will be convenient at this stage to present the structural formula of Co-enzyme A, but without comment, before proceeding to outline the work which led to the determination of its constitution.

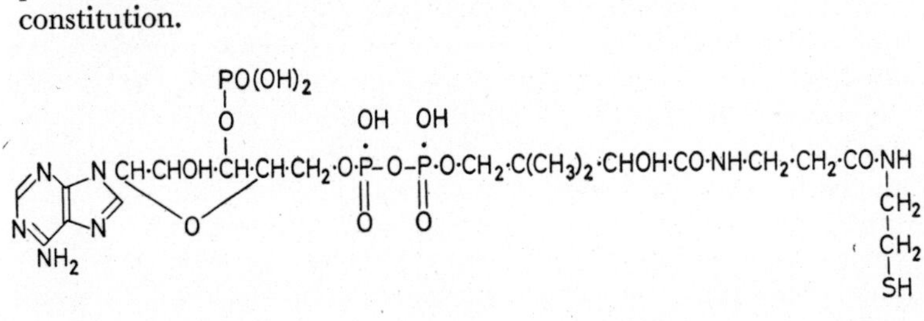

The discovery of Co-enzyme A was an outcome of the earlier work of Lipmann[3-5] on acetyl phosphate $CH_3CO \cdot O \cdot PO(OH)_2$

which he had isolated as the silver salt* during experiments on the oxidative decarboxylation of pyruvic acid with enzymes prepared from the micro-organism *Bacillus delbrückii*. The large amount of work carried out on this acid anhydride lies outside the scope of the discussion, but it was shown that the new compound can transfer its phosphate group to glucose in presence of certain bacterial enzyme preparations or in an extract of pigeon liver.

In 1948 Kaplan and Lipmann[1] showed that extracts of pigeon liver and other animal organs and of bacteria including *Clostridium butylicum* and *Escherichia coli* (*B. coli*) can transfer an acetyl group from acetic acid to sulphanilamide and *p*-aminobenzoic acid in presence of adenosine triphosphate, and although in earlier experiments[3] it seemed possible that acetyl phosphate might be the carrier of the acetyl group, this was shown not to be the case, acetyl phosphate being inactive under such conditions. Lipmann[6] also found that the acetylation of sulphanilamide $\overset{4}{N}H_2 \cdot C_6 H_4 \cdot \overset{1}{S}O_2 \cdot NH_2$ by pigeon-liver extracts was much increased in presence of acetate. Under anaerobic conditions the presence of adenosine triphosphate was necessary. The enzyme system could be re-activated by a preparation of boiled liver extract and this effect was shown to depend on the presence in such extracts of a thermostable co-enzyme (Co-enzyme A) which was finally obtained in an almost pure condition and shown by Lipmann and Kaplan to be also concerned in the acetylation of choline in enzyme systems obtained from brain tissue[7].

PREPARATION OF CO-ENZYME A

Liver, *Clostridium butylicum* and *Proteus morganii* were quickly recognized as being among the best sources of Co-enzyme A. An early method for the preparation of the crude co-enzyme was described by Lipmann and his colleagues[8]. Pig liver was added to boiling water, the extract filtered through muslin and protein precipitated by trichloroacetic acid. The co-enzyme was then converted to the insoluble mercury derivative with mercuric acetate. This was decomposed by hydrogen sulphide. Addition of acetone to the resulting solution gave an oil which was converted successively to the barium, lead and silver salts and again to the barium salt. On precipitation of the barium as sulphate, co-precipitation of Co-enzyme A occurred. This was eluted with aqueous sodium sulphate and converted to the phosphotungstate from which a barium salt was again prepared, and dissolved in hydrochloric acid. Separation of barium as sulphate and addition of excess acetone to the filtrate

---

* See also Lynen, F., *Ber. dtsch. chem. Ges.* **73** (1940) 367.

gave a white precipitate (625 mg. from 500 lb. liver). It had an activity of 130 units per mg. Two later methods for its preparation may now be described. The first employs the liquid medium on which *Streptomyces fradiae* has been grown, the second uses brewers' yeast.

1. The co-enzyme was removed from the culture medium of a large-scale fermentation, by adsorption on charcoal[9]. Elution with alkaline acetone followed by adsorption from acid solution gave a specimen having an activity of 64 units per mg. The yield was about 40 per cent. The product now contained much of the disulphide form R—S—S—R and also impurities. It was reduced by zinc and 0·5 N-hydrochloric acid and precipitated with mercuric acetate as the —S—Hg—S— derivative. This was washed with water and decomposed in aqueous suspension by hydrogen sulphide. The supernatant liquor was then passed through a column of 'Duolite CS-100' resin (H$^+$ form) and most of the impurities removed by washing with 0·2 N-hydrochloric acid. The co-enzyme was then eluted with water and freeze-dried. The product, which represented a yield of 20 per cent, now had an activity of 384 units per mg. and was dried in a vacuum at 34° C to avoid decomposition. Assuming that this procedure removed all water the preparation contained 90–93 per cent of the pure co-enzyme. After hydrolysis by acid, paper chromatography revealed the presence of β-alanine and 2 : 2'-diaminodiethyl disulphide $NH_2 \cdot CH_2 \cdot CH_2 \cdot S \cdot S \cdot CH_2 \cdot CH_2 \cdot NH_2$, but no other product which reacted with ninhydrin was detected. The pantothenic acid content of this product after hydrolysis was shown by enzymatic and microbiological assays to be 1 molar; adenine was determined spectrophotometrically (1·05 molar). Total phosphorus was 2·83 molar and mono-ester phosphate 0·96 molar. The sulphur was 1·07 molar. These figures agree with the formula given on p. 207.

2. The co-enzyme was obtained from an aqueous extract of dried brewers' yeast[10] by precipitation in strongly acid solution as the —S—Cu compound by cuprous oxide in presence of reduced glutathione. The precipitate was decomposed by hydrogen sulphide and the aqueous solution after removal of copper sulphide passed through carbon. The co-enzyme was then eluted with aqueous 5 per cent pyridine and the effluent extracted with chloroform. Concentration of the extract and precipitation with acetone gave a crude product which was again adsorbed on charcoal and eluted. Glutathione was removed by a column of Dowex (H$^+$ form) and Co-enzyme A finally obtained in about 10–15 per cent yield. It had a pantothenic acid content of about 20 per cent.

BIOLOGICAL ASSAY OF CO-ENZYME A AND RELATED COMPOUNDS

The assay of Co-enzyme A is carried out by a method described by Kaplan and Lipmann[1] who also give a useful account, with references, of the early work on the co-enzyme. Pigeon liver extracts after autolization (partial decomposition) cease to acetylate sulphanilamide. Acetylating activity is recovered by addition of Co-enzyme A. At medium concentration the reaction is proportional to the content of Co-enzyme A. The acetylation is determined by the fall in concentration of sulphanilamide which is followed colorimetrically. 'A unit of Co-enzyme A' reactivates the enzyme system to half its maximum activity.

Kaplan and Lipmann showed that *Clostridium butylicum* had a very high content of Co-enzyme A and remarked that this observation coupled with the observed role of the co-enzyme in acetate metabolism, already established in their laboratory, seems to suggest a function of Co-enzyme A in the condensation of chains of two carbon atoms (acetic acid) to those containing four atoms of the element such as butyric acid. Lipmann not only isolated Co-enzyme A but proved[2] that it is a derivative of pantothenic acid

$$HO \cdot CH_2 \cdot C(CH_3)_2 \cdot CHOH \cdot CO \cdot NH \cdot CH_2 \cdot CH_2 \cdot COOH$$

and later made the very stimulating suggestion that it might act as an acetyl carrier. The pantothenic acid was detected during an assay of the crude preparations of Co-enzyme A which proved that only traces of the known B-Vitamins were present. Details of the assay need not be given. It involved, however, a preliminary treatment with clarase–papain*. If this treatment were prolonged the pantothenic acid values as determined by the stimulation of the growth of *Lactobacillus casei E* increased slowly, evidently due to hydrolysis of the co-enzyme. The preparations were therefore hydrolysed by acid and the β-alanine determined in the product by a process depending on the stimulation of the growth of yeast. The results clearly indicated the presence of combined pantothenic acid (pantoyl-β-alanine) in the molecule of the co-enzyme. References to the biological methods of assay are given in the original communication by Lipmann *et al.* They also showed[11] that in addition to pantothenic acid Co-enzyme A contains adenosine (adenylriboside; I, R=H), a sulphur residue which they believed to be allied to cysteine $HS \cdot CH_2 \cdot CH(NH_2) \cdot COOH$, and either two or three phosphate groups. These were recognized, along with pantothenic

---

* 'Clarase' is one of the names given to proprietary preparations of an amylase of vegetable origin. Papain is well known as a proteolytic enzyme from the *paw-paw* fruit. 'Clarase–papain' is sold in America as a 'tenderizer' for meat.

acid, by separate hydrolysis of the co-enzyme with intestinal phosphatase and pigeon liver extract

The phosphatase removed the pyrophosphate link between the ribose and the pantothenic acid; the pigeon liver extract caused fission of the fragment containing sulphur from another part of the pantothenic acid molecule. Lipmann's purest preparation of Co-enzyme A contained 4·3 per cent of sulphur corresponding to one atom per molecule of pantothenic acid. Dephosphorylation of Co-enzyme A yielded a compound containing pantothenic acid and the sulphur fragment which Lipmann believed to be bound through the carboxyl group. This view was confirmed by Snell and his colleagues (*see* p. 212), who identified the simple sulphur fragment as thioethanolamine $NH_2 \cdot CH_2 \cdot CH_2 \cdot SH$ and showed that it was linked as a peptide to pantothenic acid, a linkage which was broken by Lipmann's liver enzyme.

THE WORK OF BADDILEY AND THAIN

Some account may now be given of the extended researches of Baddiley and Thain[12] which led them to propose the structural formula for the co-enzyme which is given on p. 207.

These authors, working at the Lister Institute in London, hydrolysed Co-enzyme A with mild alkali and after removing inorganic phosphates submitted the product to paper chromatography. They detected adenosine 5'-phosphate [I, $R=PO(OH)_2$] and either pantothenic acid 4'-phosphate (II) or its product of hydrolysis, pantoic acid 4'-phosphate (III). Spots corresponding to the 2'-phosphate and 2' : 4'-diphosphate of pantothenic acid were absent, suggesting the absence of such groupings in the molecule of Co-enzyme A, always assuming that they are not unstable in presence of the alkali used for hydrolysis. Baddiley and Thain[13] had already synthesized the 2'- and 4'-phosphates of pantothenic acid (IV) and (II).

THE NATURE OF THE SULPHUR FRAGMENT OF CO-ENZYME A

Hydrolysis of the co-enzyme with dilute hydrochloric acid, addition of excess sodium carbonate and distillation in nitrogen yielded mercaptoethylamine[12] $H_2N \cdot CH_2 \cdot CH_2 \cdot SH$ which was detected by

211

paper chromatography and spraying with ninhydrin (whereby a purplish colour was produced) and also with a mixture of sodium sulphite, sodium cyanide and sodium nitroprusside.

$$(HO)_2P—O—CH_2 \cdot C(CH_3)_2 \cdot CHOH \cdot CO \cdot NH \cdot CH_2 \cdot CH_2 \cdot COOH$$
$$\overset{\|}{O} \qquad\qquad\qquad (II)$$

$$(HO)_2P—O \cdot CH_2 \cdot C(CH_3)_2 \cdot CHOH \cdot COOH$$
$$\overset{\|}{O} \qquad\qquad (III)$$

$$HO \cdot CH_2 \cdot C(CH_3)_2 \cdot CH \text{——} CO \cdot NH \cdot CH_2 \cdot CH_2 \cdot CO \cdot OH$$
$$\overset{|}{O \cdot PO(OH)_2}$$
$$(IV)$$

$$HO \cdot CH_2 \cdot C(CH_3)_2 \cdot CHOH \cdot CO \cdot NH \cdot CH_2 \cdot CH_2 \cdot CO \cdot NH \cdot CH_2 \cdot$$
$$CH_2 \cdot SH$$
Pantetheine (V)

$$HO \cdot CH_2 \cdot C(CH_3)_2 \cdot CHOH \cdot CO \cdot NH \cdot CH_2 \cdot CH_2 \cdot CO \cdot OCH_3$$
Methyl pantothenate (VI)

$$[HO \cdot CH_2 \cdot C(CH_3)_2 \cdot CHOH \cdot CO \cdot NH \cdot CH_2 \cdot CH_2 \cdot CO \cdot NH \cdot CH_2 \cdot$$
$$CH_2 \cdot S]_2$$
Pantethine (VII)

The identification of 2-mercaptoethylamine was important because this thiol enters into the structure of a growth factor for *Lactobacillus bulgaricus* which was isolated by two groups of American workers[14,15], and was shown to be a thiol and a derivative of pantothenic acid and to have the structure (V). It was also synthesized from methyl pantothenate (VI) and 2-mercaptoethylamine. The names pantetheine and pantethine (VII) were suggested by Snell and his co-workers[16] to denote the thiol and disulphide forms of this compound, in analogy with cysteine and cystine. The thiol form was found to be indistinguishable from a decomposition product of Co-enzyme A[17]. It appeared probable therefore that the pantetheine fragment is a component of Co-enzyme A. Novelli, Kaplan and Lipmann[18] had already shown that Co-enzyme A is probably a dinucleotide carrying a pyrophosphate residue which links the ribose of the adenosine residue with the long aliphatic chain. On these grounds Baddiley and Thain[19] proposed the structural formula on p. 207 for Co-enzyme A.

212

Synthesis of Pantetheine

Baddiley and Thain[20] have described an improved synthesis of pantetheine (*see* p. 212), starting from 2-benzylthioethylamine. This was prepared from benzyl mercaptan and bromoethylamine in liquid ammonia. $C_6H_5CH_2SH + Br \cdot CH_2 \cdot CH_2 \cdot NH_2 = C_6H_5 \cdot CH_2 \cdot S \cdot (CH_2)_2 \cdot NH_2 \cdot HBr$. (It may be mentioned that with sodium in liquid ammonia the benzyl group is eliminated as toluene, giving 2-mercaptoethylamine. This method is the most convenient for the preparation of the thiolamine.)

Benzylthioethylamine (VIII) reacts with carbobenzyloxy-β-alanine azide (IX) in chloroform to give 2-benzylthio-N-(carbo-benzyloxy-β-alanyl)-ethylamine (X). Reduction with sodium in liquid ammonia removes the benzyl and the carbobenzyloxy groups giving N-β-alanyl-2-mercaptoethylamine (XI). This reacts with D(—) pantolactone (XII) at 100 °C in the absence of a solvent to give pantetheine, the lactone ring being opened.

$$C_6H_5 \cdot CH_2 \cdot S \cdot CH_2 \cdot CH_2 \cdot NH_2 + N_3 \cdot CO \cdot CH_2 \cdot CH_2 \cdot NH \cdot CO \cdot O \cdot CH_2 \cdot C_6H_5$$

(VIII)   (IX)

$$C_6H_5 \cdot CH_2 \cdot S \cdot CH_2 \cdot CH_2 \cdot NH \cdot CO \cdot CH_2 \cdot CH_2 \cdot NH \cdot CO \cdot O \cdot CH_2 \cdot C_6H_5$$

(X)

$$C_6H_5 \cdot CH_3 + HS \cdot CH_2 \cdot CH_2 \cdot NH \cdot CO \cdot CH_2 \cdot CH_2 \cdot NH_2$$

(XI)

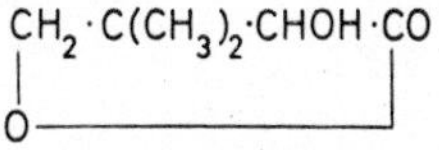

$$\begin{array}{l} CH_2 \cdot C(CH_3)_2 \cdot CHOH \cdot CO \\ | \quad\quad\quad\quad\quad\quad\quad\quad | \\ O \underline{\quad\quad\quad\quad\quad\quad\quad\quad} \end{array} \quad + \text{(XI)}$$

(XII)

$$HO \cdot CH_2 \cdot C(CH_3)_2 \cdot CHOH \cdot CO \cdot NH \cdot CH_2 \cdot CH_2 \cdot CO \cdot NH \cdot CH_2 \cdot CH_2 \cdot SH$$

Pantetheine

Pantetheine readily oxidizes in air to pantethine (VII). The synthetic product, when examined by paper chromatography, could not be distinguished from natural pantetheine. When tested as a growth stimulant for *L. bulgaricus* its activity was 26,000 units per mg. The American workers found a figure of 29,000 for their preparation.

THE PHOSPHATES OF PANTETHEINE

The Cyclic 2′ : 4′ Hydrogen Phosphate

This compound (XIII) and also the 4′-phosphate was synthesized by Baddiley and Thain[21,22] for comparison with certain phosphorylated breakdown products of Co-enzyme A which are discussed on p. 215.

Pantetheine is converted to pantethine by aeration in moist pyridine followed by treatment with phosphoryl chloride. The resulting product is indistinguishable by paper chromatography from the product obtained by hydrolysis of Co-enzyme A. On cautious hydrolysis it lost the mercaptoethylamine residue and gave the cyclic 2′ : 4′-hydrogen phosphate of pantothenic acid and also some 4′-phosphate in the same manner as did the natural degradation product.

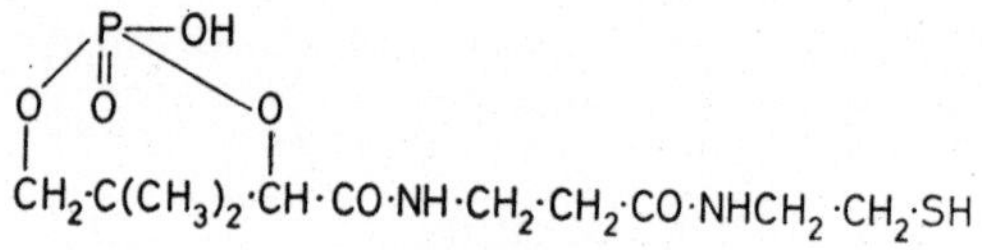

$$\begin{array}{c} P{-}OH \\ \| \\ O \quad O \quad O \end{array}$$

$$CH_2 \cdot C(CH_3)_2 \cdot CH \cdot CO \cdot NH \cdot CH_2 \cdot CH_2 \cdot CO \cdot NHCH_2 \cdot CH_2 \cdot SH$$

(XIII)

PANTETHEINE-4′-PHOSPHATE (THE ACETOBACTER STIMULATING FACTOR)
A DEGRADATION PRODUCT OF CO-ENZYME A

This was originally obtained from Co-enzyme A by the action of a mixture of unpurified liver enzymes and later with the enzyme pyrophosphatase. It is also formed by purely chemical hydrolysis of the co-enzyme with dilute acid. It stimulates the growth of *Acetobacter suboxydans* and as its structure was at first unknown it was designated A.S.F. (Acetobacter stimulating factor).

On enzymic hydrolysis the 'factor' gave pantothenic acid and phosphate in the ratio of 1 : 1 and was at first thought to be a phosphate of pantothenic acid. None of the synthetic monophosphates of this acid (the 2′-, the 4′- and the cyclic 2′ : 4′-) exhibited the stimulatory effect on *A. suboxydans* and it appeared likely that the 'factor' was either not a pantothenic acid phosphate or was contaminated with some biologically active product. Baddiley and Thain suggested that A.S.F. was the 4′-phosphate of pantetheine, i.e. the 2-thiolethylamide of pantothenic acid 4′-phosphate,

$$(HO)_2P—O—CH_2 \cdot C(CH_3)_2 \cdot CHOH \cdot CO \cdot NH \cdot CH_2 \cdot CH_2 \cdot CO \cdot NH \cdot$$
$$\overset{\|}{O}$$

$CH_2 \cdot CH_2 \cdot SH$, and that the 2-thioethylamine had not been detected in the earlier experiments on the hydrolysis of the 'factor'. This opinion was confirmed by the synthesis both of the DL- and the D-isomers by methods which are described below.

Synthesis of DL-Pantetheine-4′-Phosphate

The lactone of pantoic acid (XIV) was converted to the benzyl ether (XV) by reaction with benzyl chloride in presence of sodium ethoxide. The ether reacted with β-alanine in methanol containing dimethylamine giving pantothenic acid 2′-benzyl ether (XVI).

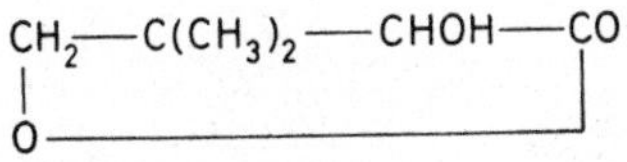

$$CH_2—C(CH_3)_2—CHOH—CO \qquad CH_2—C(CH_3)_2—\overset{O \cdot CH_2 \cdot C_6H_5}{\overset{|}{CH}}—CO$$
$$| \qquad\qquad\qquad\qquad\qquad\qquad\qquad | $$
$$O———————————— \qquad O————————————$$

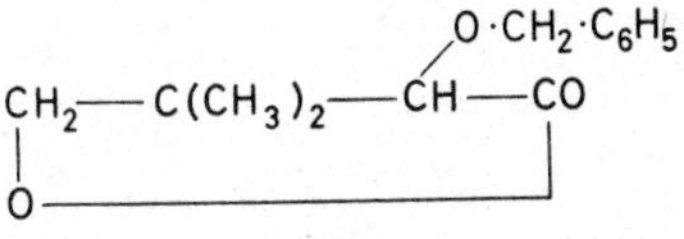

$$\text{(XIV)} \qquad\qquad\qquad\qquad \text{(XV)}$$

$$HO \cdot CH_2—C(CH_3)_2—\overset{O \cdot CH_2 \cdot C_6H_5}{\overset{|}{CH}}—CO \cdot NH \cdot CH_2 \cdot CH_2 \cdot COOH$$

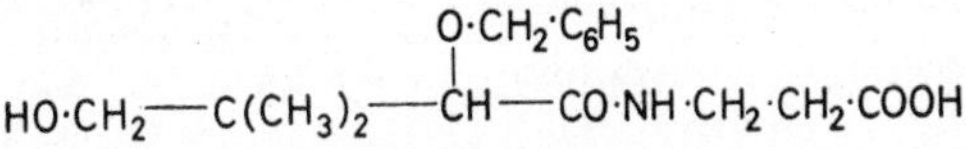

$$\text{(XVI)}$$

When (XVI) was treated with ethyl chloroformate in presence of N-methylmorpholine (XVII) to remove hydrogen chloride, a mixed carbonic anhydride (XVIII) was obtained. This lost carbon dioxide on reaction with 2-benzylthioethylamine (*see* p. 213) giving pantetheine $O^{2'}$-S-dibenzyl ether (XIX) the structure of which was proved by its reduction with sodium in liquid ammonia which gave pantetheine. Phosphorylation of the 4′-hydroxyl group with dibenzyl phosphorochloridate $Cl \cdot PO(OCH_2 \cdot C_6H_5)_2$ gave a tetrabenzyl compound (XX). With sodium and a small amount of ethanol in liquid ammonia the four benzyl groups were replaced by hydrogen giving the desired product (XXI) which was purified with an ion-exchange resin to remove bases and then through the lithium and silver salts. It was shown to be homogeneous by paper chromatography and on hydrolysis gave pantothenic acid 4′-phosphate.

The pantetheine 4′-phosphate in presence of adenosine triphosphate was tested with a partly purified enzyme obtained from pigeon liver. This enzyme mixture synthesizes Co-enzyme A from the bacterial 'acetobacter stimulating factor'. With this racemic pantetheine phosphate[22] the conversion to co-enzyme was 48 per cent, which was in very good agreement with the figure of 50 per cent calculated for a DL-mixture.

$$\underset{\text{(XVII)}}{\overset{\text{CH}_2-\text{CH}_2}{\underset{\text{CH}_2-\text{CH}_2}{\text{O}}}}\text{N}\cdot\text{CH}_3}$$ $$\underset{\text{(XVIII)}}{\text{HO}\cdot\text{CH}_2\cdot\text{C(CH}_3)_2\cdot\text{CH(O}\cdot\text{CH}_2\cdot\text{C}_6\text{H}_5)\cdot\text{CONH}\cdot\text{CH}_2\cdot\text{CH}_2\cdot\text{CO}\cdot\text{O}\cdot\text{COOC}_2\text{H}_5}$$

$$\text{HO}\cdot\text{CH}_2\cdot\text{C(CH}_3)_2\cdot\text{CH}(\cdot\text{O}\cdot\text{CH}_2\cdot\text{C}_6\text{H}_5)\cdot\text{CO}\cdot\text{NH}\cdot\text{CH}_2\cdot\text{CH}_2\cdot\text{CO}\cdot\text{NH}\cdot\text{CH}_2\cdot\text{CH}_2\cdot\text{S}\cdot\text{CH}_2^!\text{C}_6\text{H}_5$$

(XIX)

$$(\text{C}_6\text{H}_5\text{CH}_2\cdot\text{O})_2 \underset{\overset{\|}{\text{O}}}{\text{P}}-\text{O}\cdot\text{CH}_2\cdot\text{C(CH}_3)_2\cdot\text{CH(OCH}_2\cdot\text{C}_6\text{H}_5)\cdot\text{CO}\cdot\text{NH}\cdot\text{CH}_2\cdot\text{CH}_2\cdot\text{CO}\cdot\text{NH}\cdot(\text{CH}_2)_2\cdot\text{S}\cdot\text{CH}_2\cdot\text{C}_6\text{H}_5$$

(XX)

$$(\text{HO})_2\cdot\underset{\overset{\|}{\text{O}}}{\text{P}}\cdot\text{O}\cdot\text{CH}_2\cdot\text{C(CH}_3)_2\cdot\text{CHOH}\cdot\text{CO}\cdot\text{NH}\cdot\text{CH}_2\cdot\text{CH}_2\cdot\text{CO}\cdot\text{NH}\cdot\text{CH}_2\cdot\text{CH}_2\cdot\text{SH}$$

(XXI)

Synthesis of D-Pantetheine 4'-Phosphate

D (+)-Pantethine (the disulphide) in pyridine with dibenzyl phosphorochloridate $\text{Cl}\cdot\text{PO(O}\cdot\text{CH}_2\cdot\text{C}_6\text{H}_5)_2$ gave the neutral dibenzyl ester which was then reduced with sodium in liquid ammonia. The product, after purification through the barium and silver salts, was identical with pantetheine-4'-phosphoric acid. In the enzyme test, carried out as before, an 84 per cent conversion to Co-enzyme A was observed[22].

SYNTHESIS OF DERIVATIVES OF PANTOTHENIC ACID

Baddiley and Mathias[23] have described the preparation of various derivatives of pantothenic acid which from structural considerations might possibly be regarded as intermediate compounds in the biological synthesis of Co-enzyme A. The most interesting of these was pantothenoylcysteine (**XXII**) which by simple decarboxylation could yield pantetheine (**XXIII**). This peptide and the corresponding disulphide were synthesized by four methods, two of which are described below. The 4'-phosphate of pantothenoylcysteine was also prepared.

The biochemical behaviour of these compounds will first be considered. Pierpoint and Hughes[24] had shown that *Lactobacillus arabinosus* converts pantetheine (**XXIII**) into Co-enzyme A but pantothenic acid does not undergo this reaction unless cystine is present. The cystine cannot be replaced by 2-mercaptoethylamine so its action cannot be explained by a simple reduction to cysteine followed by decarboxylation, or by the similar reaction in which decarboxylation might precede reductive fission

$$[COOH \cdot CH(NH_2) \cdot CH_2 \cdot S]_2 \rightarrow COOH \cdot CH(NH_2) \cdot CH_2 \cdot SH \xrightarrow{-CO_2}$$
$$NH_2 \cdot CH_2 \cdot CH_2 \cdot SH.$$

It appeared possible that pantothenoylcysteine (XXII) might first be formed which by decarboxylation would yield pantetheine (XXIII).

$$\overset{4'}{HO} \cdot CH_2 \cdot \overset{3'}{C}(CH_3)_2 \cdot CHOH \cdot CO \cdot NH \cdot (CH_2)_2 \cdot CO \cdot NH \cdot CH \cdot CH_2 \cdot SH$$

$$(XXII) \qquad\qquad COOH$$

$$HO \cdot CH_2 \cdot C(CH_3)_2 \cdot CHOH \cdot CO \cdot NH \cdot (CH_2)_2 \cdot CO \cdot NH \cdot CH_2 \cdot CH_2 \cdot SH$$
$$(XXIII)$$

Brown and Snell[25] found that specimens of pantothenoylcysteine synthesized in their laboratory and by Baddiley and Mathias were converted to Co-enzyme A by *Acetobacter suboxydans* but not by *L. arabinosus*. They also suggested that pantothenoylcysteine-4'-phosphate might be a precursor of the co-enzyme. This phosphate has been synthesized by Baddiley and Mathias, *see* p. 218, and found to have only about 40 per cent of the activity of pantothenoylcysteine and twice the activity of pantothenic acid in stimulating the growth of *A. suboxydans*. A possible explanation is that dephosphorylation may take place before conversion to Co-enzyme A.

Synthesis of Pantothenoylcysteine

In Baddiley and Mathias' first method[23] pantothenic acid and ethyl chloroformate reacted to give a mixed carbonic anhydride (XXIV) which on treatment with S-benzylcysteine lost ethanol and carbon dioxide to give impure S-benzyl-pantothenoylcysteine (XXV). Removal of the benzyl group with sodium in liquid ammonia and purification of the product on a cellulose column yielded pantothenoylcysteine.

$$HO \cdot CH_2 \cdot C(CH_3)_2 \cdot CHOH \cdot CO \cdot NH \cdot CH_2 \cdot CH_2 \cdot CO \cdot O \cdot CO \cdot OC_2H_5$$
$$(XXIV)$$
$$+ H_2N \cdot CH(COOH) \cdot CH_2 \cdot S \cdot CH_2 \cdot C_6H_5$$

217

$$HO \cdot CH_2 \cdot C(CH_3)_2 \cdot CHOH \cdot CO \cdot NH \cdot CH_2 \cdot CH_2 \cdot CO \cdot NH \cdot CH$$
$$(COOH) \cdot CH_2 \cdot S \cdot CH_2 \cdot C_6H_5$$

(XXV)

A more convenient method of synthesis[23] was from β-alanine which with benzyl chloroformate gave benzyloxycarbonyl-β-alanine (XXVI). This was converted to the acid chloride (XXVII) which with S-benzyl-L-cysteine in sodium hydroxide followed by acidification gave S-benzyl-N-(benzyloxycarbonyl-β-alanyl)cysteine (XXVIII).

$$C_6H_5 \cdot CH_2 \cdot O \cdot CO \cdot Cl + HNH \cdot CH_2 \cdot CH_2 \cdot COOH \rightarrow HCl + (XXVI)$$
$$\rightarrow C_6H_5CH_2 \cdot O \cdot CO \cdot NH \cdot CH_2 \cdot CH_2 \cdot COCl + NH_2CH(COOH)CH_2 \cdot$$
$$S \cdot CH_2 \cdot C_6H_5 \rightarrow$$

(XXVII)

$$C_6H_5CH_2 \cdot O \cdot CO \cdot NH \cdot CH_2 \cdot CH_2 \cdot CO \cdot NH \cdot CH(COOH) \cdot CH_2 \cdot S \cdot$$
$$CH_2 \cdot C_6H_5 + HCl$$

(XXVIII)

Treatment of (XXVIII) with sodium in liquid ammonia and rebenzylation of the thiol group gave S-benzyl-β-alanylcysteine (XXIX). With pantolactone (XXX) this yielded S-benzyl-N-(D-pantothenoyl) cysteine which on removal of the benzyl group with sodium in liquid ammonia gave pantothenoylcysteine (XXXI).

$$H_2C \cdot C(CH_3)_2 \cdot CHOH \cdot CO \qquad + \qquad H_2N \cdot CH_2 \cdot CH_2 \cdot CO \cdot NH \cdot CH(COOH) \cdot CH_2 \cdot SCH_2 \cdot C_6H_5$$
$$O \underline{\hspace{4cm}}$$

(XXX)   (XXIX)

$$HO \cdot CH_2 \cdot C(CH_3)_2 \cdot CHOH \cdot CO \cdot NH \cdot CH_2 \cdot CH_2 \cdot CO \cdot NHCH \cdot CH_2 \cdot SH$$
$$\qquad\qquad COOH$$

(XXXI)

Pantothenoylcysteine-4'-Phosphate

Baddiley and Mathias[23] synthesized pantothenoylcysteine-4'-phosphate (XXXII) by a method similar to that employed for pantetheine-4'-phosphate (*see* p. 215). S-benzylpantothenoyl-cysteine (XXXIa) was phosphorylated with dibenzyl phosphochloridate in pyridine and benzyl groups removed by sodium in liquid ammonia. The 2'-hydroxyl group is unaffected under these conditions. The structure of the product was proved by alkaline hydrolysis to cysteine and pantothenic acid-4'-phosphate. On oxidation by hydrogen peroxide followed by hydrolysis with hydrochloric acid, β-alanine and cysteic acid, $COOH\cdot CH(NH_2)\cdot CH_2\cdot SO_2\cdot OH$ were detected.

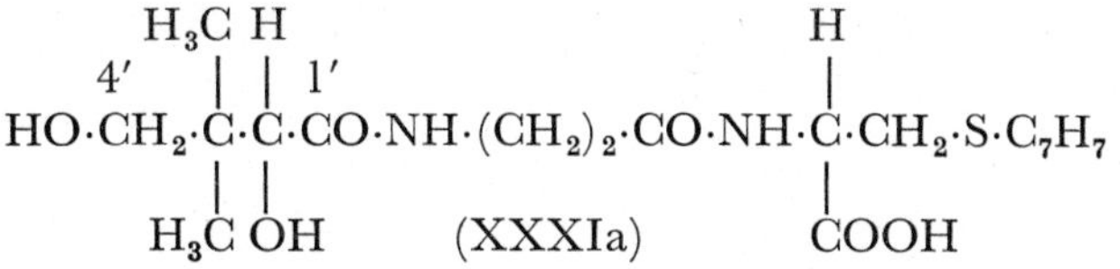

$$\underset{\substack{4' \\ }}{HO\cdot CH_2}\cdot \underset{\substack{| \\ H_3C}}{\overset{\substack{H_3C \\ |}}{C}}\cdot \underset{\substack{| \\ OH}}{\overset{\substack{H \\ |}}{\underset{1'}{C}}}\cdot CO\cdot NH\cdot (CH_2)_2\cdot CO\cdot NH\cdot \underset{\substack{| \\ COOH}}{\overset{\substack{H \\ |}}{C}}\cdot CH_2\cdot S\cdot C_7H_7$$

(XXXIa)

$$H_2O_3P\cdot O\cdot CH_2\cdot \underset{\substack{| \\ H_3C}}{\overset{\substack{H_3C \\ |}}{\underset{4'}{C}}}\cdot \underset{\substack{| \\ OH}}{\overset{\substack{H \\ |}}{\underset{1'}{C}}}\cdot CO\cdot NH\cdot (CH_2)_2\cdot CO\cdot NH\cdot \underset{\substack{| \\ COOH}}{\overset{\substack{H \\ |}}{C}}\cdot CH_2\cdot SH$$

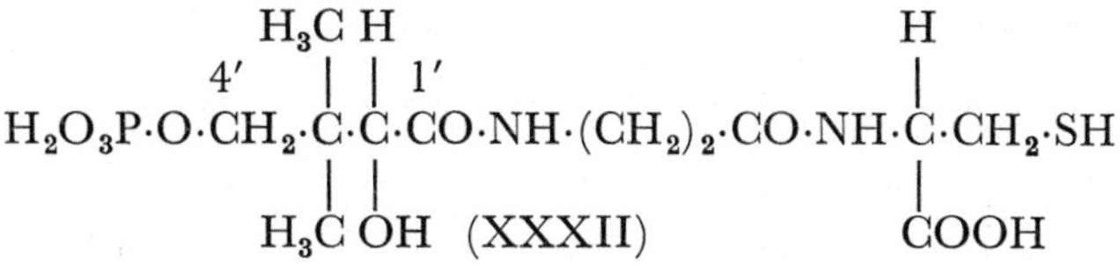

(XXXII)

THE SINGLE PHOSPHORIC ACID GROUPING IN CO-ENZYME A

It has been mentioned already that one mole of Co-enzyme A yields 2·83 moles of phosphoric acid (*see* p. 209) indicating the presence of three phosphoric acid residues. Two of these are present as a pyrophosphate link, since on enzymic hydrolysis of Co-enzyme A by a nucleotide pyrophosphatase it was found that adenosine-5'-phosphoric acid and a phosphorylated pantothenic acid were obtained[26]. This result agrees with the view that in Co-enzyme A (XXXIII) a pyrophosphoric acid residue links the adenosine (adenylriboside) fragment with the pantothenic acid chain.

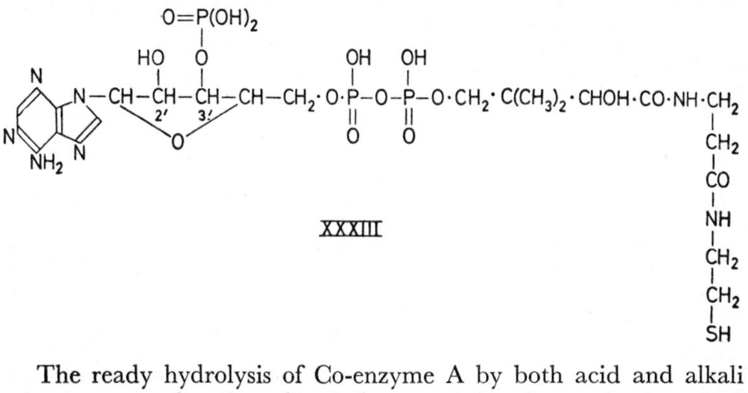

XXXIII

The ready hydrolysis of Co-enzyme A by both acid and alkali also supports the view that it is a pyrophosphate. An intestinal phosphatase which has both mono- and di-esterase activity removes all three phosphoric acid groups[27]. Gregory, Novelli and Lipmann found that a mono-esterase enzyme obtained from the prostate gland removed only one phosphoric acid group from Co-enzyme A[9,26], a result obviously compatible with the presence of a pyrophosphate linking. Baddiley and Thain[27] showed that, as in triphosphopyridine nucleotide, this single phosphate group is attached to the ribose fragment, either on carbon atom 2'- or 3'-. Nucleotides which are unsubstituted in these two positions yield dialdehydes on oxidation with sodium periodate on filter paper and these can be detected by spraying with Schiff's reagent. On application of this test to Co-enzyme A no reaction was obtained under conditions where nucleotides unsubstituted in these positions were oxidized. However, on hydrolysis of the co-enzyme with acid and application of the test, dialdehydes were easily detected. The test obviously will not distinguish between positions 2'- and 3'- but it is clear that in Co-enzyme A one of these positions is occupied by a phosphoric acid residue. The structure of the co-enzyme, therefore, presents some analogy with that of triphosphopyridine nucleotide (XXXIV). In this compound the third phosphoric acid group is situated on carbon atom 2' of the ribose fragment[28].

(XXXIV)

Triphosphopyridine nucleotide (TPN)

The position of the monophosphate residue in Co-enzyme A was finally decided by the very interesting work of Wang, Shuster and Kaplan[29] with specific enzymes (phosphoric esterases). Their paper represents an important application of this technique.

These authors employed a specific 3'-nucleotidase obtained from barley and rye-grass. This hydrolyses only a phosphoric acid group attached to the 3'-position in nucleotides, but has no effect on such groups in the 2'- or 5'- positions. This 3'-nucleotidase was found to liberate one mole of phosphoric acid from one mole of Co-enzyme A and also to hydrolyse adenosine-3'-phosphoric acid and the co-enzyme at about the same rate. In this reaction the co-enzyme must be present in the disulphide form which can be ensured by stirring or shaking at pH 7·5 until the odour of thiol compounds disappears. If this is not done the thiol group inhibits the 3'-nucleotidase. In agreement with this explanation it was found that cysteine and reduced glutathione strongly inhibit the enzyme.

As would be expected triphosphopyridine nucleotide (XXXIV)

is not attacked by the 3'-nucleotidase as its monophosphoric group
is at 2'-. There is, therefore, strong evidence for the presence of a
single phosphoric acid residue on carbon atom 3'- in the ribose
fragment of Co-enzyme A.

This conclusion is strengthened by some further work described
by the same authors[29]. By the use of pyrophosphatase obtained
from snake venom both Co-enzyme A and triphosphopyridine
nucleotide were hydrolysed to yield two fragments which were both
diphosphoadenosines, and were shown to be different by their
behaviour on paper chromatography. On treatment with the
specific 3'-nucleotidase from rye-grass or barley the diphosphoaden-
osine (XXXV) from Co-enzyme A yielded adenosine-5'-phosphate
with loss of phosphoric acid, but that(XXXVI) from triphosphopyridine nucleotide did not, in agreement with the established structure
of the latter compound, in which as already stated the monophosphate linkage is on carbon atom 2'. The diphosphoadenosines from
Co-enzyme A and triphosphopyridine nucleotide are therefore
3' : 5'- and 2' : 5'- derivatives respectively.

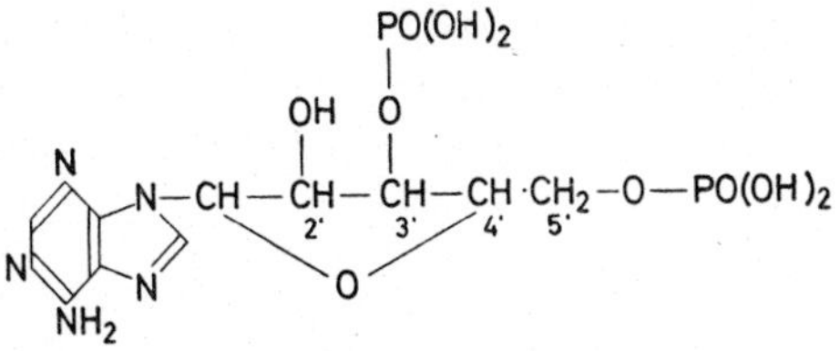

(XXXV)

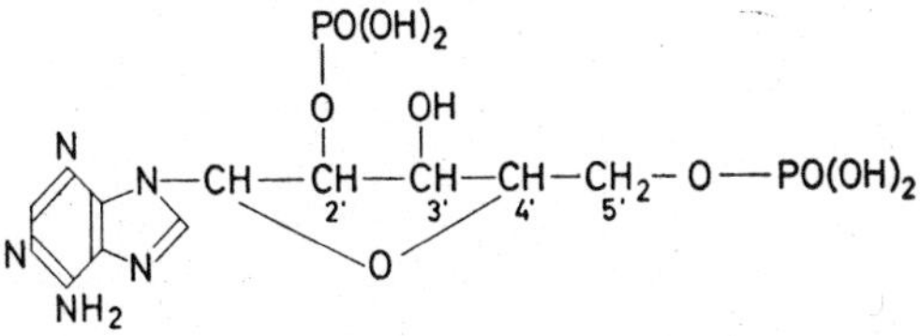

(XXXVI)

Finally Wang *et al.* studied the action of the 3'-nucleotidase on Co-
enzyme A. This gives a compound known at first as 'dephosphory-
lated Co-enzyme A'. Analysis by standard methods showed that
adenine, ribose, pantothenic acid and phosphate were present in the
molar ratios of 1 : 1 : 1 : 2. One phosphoric acid residue had been
removed from position 3'.

221

BIOLOGICAL SYNTHESIS OF CO-ENZYME A

The identification of the degradation products of the co-enzyme, i.e. pantetheine, pantetheine phosphate and dephospho-Co-enzyme A, by the use of specific enzymes as described already, affords excellent evidence that the co-enzyme has the structure formulated earlier in this chapter. These fission products were all re-converted to Co-enzyme A by crude extracts of pigeon liver, although the conversion of pantetheine was poor. By careful and complicated fractionation of the liver extracts an enzyme, *pantetheine kinase*, was separated which converted pantetheine only as far as its phosphate. The remainder of the original pigeon liver extracts ('the supernatant' portion) was shown to convert both pantetheine phosphate and dephospho-Co-enzyme A to Co-enzyme A.

Extracts of hogs' liver were then found to afford a cheap source of these enzymes and by improved processes of fractionation it was possible to separate three enzymes, (a) *pantetheine kinase* (which phosphorylates pantetheine in the 4'-position), (b) the so-called '*condensing enzyme*' which converts 4'-phosphopantetheine but not the 2'- or the 2' : 4' cyclic phosphate (*see* p. 214) to dephospho-Co-enzyme A and (c) *dephospho-Co-enzyme A kinase* which introduces the third phosphate group into the ribose molecule to give Co-enzyme A.

Adenosine triphosphate is necessary for each of these conversions. The formation of a diphospho derivative (dephospho-Co-enzyme A) from 4'-phosphopantetheine by adenosine triphosphate proceeds by loss of two phosphate residues. It seemed possible that these might be eliminated as pyrophosphate.

The first evidence for this was furnished by the observation that added inorganic pyrophosphate completely inhibited the conversion of phosphopantetheine to Co-enzyme A, but had no effect on the third stage, the phosphorylation of the dephospho-Co-enzyme A to Co-enzyme A. By freeing the enzyme almost completely from *pyrophosphatase* (which causes fission of pyrophosphate to orthophosphate) it became possible to measure the formation of pyrophosphate in the reaction. It was shown that when adenosine triphosphate was incubated with 4'-phosphopantetheine in presence of the enzyme, condensation occurs with elimination of inorganic pyrophosphate in fairly good equivalence with the Co-enzyme A synthesized. This proves the elimination of pyrophosphate in reaction (b) above and also the presence of a pyrophosphate linkage in Co-enzyme A. One molecule of pyrophosphate is eliminated from adenosine triphosphate and a new pyrophosphate link established. Fuller details are given in a review by Novelli[30] entitled 'Enzymatic Synthesis and Structure

222

$$HO \cdot \overset{4'}{CH_2} \cdot C(CH_3)_2 \cdot CHOH \cdot CO \cdot NH \cdot CH_2 \cdot CH_2 \cdot CO \cdot NH \cdot CH(COOH) \cdot CH_2 \cdot SH$$

(1) $-CO_2$ | Pantothenoylcysteine

$$HO \cdot CH_2 \cdot C(CH_3)_2 \cdot CHOH \cdot CO \cdot NH \cdot CH_2 \cdot CH_2 \cdot CO \cdot NH \cdot CH_2 \cdot CH_2 SH$$

Pantetheine

(2) Pantetheine kinase | A.T.P.

$$HO - \overset{O}{\underset{OH}{\overset{\|}{P}}} - O \cdot CH_2 \cdot C(CH_3)_2 \cdot CHOH \cdot CO \cdot NH \cdot CH_2 \cdot CH_2 \cdot CO \cdot NH \cdot CH_2 \cdot CH_2 \cdot SH \quad + A.D.P.$$

4' Phosphopantetheine

(3) Condensing enzyme | A.T.P.

$$CHOH \cdot CO \cdot NH \cdot (CH_2)_2 \cdot CO \cdot NH \quad + \quad O=\overset{OH}{\underset{OH}{P}} - O - \overset{OH}{\underset{OH}{P}}=O$$
$$(CH_2)_2$$
$$SH$$

Dephospho Co-enzyme A

(4) Dephospho Co-enzyme A | A.T.P.
Kinase

Co-enzyme A

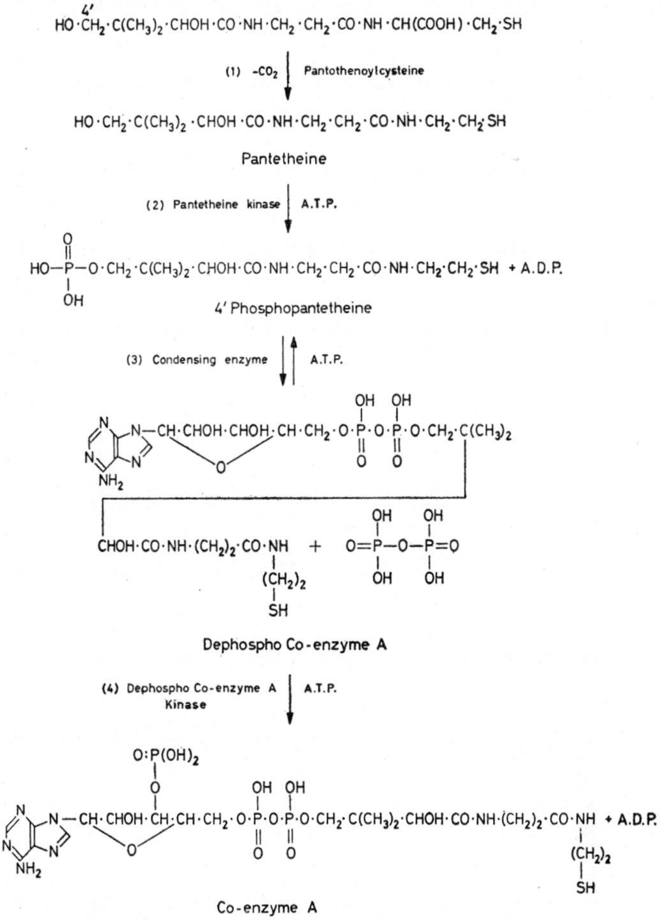

The formulae for adenosine tri-and diphosphate are shown below:

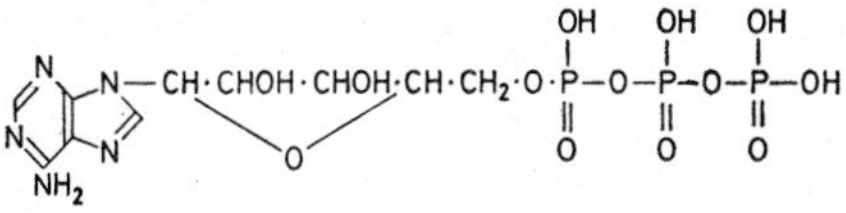

Adenosine triphosphate

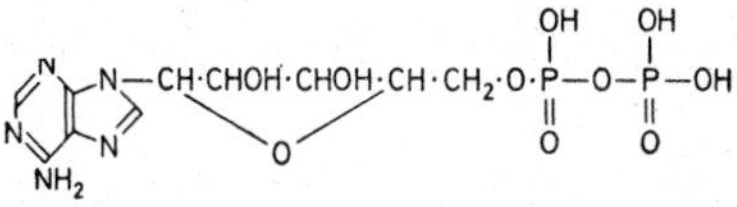

Adenosine diphosphate

223

of Co-enzyme A', from which the enzymic reactions set out under (2)–(4) are taken. The origin of pantetheine is not considered, but from the results of Brown and Snell[31] it would appear that pantothenoyl-cysteine or possibly its 4'-phosphate (*see* p. 218) may be its precursor. Novelli points out that in general reactions brought about by kinase enzymes are essentially irreversible since there is a large decrease in free energy between adenosine triphosphate and the monophosphate formed by transfer. In the above case this would be phosphopantetheine. On the other hand condensations between adenosine triphosphate and mononucleotides which involve elimination of pyrophosphate and formation of a new pyrophosphate link are theoretically reversible since there is relatively no energy fall between the reactants and the products. Novelli confirmed this by a study of the reaction (3) above.

S-ACETYL CO-ENZYME A

In 1948 Kaplan and Lipmann[32] showed that in extracts obtained from *E. coli* containing acetate and adenosine triphosphate, acetylation of sulphanilamide was observed, but that acetyl phosphate was inactive under these conditions. In the absence of an 'acetate acceptor' considerable quantities of a substance accumulated which had many of the properties of acetyl phosphate but differed from it in being inert to a specific enzyme—acetyl phosphatase—obtained from muscle. The compound was not diacetylphosphate. An interesting and significant reaction occurred when this new compound, in dialysed suspensions of *E. coli*, reacted with formate, pyruvic acid being produced. This could be explained on the basis of some such reaction as

$$R \cdot COCH_3 + H \cdot COOH = RH + CH_3 \cdot CO \cdot COOH$$

the compound being assumed to contain a mobile acetyl group. The *E. coli* suspensions were free from adenosine triphosphate and contained only traces of other organic phosphates. Synthetic acetyl phosphate undergoes a similar reaction only in the presence of adenosine diphosphate. In view of later work it is probable that this new product, which so much resembled acetyl phosphate, consisted largely of the S-acetyl derivative of Co-enzyme A.

Metabolism of Acetate by Impoverished Yeast: The Induction Period

Some six years prior to this work of Lipmann's, however, Lynen[33] had observed that when impoverished yeast[34] (obtained by shaking yeast for 15–20 hours in presence of oxygen) was treated with acetate there was a very pronounced delay in the onset of oxidation. This 'induction period' could be eliminated or greatly reduced by the addition of small quantities of readily oxidizable alcohols or aldehydes or of glucose. Lynen considered that during the oxidation of these substances the acetate became 'activated', i.e. combined in a labile form with some residue R.

It appeared possible, at first, that this 'active acetate' might be acetyl phosphate which was shown by Lipmann[3-5] to be produced by certain bacteria from pyruvic acid either by oxidation (dehydrogenation) or by a phosphoroclastic reaction.

$$CH_3 CO \cdot COOH + H \cdot O \cdot PO(OH)_2 = CH_3CO \cdot O \cdot PO(OH)_2 + H \cdot COOH$$

It was also detected in the bacterial dehydrogenation of acetaldehyde or the fission of acetoacetic acid. A typical reaction in which 'active acetic acid' is concerned is the condensation of acetic and oxaloacetic acids to give citric acid[35,35a]. Acetyl phosphate was shown by Stadtman and Barker[36] to be quite ineffective in this connection and was clearly not identical with 'active acetic acid'. It was found, however, that the acetylation of choline and of sulphanilamide in extracts of animal organs and of pigeon liver respectively, which was observed with 'active acetic acid', could be effected in its absence by a mixture of acetate and adenosine triphosphate. It seemed, therefore, that in animal enzyme systems acetyl phosphate was inactive as an acetyl donor but that adenosine triphosphate (presumably a source of phosphate) *plus* acetate was effective. This was explained when it was shown that the crude enzyme preparations contained a compound, later known as Co-enzyme A, which was found to be concerned with the acetylations[1,7,37]. Adenosine triphosphate, acetate and Co-enzyme A appeared to be equivalent to active acetic acid in acetylating power and, in presence of the appropriate enzyme, this mixture not only acetylated choline and sulphanilamide but was able to synthesize citric acid from oxaloacetate and to convert acetoacetate to acetate, as discussed on p. 237.

From a consideration of these results and his earlier work on the 'induction period' that was necessary before the oxidation of acetate by impoverished yeast could proceed effectively (*see* above) Lynen[38] suggested that Co-enzyme A might play some part during this induction period. This possibility was supported by the observation of Novelli and Lipmann that yeast cells, cultivated in a medium deficient in pantothenic acid, contained only 150 units of Co-enzyme A per gram of dry matter (fresh yeast[38] may show 190) and had a considerably diminished capacity to oxidize acetate. Lynen then showed that in four experiments impoverished yeast contained 25 per cent less Co-enzyme A than normal specimens; the assay was carried out by the sulphanilamide process already described. By the use of fresh yeast cultures Lynen showed that on addition of acetate the amount of Co-enzyme A rose rapidly in about 15 minutes to a maximum of 320–360 units per gram of dry yeast. In a corresponding experiment with impoverished yeast the rate of increase was much slower and even after 160 minutes only about 250 units of Co-enzyme A were present. It was also found that the rate of oxygen consumption, i.e. the oxidation of acetate, was very much slower in the experiments with impoverished yeast than with fresh yeast.

As the increase in the amount of Co-enzyme A in yeast–acetate cultures is accompanied by increased consumption of oxygen and of acetate Lynen suggested that a compound of Co-enzyme A and acetic acid (active acetic acid) is involved in the metabolism of acetate by yeast. There remained, however, the remarkable fact (considered on p. 225) that impoverished yeast, even when containing appreciable amounts of Co-enzyme A, is unable to metabolize acetate until about 100 units per gram of the Co-enzyme A are present. Between 100 and 400 units, however, the content of Co-enzyme A and rate of disappearance of acetate were found to be directly proportional.

ISOLATION OF ACTIVE ACETIC ACID—S-ACETYL CO-ENZYME A

Preparation of an Aqueous Extract of Yeast

Lynen[38] found that the best source was an aqueous extract of yeast. Prior to extraction the yeast was suspended in aqueous glucose or sucrose which was maintained mildly alkaline with sodium hydrogen carbonate. A stream of oxygen was introduced during 15 minutes at 30°C. This procedure ensures the maximum production of the 'active acetic acid'. The resulting yeast suspension was added in portions to vigorously boiling water containing sufficient acetic acid to neutralize the sodium hydrogen carbonate; the temperature was not allowed to fall below 70°–80°C. After the last addition the mixture was quickly raised to the boiling point and quickly cooled to 10°C. Solid matter was then removed by centrifugation. 750 grams of yeast gave about 1,690 c.c. of a clear yellow extract. In order to avoid loss of 'active acetic acid' the extract was not maintained at 100°C longer than necessary. We may now use the term 'acetyl

Co-enzyme A' instead of 'active acetic acid'. Approximate indications of the relative concentrations of this substance in different preparations can be gained from the violet colour produced by ammoniacal sodium nitroprusside. This depends on the prior hydrolysis of the $RS \cdot COCH_3$ to a thiol $R \cdot SH$ and about one minute elapses before the colour appears. Addition of solid ammonium sulphate increases the sensitivity of the reaction and the persistence of the colour. The total volume in the test should be about 0·09 c.c. contained in a test tube of 0·9 cm. Under these conditions quantities of over 2γ of acetyl Co-enzyme A can readily be detected. Thiols naturally interfere with this reaction so they must be oxidized by alcoholic iodine solution to disulphides which are inert under the conditions of the test. The presence of disulphides in the yeast extract can be detected by addition of potassium cyanide to the ammoniacal solution before the nitroprusside is added. Thiol is produced according to the reaction

$$R \cdot S \cdot S \cdot R + KCN = R \cdot S \cdot CN + RSK$$

Separation of S-Acetyl Co-enzyme A from the Yeast Extract

After addition of alcoholic iodine the yeast extract was treated with much solid ammonium sulphate and extracted four times with liquefied phenol. This removed the desired product along with other nucleotides. The united extracts were diluted with an equal volume of ether and repeatedly extracted with water. The extracts were freed from phenol by shaking with ether and then evaporated in a vacuum at a low temperature to a small volume. The resulting solution was precipitated with barium acetate in presence of alcohol and ammonia. The barium salt was decomposed by dilute sulphuric acid and after centrifugation the acetyl Co-enzyme A removed by adsorption on charcoal. Thiols and disulphides were shown to be absent from the residual liquor. The charcoal was washed with water to remove sulphate and extracted with aqueous pyridine till the extract gave negative tests for thiols and disulphides. Pyridine was removed by extraction with chloroform and the aqueous solution evaporated to a very small bulk as before, and treated with acetone. After remaining overnight at —20°C the precipitated S-acetyl Co-enzyme A was centrifuged and dried in a vacuum over silica gel. At 0°C under these conditions the compound can be stored without decomposition. Three kilograms of yeast gave 180–250 mg. of the S-acetyl compound with an acetyl content which varied from 1 to 5·5 γ $CH_3CO \cdot$ per mg.

227

Chemical Properties of S-Acetyl Co-enzyme A

The reactions of 'active acetic acid' confirmed the conclusion that its structure was that of an acetylated Co-enzyme A, with acetyl attached to sulphur. At the time Lynen's paper in *Liebig's Annalen der Chemie*[38] was submitted the exact structure of Co-enzyme A had not been determined. The belief that an S-acetyl group was present was greatly strengthened by the behaviour of 'active acetic acid' in the ammoniacal nitroprusside test which has already been described. Compounds such as ethyl S-acetyl-2-thiopropionate, $CH_3 \cdot CO \cdot S \cdot CH_2 \cdot CH_2 \cdot CO \cdot OC_2H_5$ and diacetylthioethanolamine $CH_3 \cdot CO \cdot NH \cdot CH_2 \cdot CH_2 \cdot S \cdot CO \cdot CH_3$ behave in a similar manner and exhibit the slow production of the violet colour already mentioned. With these two pure compounds as standards Lynen[38] has placed this nitroprusside colour reaction on a quantitative basis. If a graph be drawn between the concentration of the acetylthio-group, $CH_3CO \cdot S$— and the intensity of the colour, the values obtained for both these compounds lie on the same straight line. Since acetyl Co-enzyme A has the same degree of stability to alkali as the two standards mentioned above it is permissible to apply this method to the determination of $CH_3CO \cdot S$— in this substance. Four different specimens of acetyl Co-enzyme A were examined. With these preparations the quantity of sulphanilamide acetylated in the enzymic reaction already discussed, was also determined.

The relation of $CH_3 \cdot CO \cdot S$— content to sulphanilamide acetylated, is represented by the same straight line for each of the four preparations. The graph shows that 172 parts of sulphanilamide correspond to 32 parts of sulphur, i.e. one mole of the amide to one mole of the acetylthio-group, a result which strengthens still further the formulation of 'active acetic acid' as S-acetyl Co-enzyme A[39]. Further confirmation of the structure of 'active acetic acid' was furnished by the observation that like several S-acetylmercaptans $R \cdot S \cdot CO \cdot CH_3$ it is stable to acids but not to alkalis.

De-acetylation of S-acetyl Co-enzyme A—Finally, the behaviour of Lynen's product towards aqueous mercuric acetate in slightly acid solution, afforded conclusive evidence that it is the S-acetyl derivative of Co-enzyme A. Sachs[40] had already shown that the ethyl ester of thioacetic acid $CH_3 \cdot CO \cdot S \cdot C_2H_5$ undergoes fission in presence of aqueous mercuric acetate giving acetic acid and the mercury derivative of ethanethiol $(C_2H_5 \cdot S)_2Hg$. Lynen showed that a number of acyl mercaptans $R \cdot CO \cdot S \cdot R'$ also exhibited this reaction. On treatment of 'active acetic acid' with mercuric acetate a precipitate containing mercury was obtained. Separation of this, suspension in water, removal of mercury with hydrogen sulphide, filtration and removal of excess hydrogen sulphide gave an aqueous solution containing free —SH groups, which was quite inert in the enzymic sulphanilamide test for acetyl groups. This substance, assuming Lynen's view to be correct, should be Co-enzyme A. As will be shown below this assumption was upheld and it was found convenient to use this fission reaction exerted by mercuric acetate on S-acetyl Co-enzyme A for the preparation of specimens of the co-enzyme free from its S-acetyl derivative:

(1) $2R \cdot S \cdot CO \cdot CH_3 + 2HOH + Hg(O \cdot CO \cdot CH_3)_2 = (RS)_2 Hg +$
    S-acetyl Co-enzyme A $\qquad\qquad\qquad\qquad\qquad 4CH_3CO \cdot OH$

(2) $\qquad\qquad\qquad (RS)_2Hg + H_2S = HgS + 2RSH$
$\qquad\qquad\qquad\qquad\qquad\qquad\qquad\qquad\qquad$ Co-enzyme A

The pure, or almost pure, preparation of Co-enzyme A obtained through the mercury derivative was treated in aqueous solution with sodium amalgam to ensure that any of the $R \cdot S \cdot S \cdot R$ form of the co-enzyme was reduced to the $R \cdot SH$ form. It was found to be almost completely inactivated (95 per cent) by sodium iodoacetate as shown by Lipmann's sulphanilamide test (using acetate and adenosine triphosphate). Iodoacetate is a specific inactivator for —SH compounds as was shown by Dickens[41] and others in the case of the reduced (—SH) form of glutathione. This is due to the reaction $—SH + I \cdot CH_2 \cdot COONa = —S \cdot CH_2 \cdot COONa + HI$.

The Enzymic Synthesis of Acetyl Co-enzyme A

Stadtman[44] has amplified the results of Lynen, Reichert and Rueff[38] and obtained strong evidence for the production of acetyl Co-enzyme A from acetyl phosphate and the co-enzyme by the enzyme phosphotransacetylase, obtained from extracts of *Clostridium kluyveri*, and has discussed the energy content of the $CH_3CO \cdot S—$ bond.

$$CH_3CO \cdot O \cdot PO_3H_2 + CoA \cdot SH \rightarrow CH_3CO \cdot S \cdot CoA + PO(OH)_3$$
$\qquad\qquad\qquad$ Co-enzyme A $\qquad\qquad$ Acetyl Co-enzyme A

Only a brief outline of the experimental procedure can be given here.

A mixture containing acetyl phosphate labelled with ^{14}C in the carbonyl group, Co-enzyme A, hydrogen sulphide and the enzyme were incubated at 28°C. (The hydrogen sulphide was used in place of the —SH form of glutathione or cysteine in order to maintain the Co-enzyme A in the thiol form, *see* above.) After 30 minutes excess acetyl phosphate was hydrolysed by heating at 100°C. The mixture was then chromatographed on paper. A band which showed the reactions of an acetylmercaptan with hydroxylamine (*see* below) was cut out and eluted with water. On the expectation that the eluate contained the S-acetyl derivative of Co-enzyme A the acetylmercaptan content was determined by the hydroxylamine procedure (*see* below), the ^{14}C by the usual radioactive assay, and the content of Co-enzyme A by the arsenolysis reaction (*see* p. 231). Furthermore the capacity of the eluate to synthesize citric acid from oxaloacetic acid in presence of the crystalline condensing enzyme of Stern and Ochoa[35,35a,58] (*see* p. 237) was also measured. The results showed that the eluate contained equivalent amounts of acetyl Co-enzyme A, ^{14}C, Co-enzyme A and of citrate precursor.

Similar data were obtained in other experiments; it was shown that the eluate was active in the acetylation of *p*-aminobenzoic acid in pigeon liver extracts, an established reaction of acetyl Co-enzyme A. Moreover acetyl Co-enzyme A and Stadtman's product were both stable to heat at acid pH and showed no nitroprusside reaction. They were, however, readily hydrolysed by alkali and the presence of a free thiol group could then be demonstrated. They both showed the reaction of acetylmercaptans with neutral hydroxylamine to give a hydroxamic acid and a mercaptan, both of which can be detected on paper.

$$CH_3CO \cdot S \cdot R + NH_2OH = R \cdot SH + CH_3C \overset{\textstyle OH}{\underset{\textstyle N \cdot OH}{<}}$$

Inorganic phosphate has a pronounced influence on the formation of acetyl Co-enzyme A from acetyl phosphate by phosphotransacetylase, as would be expected if the equation shown on p. 229 represents the reaction. Reduction of the yield to the extent of 55 per cent was observed by addition of increasing amounts of phosphate. This is not due to an inhibition of the enzyme, but to a shifting of the equilibrium. If, when the system is at equilibrium, phosphate is added the concentration of acetyl Co-enzyme A diminishes to a value identical with that obtained when the same amount of phosphate is added initially. Moreover, if the acetyl co-enzyme (obtained by paper chromatography) and inorganic phosphate be incubated in the absence of any enzyme an almost quantitative conversion to acetyl phosphate occurs.

It will be recalled that similar conclusions as to the effect of phosphate were put forward by Lynen, Reichert and Rueff[38] in their study of the induction period which is observed prior to the oxidation of acetate by impoverished yeast (*see* p. 226). Other mercaptans are acetylated by acetyl phosphate, Co-enzyme A and the phosphotransacetylase enzyme, e.g. glutathione and thioacetic acid, $HS \cdot CH_2 \cdot COOH$, giving compounds which are stable to heat; others such as cysteine probably yield unstable products. Apparently acetyl phosphate in presence of phosphotransacetylase acetylates Co-enzyme A which then acetylates the added thiol compound. This second reaction is believed not to be enzymic, a conclusion strengthened by the observation that acetylthioacetate and gluta-thione at pH 8·1 and 26°C in the absence of any enzyme yield acetylglutathione

$$CH_3 \cdot CO \cdot S \cdot CH_2 \cdot CO\bar{O} + G \cdot SH = G \cdot S \cdot CO \cdot CH_3 + HS \cdot CH_2 \cdot CO\bar{O}$$

A similar formation of acetylglutathione occurs with acetylthio-phenol $CH_3 \cdot CO \cdot S \cdot C_6H_5$, and with aniline and thioacetic acid[42,43] $CH_3 \cdot CO \cdot SH$ a vigorous reaction occurs giving acetanilide.

Arsenolysis of Acetyl Phosphate

It has been shown by Stadtman and Barker[44] and by Stadtman, Novelli and Lipmann[45] that, in presence of arsenate, enzyme preparations obtained from *Cl. kluyveri* catalyse a rapid and complete hydrolysis of acetyl phosphate to acetate and inorganic phosphate. This arsenolysis is specific for acetyl phosphate; arsenate has no influence on the rate of decomposition of other acyl phosphates. The reaction is due to a phosphotransacetylase and its rate is directly proportional to the concentration of Co-enzyme A. For a discussion of the origin of the study of arsenolysis, its relation to the hydrolysis of glucose-1-phosphate by an enzyme obtained from *Pseudomonas saccharophila* and the part played by Co-enzyme A, the papers by Stadtman and his colleagues should be consulted.

THE RELATION OF CO-ENZYME A TO FATTY ACID METABOLISM

So far, in this chapter, attention has been directed to the isolation and structure of Co-enzyme A, to its breakdown products and to its biological synthesis. A similar treatment has been accorded to the S-acetyl derivative of the co-enzyme. During the course of the discussion the acetylating powers of the co-enzyme plus an acetate donor or of its S-acetyl derivative have been mentioned in connec-tion with choline and with sulphanilamide. It is also probable that the N-acetyl group of the acetylated cysteine fragment of the various mercapturic acids, which are excreted when certain aromatic compounds are administered to animals, is furnished through the activity of Co-enzyme A. Thus, bromobenzene gives rise to p-bromophenylmercapturic acid

$$Br-\langle\quad\rangle-S\cdot CH_2\cdot \overset{\overset{\displaystyle NH\cdot CO\cdot CH_3}{\displaystyle |}}{CH}\cdot COOH$$

The analogous conjugation of glycine with benzoic acid which occurs in many animals, including the horse, giving hippuric acid $C_6H_5CO\cdot NH\cdot CH_2\cdot COOH$, has recently been shown to involve the participation of S-benzoyl Co-enzyme A. These and many other so-called detoxication mechanisms have been fully discussed by Williams[46]. The biochemical functions of Co-enzyme A are, however, much more far-reaching and complicated than the simple acylations which have just been mentioned[47-51]. One of these functions, its participation in the metabolism of fatty acids, must now be considered.

At this stage the reader may be reminded of some well-known facts which have a bearing on the metabolism of fatty acids in animals and plants.

1. Very many, but not all, natural fatty acids, e.g. butyric, lauric, palmitic, stearic and oleic, contain an even number of carbon atoms.

2. Rancidity of fats caused by mould infection is often due to ketones, e.g. methyl n-nonyl ketone, which are formed by the β-oxidation of fatty acids followed by decarboxylation. Thus with lauric acid[52]:

$$CH_3\cdot(CH_2)_8CH_2\cdot CH_2COOH \rightarrow CH_3(CH_2)_8CO\cdot CH_2\cdot COOH \rightarrow$$
$$CH_3(CH_2)_8CO\cdot CH_3 + CO_2$$

3. Similar reactions, no doubt, account for the presence of methyl n-nonyl and methyl n-heptyl ketone in oil of rue[53].

4. The incomplete metabolism of fats, as in diabetes, gives rise to the excretion of acetoacetic acid and acetone.

5. Oxidation of the ammonium salts of fatty acids by hydrogen peroxide occurs in the β-position giving ketones (e.g. methyl-n-heptyl ketone from capric acid $C_9H_{19}COOH$) and fatty acids[54].

These and many other investigations led to the conclusion that the normal biological degradation of even-membered fatty acids occurs by successive loss of two atoms of carbon, though in animals the only intermediate compound which could be detected was acetoacetic acid, and even this only under pathological conditions. The results obtained by a study of the relation of Co-enzyme A to fatty acid[38,39,55-57] metabolism are in keeping with this earlier view. By the use of modern methods of enzymology and spectroscopy, however, quantitative results have been obtained which have provided a much more definite and detailed explanation (*see* below). Nevertheless, although many even numbered fatty acids have been submitted to enzymic oxidation in presence of Co-enzyme A, here again the only intermediate product which has been isolated is aceto-acetic acid in the form of its Co-enzyme A derivative $CH_3CO \cdot CH_2 \cdot CO \cdot S \cdot CoA$. The reason for this will be considered later (*see* p. 240).

The work of Lipmann, Novelli and their colleagues which has been discussed already was followed by their demonstration that not only was Co-enzyme A responsible for the transfer of acetyl and other acyl groups, but also for the production of such groups from fatty acids with short chains in presence of adenosine triphosphate or acetyl phosphate. Stadtman and Barker[58],[59] then showed in 1949 that extracts of *Clostridium kluyveri* catalysed the aerobic oxidation of caproic acid $C_5H_{11} \cdot COOH$ or butyric acid giving acetic acid and acetyl phosphate. They also observed the reverse type of reaction by which, in absence of air, caproic and butyric acids were synthesized from ethanol and acetate. This was one of the earliest experiments on the oxidation of fatty acids with a soluble enzyme preparation although in 1943 Muñoz and Leloir[60] obtained a cell-free preparation from liver which also oxidized fatty acids.

As a consequence of this and of Stadtman's work on the enzyme *phosphotransacetylase* (*see* p. 229) Barker[61], in 1951, put forward certain suggestions as to the possible course of the biological oxidation of fatty acids which were very similar to the views which are now held as a result of the work of Lynen, Ochoa, Mahler and others. Some aspects of these investigations must now be described, but for fuller particulars a valuable review by Mahler[56] should be consulted. For some years he had been engaged in the study of fatty acid oxidation and, by the use of an enzyme preparation from heart muscle had concluded that the conversion of butyrate to acetoacetate required more than one enzyme and, in addition, Co-enzyme A, diphospho-pyridine nucleotide (DPN)—for structure *see* p. 234—adenosine triphosphate (ATP) and magnesium ions. While this work was in progress Drysdale[62] described the preparation of a fatty acid oxidase system obtained from the mitochondria of rat liver. Mahler then developed a method for the preparation on a large scale of active mitochondrial suspensions from animal tissues obtained from abattoirs and for the production of large quantities of Co-enzyme A.

The Enzymic Breakdown and Synthesis of Fatty Acids

With the plentiful material thus available Mahler and his colleagues were able to identify and separate in a high degree of purity all the five enzymes concerned in the conversion of fatty acids to S-acetyl

Co-enzyme A. Mahler gives the following details of the reactions and enzymes involved in the enzymic oxidation of butyrate. In these abbreviated equations CoA·SH implies the reduced thiol form of Co-enzyme A, A.M.P., the 5′-monophosphate of adenosine, F.A.D.$_{ENZ}$ flavine adenine dinucleotide fixed on protein, DPN$^+$ and DPNH diphosphopyridine nucleotide and its reduced form and PP, inorganic pyrophosphate, $(HO)_2OP·O·PO(OH)_2$. For structures *see* below.

(1) $CH_3·CH_2·CH_2·CO\overline{O} + ATP + CoA·SH \xrightarrow[\text{Activating enzyme}]{\text{Mg}^{++} \text{ and Fatty acid}}$

$CH_3·CH_2·CH_2·CO·S·CoA + AMP + PP$
S-Butyryl Co-enzyme A

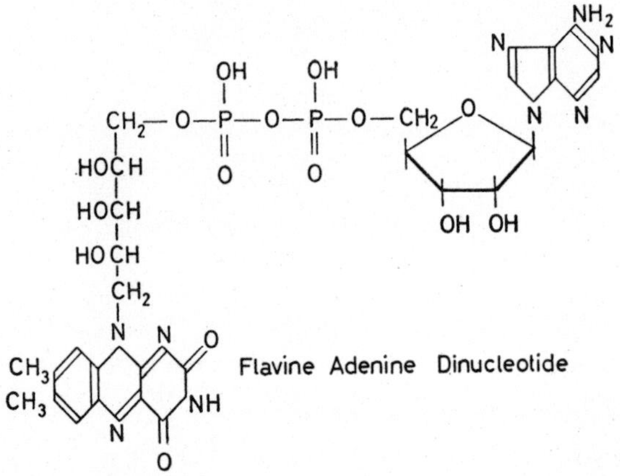

Flavine Adenine Dinucleotide

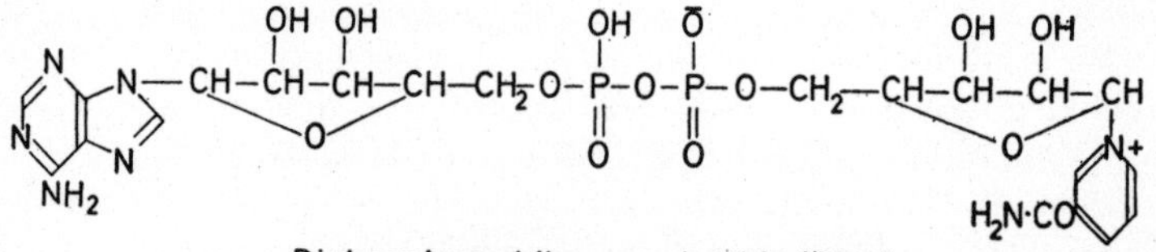

Diphosphopyridine nucleotide (DPN)

(2) $CH_3·CH_2·CH_2·CO·S·CoA + FAD_{ENZ} \xrightarrow{\text{Butyryl CoA dehydrogenase}}$

$CH_3CH : CH·CO·S·CoA + FADH_{2ENZ}$
S-Crotonyl Co-enzyme A

(3) $CH_3·CH : CH·CO·S·CoA + HOH \xrightarrow[\text{CoA hydrase}]{\alpha\beta\text{-unsaturated acyl}}$

$CH_3·CHOH·CH_2·CO·S·CoA$
β-hydroxybutyryl Co-enzyme A

(4) $CH_3 \cdot CHOH \cdot CH_2 \cdot CO \cdot S \cdot CoA + DPN \xrightarrow[\text{dehydrogenase}]{\beta\text{-hydroxyacyl CoA}}$

$CH_3 \cdot CO \cdot CH_2 \cdot CO \cdot S \cdot CoA + DPNH + H^+$
Acetoacetyl Co-enzyme A

(5) $CH_3 \cdot CO \cdot CH_2 \cdot CO \cdot S \cdot CoA + CoA \cdot SH \xrightarrow[\text{cleavage enzyme}]{\text{Acetoacetyl CoA}}$

$2\ CH_3 CO \cdot S \cdot CoA$

The last reaction has been termed a 'thiolysis' by Lynen[38].

A full discussion of these reactions and of the purification of the enzymes concerned appears in Mahler's review and in numerous original papers where the chemical and spectrometric methods employed during the isolation of the enzymes and products will be found. Nevertheless it will be useful to append some notes on the reactions represented by each of the equations 1–5. It will be sufficient to give an outline of the purification of only one of the enzymes as the procedure may be regarded as typical of, though not identical with, that employed in other cases.

Reaction (1)—The activity of the enzyme may be measured by using the nitroprusside reaction to follow the disappearance of the free —SH group of Co-enzyme A or by spectrophotometric measurement of the S-acyl group which is formed in the reaction. By these methods it was shown that the stoichiometry of reaction 1 is in agreement with the equation.

n-Fatty acids from C_2 to C_{10} were shown to form —S·CoA derivatives by this method, which has been used for their preparation in quantity. Branched chain and phenyl-substituted fatty acids also combine with Co-enzyme A. The reaction was found to be strictly reversible with an equilibrium constant essentially equal to unity. From this measurement and the known free energy change Δ_F° for the reaction $ATP = AMP + PP$ it follows that the acyl Co-enzyme A derivatives are high energy compounds with a free energy of hydrolysis (reaction 6) of approximately 11,000 cal.

(6) $R \cdot CO \cdot S \cdot CoA + HOH = R \cdot CO \cdot OH + CoA \cdot SH$

Δ_F° approx. $-$ 11,000 cal.

Reaction (2)—The enzyme which catalyses the conversion of butyryl Co-enzyme A to crotonyl Co-enzyme A is green in colour and was isolated from the extract of beef mitochondria by treatment with acetone to give a solid which then underwent the following processes: (1) Ammonium sulphate fractionation; (2) Treatment with zinc

235

hydroxide gel; (3) Fractionation with alcohol; (4) Adsorption on alumina; (5) Further alcohol fractionation and (6) Electrophoresis at pH 8. The enzyme so isolated was shown to be homogeneous in the ultracentrifuge. Absorption spectra showed the presence of a flavo-protein. The enzyme can be converted to an almost inactive apo-enzyme by ammonium hydrogen sulphate. Addition of flavine adenine nucleotide (*see* p. 234) or a boiled extract of the purified enzyme restores activity. This boiled extract has an absorption spectrum identical with that of flavine adenine nucleotide.

By the use of a recording spectrophotometer it can be shown that the enzyme is reduced in less than three seconds by butyryl Co-enzyme A but—and here we see the essential importance of Co-enzyme A—not by butyrate itself. Octanoyl Co-enzyme A does not cause this rapid reduction—a different enzyme being required, *see* below. The reversibility of reaction (2) is shown by the fact that the reduced enzyme (reduced flavoprotein) can be rapidly re-oxidized by crotonyl Co-enzyme A.

Reactions (3) *and* (4)—The hydrase which catalyses the addition of water to the unsaturated acyl Co-enzyme A in reaction (3) and the dehydrogenase which converts the resulting hydroxy acid to the β-keto-acid in reaction (4) are obtained from the beef mitochondria by methods which are very similar to those described for the flavo-protein enzyme. They can be separated completely but the necessary fractionations are very prolonged. The addition of water to the double bond of the crotonyl Co-enzyme A, to give β-hydroxybutyryl Co-enzyme A, is reversible and, at least in the case of the C_4 acids, the elimination of water can proceed in two directions to give a crotonyl and a vinylacetic acid derivative.

These relations are summarized below

$$CH_2 : CH \cdot CH_2 \cdot CO \cdot S \cdot CoA \rightleftharpoons d\text{-}CH_3 \cdot CHOH \cdot CH_2 \cdot CO \cdot S \cdot CoA \rightleftharpoons CH_3 \cdot CH : CH \cdot CO \cdot S \cdot CoA$$

A number of αβ-unsaturated acyl Co-enzyme A derivatives containing from 4 to 12 carbon atoms were found to undergo addition of water in presence of the *hydrase*. The free acids, however, are completely inert to the appropriate enzyme, again indicating the dominant part played by Co-enzyme A. The dehydrogenation of the β-hydroxybutyryl Co-enzyme A by the dehydrogenase in reaction (4) is confined to the *d*-isomer, and with, of course, less efficiency the *dl*-compound. The *l*-isomer is quite inert. It follows, as shown in the equation above, that the *d*-isomer only is involved in the addition and elimination of water catalysed by the hydrase.

The conversion of the hydroxyacyl- to the ketoacyl-derivative in reaction (4) requires diphosphopyridine nucleotide as a hydrogen acceptor. With β-hydroxybutyryl Co-enzyme A, acetoacetyl Co-enzyme A, $CH_3 \cdot CO \cdot CH_2 \cdot CO \cdot S \cdot CoA$, has been isolated by extraction with a mixture of phenol and benzyl alcohol and characterized (a) by determination of the acetyl Co-enzyme A produced and —SH removed when the acetoacetyl Co-enzyme A and free Co-enzyme A are incubated with the cleavage enzyme, the change being shown in reaction (5) and (b) by the chemical reactions of the acetoacetic acid obtained by hydrolysis. Finally the identity of the acetoacetyl Co-enzyme A has been established by an interesting and important reaction, whereby the relation of Co-enzyme A to the tricarboxylic acid cycle has been demonstrated. It has been mentioned already (see p. 225) that acetyl Co-enzyme A and oxaloacetate yield citric acid in presence of Ochoa's 'condensing enzyme'. Mahler has effected a similar conversion of acetoacetyl Co-enzyme A to citrate by its interaction with malate, $COOH \cdot CH_2 \cdot CHOH \cdot CO\overline{O}$, malic acid *dehydrogenase* (which converts malate to oxalo-acetate $COOH \cdot CH_2 \cdot CO \cdot CO\overline{O}$), Co-enzyme A, diphosphopyridine nucleotide and Ochoa's 'condensing enzyme'. The pyridine derivative takes up the hydrogen removed from the malate. The overall reaction is represented by the equation:

Acetoacetyl S— CoA $+ 2$ malate$^{--} + 2DPN^+ + 2O\overline{H} \rightarrow 2$ citrate^{---} $+ 2$ DPNH $+ 2H^+ +$ CoA $\cdot$ SH

Since no mention is made by Mahler of the addition of the cleavage enzyme [see reaction (5) p. 235 and below] it is to be assumed that the condensing enzyme is able to convert acetoacetyl Co-enzyme A to acetyl Co-enzyme A. This then reacts with the oxaloacetic acid thus:

$$COOH \cdot CH_2 \cdot CO \cdot COOH + CoA \cdot S \cdot CO \cdot CH_3 \rightarrow$$

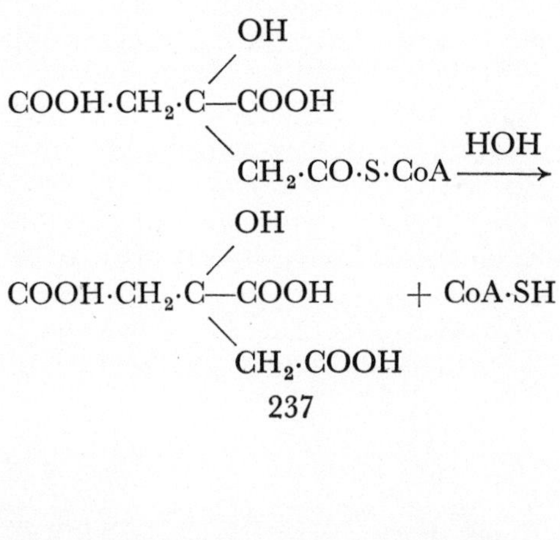

$$COOH \cdot CH_2 \cdot \overset{\displaystyle OH}{\underset{\displaystyle CH_2 \cdot CO \cdot S \cdot CoA}{C}} - COOH \xrightarrow{\quad HOH \quad}$$

$$COOH \cdot CH_2 \cdot \overset{\displaystyle OH}{\underset{\displaystyle CH_2 \cdot COOH}{C}} - COOH \quad + CoA \cdot SH$$

237

The reaction follows a well-known synthesis of citric acid, and it should be noticed thatthe CH_3^- group of $CH_3 \cdot CO \cdot S \cdot CoA$ contains an active hydrogen capable of undergoing a reaction of the aldol type. Higher homologues of acetoacetyl Co-enzyme A behave in a similar manner.

Reaction (5)—The 'cleavage enzyme' has been found to cause fission of all the β-ketoacyl Co-enzyme A derivatives from C_4 to C_8 which were tested. The course of reaction (5) has been confirmed by an experiment which depends on the fact that whereas the β-hydroxybutyryl Co-enzyme A and also S-acetyl Co-enzyme A react with hydroxylamine to give hydroxamic acids:

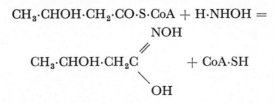

$$CH_3 \cdot CHOH \cdot CH_2 \cdot CO \cdot S \cdot CoA + H \cdot NHOH =$$

the β-ketobutyryl Co-enzyme A (acetoacetyl Co-enzyme A) does not. Thus when $0.25\mu m$ of β-hydroxybutyryl Co-enzyme A were dehydrogenated according to reaction (4) in presence of diphospho-pyridine nucleotide, $0.25\mu m$ of the corresponding hydrogenated nucleotide were obtained and an equal amount of material reacting with hydroxylamine disappeared. No free —SH was produced. On addition of the cleavage enzyme and free Co-enzyme A, $0.47\mu m$ of a compound reacting with hydroxylamine were obtained (acetyl Co-enzyme) and $0.24\mu m$ of Co-enzyme A disappeared as required by reactions (4) and (5). The β-hydroxybutyryl Co-enzyme A had been dehydrogenated to the β-keto-derivative and this by reaction with free Co-enzyme A in presence of the cleavage enzyme yielded 2 molar proportions of acetyl Co-enzyme A.

Enzymic Oxidation of Octanoic Acid

It will be appreciated that the five reactions discussed above have been worked out for the—apparently—simple oxidation of butyrate to acetate, which it must again be emphasized is exerted not on butyrate itself but on butyryl Co-enzyme A. The question arises— are the same reactions and enzymes concerned with the oxidation of the higher acids? There is little doubt that in the main this question can be answered in the affirmative, but there is at least one exceptional case. When Mahler and his colleagues began to study the enzymic oxidation of the higher fatty acids such as octanoic acid $CH_3 \cdot (CH_2)_6 \cdot COOH$ they found that the system containing all the enzymes described in the preceding pages was incapable of converting this acid to acetic acid (in presence of Co-enzyme A) unless an additional enzyme were present. This was yellow in colour and, in the case of fatty acids higher than hexanoic, must be added in order to replace the green butyryl Co-enzyme A dehydrogenase which, it may be mentioned, was found to contain copper and flavin in the ratio of 2 : 1. This yellow enzyme is a more general acyl Co-enzyme A dehydrogenase. It was also active for decanoyl Co-enzyme A. With this enzyme *plus* those already described the graded oxidation of octanoic acid to acetic acid was effected, through the Co-enzyme A derivatives, without, of course, any isolation of intermediate compounds.

It appears to follow from Mahler's results that this graded oxidation of octanoate to acetate proceeds thus:

Octanoic Acid $\quad\quad CH_3 \cdot (CH_2)_4 \cdot CH_2 \cdot CH_2 \cdot CO \cdot OH$
$\downarrow$

Octanoyl-CoA $\quad\quad CH_3 \cdot (CH_2)_4 \cdot CH_2 \cdot CH_2 \cdot CO \cdot S \cdot CoA$
$\downarrow$

$\alpha\beta$-Octenoyl-CoA $\quad\quad CH_3 \cdot (CH_2)_4 \cdot CH : CH \cdot CO \cdot S \cdot CoA$
$\downarrow$

β-Hydroxyoctanoyl-CoA $\quad CH_3 \cdot (CH_2)_4 \cdot CHOH \cdot CH_2 \cdot CO \cdot S \cdot CoA$
$\downarrow$

β-Ketooctanoyl-CoA $\quad\quad CH_3 \cdot (CH_2)_4 \cdot CO \cdot CH_2 \cdot CO \cdot S \cdot CoA$
$\downarrow$

Hexanoic acid $+$ Acetyl-CoA $\quad CH_3 \cdot (CH_2)_4 \cdot COOH \;+$
$\downarrow \quad\quad\quad\quad\quad\quad\quad\quad\quad CH_3 \cdot CO \cdot S \cdot CoA$

Hexanoyl-CoA $\quad\quad CH_3 \cdot (CH_2)_2 \cdot CH_2 \cdot CH_2 \cdot CO \cdot S \cdot CoA$
$\vdots$

$\quad\quad\quad\quad\quad\quad$ 2 stages omitted

β-Ketohexanoyl-CoA $\quad\quad CH_3 \cdot (CH_2)_2 \cdot CO \cdot CH_2 \cdot CO \cdot S \cdot CoA$
$\downarrow$

Butyric acid $+$ Acetyl-CoA $\quad CH_3 \cdot (CH_2)_2 \cdot COOH \;+$
$\quad\quad\quad\quad\quad\quad\quad\quad\quad\quad CH_3 CO \cdot S \cdot CoA$
$\vdots \quad\quad\quad\quad\quad$ 3 stages omitted

Acetoacetyl-CoA $\quad\quad CH_3 \cdot CO \cdot CH_2 \cdot CO \cdot S \cdot CoA$
$\downarrow$ CoA

2 Acetyl-CoA $\quad\quad 2CH_3 \cdot CO \cdot S \cdot CoA$

Mahler points out once again that the Co-enzyme A derivatives of the fatty acids are the true intermediates in the oxidation of these acids. All the intermediate compounds in the scheme including the first and last stages are bound to Co-enzyme A by the thio-ester link as in $R \cdot CO \cdot SR'$. The processes leading to β-oxidation and the loss of two carbon atoms are effected only through acyl-Co-enzyme A derivatives. Consequently the total concentration of true intermediate compounds in the process of fatty acid oxidation can never exceed, and is probably much lower than, the total concentration of firmly bound Co-enzyme A in the mitochondria. This is as low as one mg. per gram of dry liver mitochondria.

From a consideration of the 'turnover numbers' of the enzymes concerned (i.e. moles of substrate metabolized $\times$ moles^{-1} enzyme $\times$ min^{-1} at 38°C) the conclusion is reached that the β-ketoacyl-Co-enzyme A derivatives form the only group in the whole sequence which are formed much more rapidly than they are metabolized. Consequently the majority of the Co-enzyme A which takes part in fatty acid oxidation should be combined as the β-ketoacyl derivatives at any moment and in the absence of any competing reactions.

The part played by Co-enzyme A in fatty acid metabolism is also discussed by Krebs[63] in a comprehensive review entitled *The Control of Metabolic Processes*.

REFERENCES

[1] Kaplan, N. O. and Lipmann, F., *J. biol. Chem.* **174** (1948) 37
[2] Lipmann, F., Kaplan, N. O., Novelli, G. D., Tuttle, L. C. and Guirard, B. M., *ibid.* **167** (1947) 869
[3] Lipmann, F., *Enzymologia* **4** (1937) 65
[4] Lipmann, F., *Advances in Enzymology* **6** (1946) 231; *J. biol. Chem.* **134** (1940) 463; **155** (1944) 55
[5] Lipmann, F., *Harvey Lectures* **44** (1948–9) 99
[6] Lipmann, F., *J. biol. Chem.* **160** (1945) 174
[7] Lipmann, F. and Kaplan, N. O., *ibid.* **162** (1946) 743
[8] Lipmann, F., Kaplan, N. O., Novelli, G. D. and Tuttle, L. C., *ibid.* **186** (1950) 235
[9] Gregory, J. D., Novelli, G. D. and Lipmann, F., *J. Amer. chem. Soc.* **74** (1952) 854
[10] Beinert, H., *ibid.* **74** (1952) 854
[11] Novelli, G. D., Kaplan, N. O. and Lipmann, F., *J. biol. Chem.* **177** (1949) 97
[12] Baddiley, J. and Thain, E. M., *J. chem. Soc.* (1951) 2253
[13] Baddiley, J. and Thain, E. M., *ibid.* (1951) 246
[14] McRorie, R. A., Masley, P. M. and Williams, W. L., *Arch. Biochem.* **27** (1950) 471

[15] Brown, G. M., Craig, J. A. and Snell, E. E., *Arch. Biochem.* **27** (1950) 473

[16] Snell, E. E., Brown, G. M., Peters, V. J., Craig, J. A., Wittle, E. L., Moore, J. A., McGlohon, V. M. and Bird, O. D., *J. Amer. chem. soc.* **72** (1950) 5349

[17] Novelli, G. D., Kaplan, N. O. and Lipmann, F., *J. biol. Chem.* **177** (1949) 97

[18] Novelli, G. D., Kaplan, N. O. and Lipmann, F., *Fed. Proc.* **9** (1950) 209

[19] Baddiley, J. and Thain, E. M., *J. chem. Soc.* (1951) 2255; *Chem. & Ind.* (1951) 337

[20] Baddiley, J. and Thain, E. M., *J. chem. Soc.* (1952) 800

[21] Baddiley, J. and Thain, E. M., *ibid.* (1953) 903

[22] Baddiley, J. and Thain, E. M., *ibid.* (1953) 1610

[23] Baddiley, J. and Mathias, A. P., *ibid.* (1954) 2803

[24] Pierpoint, W. S. and Hughes, R. E., *Biochem. J.* **56** (1954) 130

[25] Brown, G. M. and Snell, E. E., *J. Amer. chem. Soc.* **75** (1953) 2782

[26] Novelli, G. D., in McElroy, W. D. and Glass, B., *Phosphorus Metabolism*, Baltimore, Vol. 1 (1951), p. 414

[27] Baddiley, J. and Thain, E. M., *J. chem. Soc.* (1951) 3421

[28] Kornberg, A. and Pricer, W. E., *J. biol. Chem.* **186** (1950) 557; **193** (1951) 481

[29] Wang, T. P., Shuster, L. and Kaplan, N. O., *ibid.* **206** (1954) 299

[30] Novelli, G. D., *Fed. Proc.* **12** (1953) 675

[31] Brown, G. M. and Snell, E. E., *J. Amer. chem. Soc.* **75** (1953) 2782

[32] Kaplan, N. O. and Lipmann, F., *J. biol. Chem.* **176** (1948) 449

[33] Lynen, F., *Liebig's Ann.* **552** (1942) 270; **554** (1943) 40

[34] Wieland, H. and Sonderhof, R., *ibid.* **499** (1932) 213

[35] Stern, T. R. and Ochoa, S., *Fed. Proc.* **9** (1950) 234

[35a] Stern, T. R., *J. biol. Chem.* **193** (1951) 161, 703

[36] Stadtman, E. R. and Barker, H. A., *ibid.* **196** (1952) 527,535

[37] Lynen, F. and Reichert, E., *Angew. Chem.* **63** (1951) 48

[38] Lynen, F., Reichert, E. and Rueff, L., *Liebig's Ann.* **574** (1951) 1

[39] Lynen, F., *Harvey Lectures* **48** (1952–3) 210

[40] Sachs, G., *Ber. dtsch. chem. Ges.* **54** (1921) 1849

[41] Dickens, F., *Biochem. J.* **27** (1933) 1141

[42] Pawlewski, B., *Ber. dtsch. chem. Ges.* **31** (1898) 661

[43] Pawlewski, B., *ibid.* **35** (1902) 110

[44] Stadtman, E. R. and Barker, H. A., *J. biol. Chem.* **184** (1950) 769

[45] Stadtman, E. R., Novelli, G. D. and Lipmann, F., *ibid.* **191** (1951) 365

[46] Williams, R. T., *Detoxication Mechanisms*, Chapman and Hall, London, 1947

[47] Lynen, F., *Fed. Proc.* **12** (1953) 683

[48] Soodak, M. and Lipmann, F., *J. biol. Chem.* **175** (1948) 999

[49] Stern, J. R. and Ochoa, S., *ibid.* **179** (1949) 491

[50] Novelli, G. D. and Lipmann, F., *ibid.* **182** (1950) 213

[51] Lynen, F., *J. Amer. chem. Soc.* **75** (1953) 2788

[52] Derx, H. G., *Proc. K. Akad. Wet. Amst.* **28** (1925) 96

[53] Stokoe, W. N., *Biochem. J.* **22** (1928) 80

[54] Dakin, H. D., *J. biol. Chem.* **4** (1908) 221

[55] Ochoa, S., *Harvey Lectures* **46** (1950–1) 153

[56] Mahler, H. R., *Fed. Proc.* **12** (1953) 694

[57] Popják, G., 'Chemistry, Biochemistry and Isotopic Tracer Technique, *Lectures, Monographs and Reports, Roy. Inst. Chem.* (1955) No. 2

[58] Stadtman, E. R. and Barker, H. A., *J. biol. Chem.* **180** (1949) 1085, 1095, 1117

[59] Stadtman, E. R. and Barker, H. A., *ibid.* **181** (1949) 221

[60] Muñoz, J. M. and Leloir, L. F., *ibid.* **147** (1943) 355

[61] Barker, H. A., in McElroy, W. D. and Glass, B., *Phosphorus Metabolism*, Baltimore, Vol. 1 (1951) p. 204

[62] Drysdale, G. L., *Fed. Proc.* **11** (1952) 204

[63] Krebs, H. A., *Endeavour* **16** (1957) LXIII, 125

INDEX